IN CROSSFIRE
OF HATE

by

Martha Wall

MOODY PRESS
CHICAGO

266.0230986l
W18i

Contents

38437

PROPIETARIO Y
DIRECTOR - GERENTE
ALEJANDRO GALVIS GALVIS

VANGUARDIA LIBERAL

Y JEFE DE REDACCIÓN
MANUEL MONTAGU BLANCO

DECANO DE LOS DIARIOS DE SANTANDER FUNDADO EN 1919

Valor del ejemplar $ 0.10

AÑO XXXI   Nº 9.297   REGISTRO POSTAL Nº 256   BUCARAMANGA — COLOMBIA   MARTES, SEPBRE. 20 DE 1.949   Número circante $ 0.10

El cabildo de San Gil aprobó enérgica protesta contra actos de la policía

LA CIUDAD CONVERTIDA EN EL PEOR VILLORIO POR CULPA DE LAS AUTORIDADES.—

Santander bajo el régimen del terror

Cinco agentes de policía y dos civiles, muertos en 'La Ceiba'

Como ¡Ocurrieron Antier los Hechos

200 Familias de Matanza Llegaron Ayer a B/manga.

Abaleo en Piedecuesta y San Gil, por la Policía, Antier

TRES MUERTOS EN SAN GIL.— DESTRUIDAS LAS PUERTAS DE CASAS DE LIBERALES EN PIEDECUESTA Y DE UN COLEGIO DE ANGLO-AMERICANOS.

AÑO XXXI   Nº 9.293   BUCARAMANGA — COLOMBIA   DOMINGO, SEPBRE. 25 DE 1.949

NO HA PASADO NADA

57 CASAS DE "EL PLAYON", SON CONVERTIDAS EN CENIZAS

--Pérdidas por más de un millón--

...smo Colombiano no ...atible con la Religión

Los cadáveres no han sido levantados de la carretera

Es Clausurado "El Colombiano"
--- Reacción Contra la Dictadura del Gobierno ---

...licación de divisas y las industrias

Dice el Papa en Circular al Clero Nacional

AÑO XXXI   Nº 9.294   REGISTRO POSTAL Nº 256   BUCARAMANGA — COLOMBIA   MIERCOLES, SEPBRE. 28 DE 1.949

Numerosos Almacenes Saqueados Después del Abaleo, en Piedecuesta

¿SE PREPARAN NUEVOS ASALTOS?

INCLUIDO VALENCIA, PERO SE AFIRMA QUE NO ACEPTARA.—

Noche de Terror fue la del Lunes
Identificados un muerto. Varios heridos

Los atacantes de El Playón planean con Vegueros asalto.-Se retira el ejército

EN REGION DEL NORTE SIGUEN CERCA DE 80 AGENTES DE SAN TANDER.—

Demandada la Disposición del Gobierno Sobre los Sindicatos

AÑO XXXI   Nº 9.296   REGISTRO POSTAL Nº 256   BUCARAMANGA — COLOMBIA   VIERNES, SEPBRE. 30 DE 1.949

Cincuenta mil liberales harán mitin el domingo en la capital

1.500 Delegados a la Gran Convención Liberal

Conjurada una Huelga

Renunció...

EL PAIS EN MARCHA

Numerosos Liberales Asesinados y Cerca de 100 Casas Quemadas, en Municipio de Onzaga

Las Autoridades

AÑO XXXI   Nº 9.292   REGISTRO POSTAL Nº 256   BUCARAMANGA — COLOMBIA   MARTES, SEPBRE. 27 DE 1.949

ABALEO EN PIEDECUESTA AYER TARDE Y ANOCHE

Cuadrillas atacantes

LISTA DE LAS VICTIMAS:

La población bajo el Régimen del Terror

La Policía Enc... a los Liberales

Hay varios heridos.- Atacadas algunas casas.-

INCENDIOS UN TRAPICHE Y UNA CASA.—

Cosecha de Café En Palmira, Ahora

La Policía Tiene muy Mala Reputación y no Tiene Carácter de Carrera Honorable

El Proyecto Sobre Nacionalización de la Cédula Electoral Será Ahora Estudiado

Muertos el recaudador, el registrador y un agente de policía, en San Benito

Atacados Varios Choferes por un Grupo de Policías

Nuevos Gobernadores para Caldas y Norte de Stder.

Nuevos Cambios en los ministerios, habrá

Preface

WHICH OF THE TWELVE DISCIPLES chosen by our Lord Jesus Christ would have passed a twentieth century mission board? James and John—so hotheaded that they had been nicknamed the sons of thunder? They smelled of fish! Simon, member of an underground revolutionary party? How would the zealot get along with Matthew, who openly had been collaborating with the occupying military government of Rome? He was a publican. He had made a fortune by extorting taxes from his own countrymen. Or Peter, a brash, unlettered peasant who spoke before he thought? For a man who tried to settle his master's quarrels with a sword, his aim was atrociously poor.

Don Marco Franco, of Aspasica, Colombia—another man chosen by the Lord Jesus Christ as a disciple—fits right in with this assortment of poor leadership risks. Illiterate, hot of temper and quick of tongue, Don Marco was such a zealot for the cause of Christ that he seemed to be looking for trouble. And during Colombia's ten years of political revolution, he did not have to go far to find it.

Readers of my previous book, *As a Roaring Lion,* have met Don Marco, audacious host whose home became the nucleus of a spiritual explosion and vortex of a storm of violent opposition. Now, from Rosa de Franco's viewpoint, here is the story of how this resolute, fiery hard drinker was chosen to be one of Jesus' apostles to the rugged people of the Andean mountains.

I believe that all who meet this valiant man and his wife in the reading of their story will be humbled as I was in the writing. Each of us will need to reevaluate our own commitment,

5

the depth of our loyalty. Like the Lord he served, Don Marco in his faithfulness knew "no variableness, neither shadow of turning."

MARTHA WALL

1

Fateful Dilemma

IN THE SALA of Don Marco Franco's adobe home, a barefoot mestizo boy hitched himself across the unpainted counter to get a better look at yuca[1] piled on the cement floor together with a dozen tomatoes and scattered onions.

The board counter—hammered together with twelvepenny nails clinched back to make it sturdy and durable—extended across the center of the dwelling's front room, which served as the local *tienda*—a mountaineer version of a village store. Together with a rectangular wooden bin set up on legs and roughly sectioned off to hold salt, beans, rice, corn, and eggs, the counter formed a sort of partition to keep customers from wandering into family privacy.

"Is the yuca fresh, Doña Rosa? 'From today,' Mamá said."

The proprietor's wife, a charming wisp of a woman, reached accommodatingly to a shelf below the counter for the ever handy machete and slashed an end from one of the tubers to reveal the glistening white succulence of Colombia's most common vegetable.

"Toño just brought them in from the farm," she said. "Look, the dirt's still damp."

"Bueno, give me that big one, and two ounces of lard."

The young mestizo counted out change from a pocket. Rosa Saravia took the trivial purchases for granted. Many of her customers bought only what they needed for the next meal. As a matter of fact, Rosa rarely had twenty pesos of change on hand.

[1]Cassava.

Marco Franco stocked a practical assortment of daily necessities and profitable luxuries for the convenience of the citizens of Aspasica, a tiny crow's nest of dwellings that had perched itself high in Colombia's western chain of Andes Mountains. From saplings supporting the thatching grass above, or from log beams that held the roof in place, hung clusters of dried chilis, guama pods, straw hats, buckets, and gourds cut and ready for use. Papayas the size of a sheep's head were lined up on the floor against the whitewashed wall. Large hands of green plantains[2] had been piled up nearby.

On the wall behind the counter were shelves displaying liquor and *gaseosas*.[3] Before the New Year's celebration of that year, 1946, he had even begun to include a few bottles of the bitter foreign Coca Cola in his stock. Another section of shelves was reserved for such luxury items as tinned sardines, oatmeal, powdered milk, and boxes of matches. The oatmeal was powdered and spiced, especially prepared for *broma,* a gruel used as a holiday beverage. Indeed, any tinned item would be used only for fiestas or other special occasions by any of their Aspasica customers.

More people drifted in and Rosa chatted genially with her neighbors as she darted about, finding for them what they had not already selected for themselves. A woman shoved at the heap of plantains with the tip of her shoe, dislodging a hen which sprang up in a flutter of excited cackling, then resumed her choice nesting place with a casual shake of ruffled feathers.

"Don't you have any bananas, Rosa?"

"The iguanas are getting them, Doña Anita."

"Well, you should cut them when they're green, like plantains."

"Is the bread good?" asked another woman, peering at the slender loaves which lay, unwrapped, in a small glass-enclosed case that was used chiefly to keep flies from a three-kilo cake of solidly pressed cottage cheese.

"Marco brings it in fresh nearly every week, Eloísa," Rosa

[2]Large green cooking banana.
[3]Carbonated beverages.

replied. "He may bring some that's fresher tonight, if he had space in his saddlebags."

Bread, a luxury that Marco seldom permitted on his own table, seemed a queer, foreign food to Rosa. Usually, when they ate a loaf they had been unable to sell, it was dry and turned to a flat, tasteless powder in the mouth. But she was not prepared for her customer's next demand.

"Well, then, do you have any *arepas?*"

"*Arepas?*" Rosa repeated, in surprise. Women in rural Colombia do not buy those heavy flat cakes. They pound their own corn and make their own *arepas.* For the quality of their *arepas* some women find husbands, but no woman evades the tedious hard work of making this everyday staple.

A man in fringed chaps who had been weighting a chain in his hand speculatively, swung around, voicing Rosa's own wonder in typically male derision. "What's the matter, Doña Eloísa? Did you get so busy gossiping you couldn't cook any?"

"Now, Hernando, you know better than that," the woman retorted, blushing nevertheless. "Ramón's brothers—all three of them—just rode in. They want to come to this party of Don Marco's, so I haven't time to fix anything."

"So you'll need two apiece?" Rosa turned to a brown elfin child in a frilled organdie frock who had just wandered in. "Emalina, go and ask Alicia if there are six *arepas.*"

In a moment, a vivacious, starry-eyed teenage girl, Rosa's oldest daughter, hurried into the sala. "What's Emalina talking about?" she demanded. "Did you send her for *arepas* to be sold?"

Doña Eloísa began her explanations all over, showing more embarrassment than before. Alicia admitted, with evident displeasure, that they had more than her father would eat.

"Well, I don't want to take your supper, Rosa, or your children's."

"Everybody's eaten but Marco," replied Rosa. "When you have to care for eight children and run a store, you start getting ready early."

"Just so Papá doesn't bring anybody with him. That's why I made extra." Alicia's tone suggested that other women could also foresee and provide for such emergencies. She brought them from the kitchen—a roofed area of the back patio, where pots steamed over an open fire on a raised earthern platform. The *arepas* were still warm, and Alicia had wrapped them separately in clean banana leaves. Doña Eloísa departed with a large slab of the cottage cheese which, because it is oversalted just as regularly as the *arepas* are made without any salt, makes a tasty and filling sandwich with the flat corn cakes.

A few men loafed in the sala, guests who had ridden in, arriving early for the party. A boy of eleven, small for his age, appeared from the patio.

"You washed your neck, Jorge—and ears?"

"And scrubbed up to my elbows," he retorted, holding up his sturdy brown arms for inspection with proud self-assurance. Jorge was happily unaware of the uneven line of demarcation that certified his most recent, soapy ablutions. Three other children skipped in, took a wild cavorting swing around Rosa's skirts, then darted off as suddenly as they had appeared.

The setting sun cast a ruddy glow over Rosa's swarthy features as she stepped into the doorway of her unpretentious home, which fronted the burro trail leading into Aspasica. She flicked back a strand of the shining black hair with which the light breeze was caressing her comely face.

Her eyes scanned the serrated spine of the mountain range to the east over which the setting sun had poured a molten topping which had run, still glowing, down the steep slopes, to spread along the far walls of ragged gorges. There the retreating day had cast long purple shadows. The light in Rosa's eyes had faded, too.

Several hours of hard riding away, along that serpentine mountain trail, lay Ocaña. Marco had ridden down at dawn to get supplies for the store and for tonight's party. He would not have been late to this fiesta he himself had planned if he could have helped it. Rosa felt a chill of apprehension crawl up her spine. Somewhere along that treacherous trail Marco, always reckless, would be riding at a more furious, death defying rate than usual. Rosa's full red lips silently formed the petition that could be read in her anxious dark eyes.

"Mamá," chirped five-year-old Emalina, unceremoniously interrupting the silent prayer by a sharp tug at her mother's sleeve. When Rosa did not reply at once, the child poked excitedly at her ribs to gain attention. "Is it time for Papá to come?"

"Yes, Nina," replied Rosa, stroking the dark hair so much like hers which, for today's festive occasion, had been combed into soft curls. "Papá should be here now."

Two boys, one older, one younger than Emalina, shoved their sister out of the doorway with an exuberant whoop of delight and padded out to the trail in their bare feet. Emalina followed.

Having climbed a gargantuan boulder that hung precariously to the flank of the mountain, they began a giggling, squirming vigilance. Almost as though on signal, three little girls burst out of another house not more than a long stone's throw from where Rosa stood. They also scrambled up the rock, and their excited shrieks were easily intelligible.

"There go the others!"

Jorge's voice cut into Rosa's private reverie, startling her. She had been oblivious to the fact that the lad had quietly joined her on the veranda.

"Oh, it's you, Jorge."

Jorge came to stand within the circle of her outstretched arm. Strange that she had never noticed before that Jorge now spoke as one of hers. He belonged to that other brood of Marco's. He was himself one of the "others."

Rosa had not failed to notice that the little girls—the *other* little girls—were wearing new party frocks far prettier than those that Rosa's daughters were wearing. Marco was spending more on Efigenia Castilla and her children than he ever had on Rosa's. When Marco chortled with pride in these children, fair complexioned like their mother, Rosa boiled with a futile, jealous rage which, she knew, must be suppressed at all costs.

How incredibly arrogant and shameless a hussy, to have permitted Marco to set her up in housekeeping so casually convenient to his established household! Even harder to endure were the insulting, supercilious airs that Efigenia affected when chance brought them together. Rosa was also aware of Efigenia's snide insinuations, constantly dropped into conversations with little subtlety, that Marco soon would be hers—all hers. Possibly they were confirmed, outside Rosa's presence, by Marco himself.

So far—Rosa could still console herself—this was Marco's home, and the whole community considered Rosa to be Marco's wife. Efi, whatever Marco's favors to her, was still "the other woman."

How long would it remain so? Would she always be able to control the smoldering volcano of her envy of this contemptuous paramour and of anger toward Marco for his unfaithfulness? Would she erupt some day in such an unseemly display of pent up animosities that Marco, who abhorred scenes, would desert her altogether? In conjugal situations like this—and they were far from rare in Colombia—didn't the younger woman usually win out? Rosa was middle-aged, older than Marco and twelve years older than Efigenia. Marco was only thirty-seven; Efi was still a young woman. Rosa might succeed in fighting her temper, but she could not win out against the passing years.

"Ouch, Doña Rosa!" Jorge giggled and moved abruptly from under her hand. She realized that she had clutched him unconsciously in a convulsive reaction of hidden despair. She pulled his ear and cupped the soft smoothness of his chin in her work-coarsened hand in a gesture of affectionate contrition.

"Oh, there you are!" called another voice. "Is Papá coming?"

"I can't see anything of him, Tive," said Rosa. "Come out here so we can see you."

A charming, roguish girl of twelve pirouetted proudly in her best party dress. Like the others, Natividad was brown as a berry, her dark eyes brimful of vitality and merriment, her full lips curved in the same inscrutable allure that made her mother still strikingly attractive. Rosa patted her dark hair approvingly.

"Doesn't Alicia need you? Have you washed the dishes?"

Alicia answered for her sister. "Everything's ready, except that Papá isn't here. Do you think . . ."

Alicia allowed her thought to trail in unspoken worry. For the party, Marco had needed to add to his supply of liquor. All too often, liquor spelled trouble for Marco. Alicia was suggesting the painful possibility that had been harassing Rosa. But Natividad propounded another, of graver import.

"What if he forgets about the party?"

"*Ai,* no, no, no! The things you'll think of!" cried Alicia in sharp reproach, as though Natividad's thought could evoke the disaster.

If Marco had begun to drink in the Ocaña tavern, by now he could be oblivious to any party. How would he react when he got back too late and found he had missed it? Rosa felt a tense foreboding. Liquor turned Marco, the man all of them adored to the point of worship, into a belligerent and unreasoning tyrant.

"The saints preserve us!" muttered Natividad. She knew, as did Rosa, that it would be impossible to explain that the guests had simply arrived. On whom would Marco vent his chagrin?

"Maybe somebody just got him into an argument," offered Jorge, more hopefully. "You know how he likes to talk."

"Just so he gets here before it's dark. That's no trail to be hurrying on, and at night, with a big load."

The arrival of several young guests took the girls to the back veranda, where Antonio was pumping up the gasoline pressure lantern. The shadows of the approaching evening had, even now, crept into the corners of the house.

"Go tell the children to come in out of the cold, Jorge," Rosa said. "The others too since they're coming to the party."

Jorge started off obediently. He was a good boy, thought Rosa, recalling vividly her violent, tearful outburst of outraged fury when Marco had announced that the boy was useful to him and that he wanted him here in his home.

It had begun then, this gnawing uncertainty of her own position. Marco had allowed her to choose between rearing Efigenia's son Jorge or losing both Marco and her own firstborn—her Antonio—to Efigenia.

Jorge's presence in the house no longer caused her to cringe with humiliation as though Marco were flaunting his other love before her. Sometimes the children all dashed off to play at the other house; more often they were all here. Was Efi's smug assurance sometimes also secretly torn by jealousy, by insecurity? Had she made a scene at the thought of losing Jorge to Rosa? Why, Rosa wondered now as she had done thousands of times, had Efi named her second daughter after her?

"Rosalia," Marco had reported flippantly on the morning the child was born. "After you."

In giving birth to her fourth child for Marco, had Efi become convinced that she had displaced Rosa in Marco's regard? Surely Efi was not so obnoxiously crass that she could force upon her own baby a name symbolizing her conquest of a rival? Or did the "other" woman also need to make rueful conciliatory gestures when, by some outburst, she had offended Marco's volatile temper?

In the fourteen years since Marco had begun his affair, Efi had borne him six children. Her oldest had been a son, born when Rosa's Antonio had been three and Alicia just a few months old. That boy had died. Jorge was Efi's oldest child now—and her only son. After that she had had four girls, one right after the other.

Would Marco have remained true to her, Rosa wondered, if she had not borne him four sons? Now that Alicia was fifteen, and Natividad was developing into a very attractive teenager, Marco often glowed with pride. Still, he had always crowed delightedly when she had presented him with a son. Except for

Santander. Their youngest child's deformity had been a blow
to both of them.

A night breeze had sprung up. Rosa could see it tugging at
the children's thin clothing. Though they were huddled down
to the huge boulder's warmth, they paid no more attention to
the cold than they did to the sounds from their home behind
them.

Someone in the house had started rasping a tune on a fiddle,
and a trumpet tentatively blasted a few notes off key. The children were interested in nothing but the arrival of their father,
and Jorge had remained to wait with them rather than relaying
her request that they come into the house. All of them, all of
those children out there on that boulder, shared with Rosa a
fierce adoration for Marco Franco.

"Tive!" called Rosa, bestirring herself from her somber re-
flections. "The children have to come in. It's getting cold."

Natividad, still childishly chubby, skipped across the slanted
parallelogram of yellow light cast by a blazing gasoline lantern,
and down the rocky path the children had taken. She raised
her voice with all the superiority of her twelve summers.

"Come in."

"No." It was a trio of emphatic resistance.

"Mamá says so. It's time to go to bed."

Rosa smiled. Natividad's psychology would improve when
she had her own children to rear. Since her argument evoked
nothing but resistance, the girl concluded that other measures
would be necessary. With practiced agility, she climbed to the
children's perch and grabbed Marco, the youngest of the group,
by the arm and started pulling him down.

"No, Tive," he bawled, furiously, fighting her all the way
down. Then he slumped, a dead weight, refusing to take another step. He complicated matters for Natividad by kicking
purposefully at her shins. She slapped him, and he roared with
renewed vigor.

"Leave Chico[4] be," shrilled Emalina, using the name Rosa

[4]Little chap, a title of endearment.

had fondly given to the boy in order to distinguish him from Marco Sr.

"We're just watching for Papá," said Jorge reasonably.

"Mamá said to come in."

"Well, I'm not," retorted Emalina and stamped her foot to emphasize her point, losing her footing in her vehemence.

Natividad eyed the little bundle of determined disobedience, and took a short, uncertain step forward as though in a mood to assert her authority. Emalina got up from the sloping surface of the stone with the lithe caution of a cat preparing to spring. The older girl, probably recalling previous encounters with her smaller sister when the claws had been unsheathed, decided on a less hazardous strategy. Swooping the toddler into her arms— he was actually heavier than Emalina—she started off toward the house with him, though it was as much as she could do to hold on to the struggling youngster.

"You'll be sorry," she called over her shoulder. "Just wait till Mamá comes after you with the strap." And so, having had the last word, she swung around and darted back with the squealing child. The remaining children squatted on the stone now grown cold and waited, arms doubled to their bodies against the cool mountain breeze. Crickets creaked cheerfully, and tree toads added their bell-like voices to the night's soft symphony.

"Emalina!" Rosa called. "Come on in out of that cold." When the children appeared not to have heard her, she added, "At once."

"Melo," proposed Emalina hesitantly, using the nickname Carmelo had himself created in his early babyish lispings. "Should we?"

Carmelo rocked back and forth on his haunches, hugging his knees, pondering possibilities. He had not decided whether to follow the path of discretion or of valor, when Emalina's sharp eyes detected the glint of moonlight on metal down the valley.

"It's Papá!" Emalina clapped her hands excitedly. Seconds later Rosa heard the rhythmic click of hoofs.

Don Marco Franco dug in his spurs as he came within sight of the festivities, clattering by the children's lookout in a gallop. The children raced after him on the very heels of his mule, arriving well out of breath just as their tall, wiry father swung from the saddle. He stooped to brush their smudgy foreheads with a kiss.

"Why aren't you kids asleep?"

"There's a party."

"Well, what of it? You're too small to dance, aren't you?"

"Did you bring us some candy?" said Emalina, coming right to the important point.

A group of young people burst from the door, and one of the young men offered to lead the horse away and see that it was fed and watered.

"Where's Toño?"

"He's here, Don Marco. He's trying to toot Alberto's horn."

Marco turned toward the house; and, even while he put an arm around Rosa's waist in a momentary, preoccupied gesture of affection taken for granted Emalina's quick fingers had found the bulge in her father's coat and extricated the bag of candy. Don Marco slapped the empty pocket and laughed.

"All right, then. Now you kids make yourselves scarce. We oldsters are going to make some real genuine whoopee."

"If the others can come to the party," chirped Emalina, with her usual show of spirit, "we can stay up for it!"

Marco laughed indulgently. "Mamá'll have the trouble of putting the whole lot of you to bed, I'm thinking." He merely tousled her hair and strode off. Emalina, assured that he had bowed to her logic, did an ungirlish cartwheel in her party dress.

Undoubtedly, though he had two attractive teenage daughters and a son who was just at that awkward age of uncertain vocal sounds and a growing interest in the opposite sex, Marco Franco was the accepted life of the party. To get him there sooner, willing hands lifted his saddle bags and carried them into the sala.

Rosa served Marco his supper in the back patio. He ate

hastily, conversing the while with the young people who gravitated to the back of the house and stood around in churning
clusters. As soon as he had finished, Marco led them back into
the lighted area of the veranda where the dance was in progress.
His attitude betrayed his eagerness to participate in the revelries.

With that flash of pride she had never lost when she compared Marco with other men, Rosa decided that, though he was
nearly forty, he was still the handsomest of all the men there.

"Where are the drinks?" Marco asked.

"Inside. On the counter."

"Well, come on in. What are we waiting for?"

From the thick speech of some and the exaggerated gaiety of
others, it was quite obvious that Antonio and Alicia had not
made the guests wait for Marco's arrival. They crowded in,
nevertheless, to accept Marco's invitation. Marco was generous,
Rosa thought as she cleared the patio table. Marco always was
congenial and generous with his guests.

"What have you got in those bags I brought in?" someone
asked.

"Oh, stuff for the store."

"What kind?"

"Oh, just the regular stuff. Salt, matches, soap, some sewing
thread for the ladies. And shoes."

"Shoes? Let's have a look. I need shoes."

"Well, I'll unpack it all tomorrow."

A general chorus of disapproval and importunity followed.
"What better time to break in new shoes than to dance in
them?"

"We can't come back up this far for a couple of weeks, maybe. What'll be left by then?"

"Aw, Don Marco. Let's see the shoes."

Marco set his glass down reluctantly. He swung the machete
from his belt and deftly severed the cords that held the pack
together. The bundle of shoes scattered freely over the counter,
some falling to the floor.

"Don't mix them up now," he said sharply, as his guests

pounced on them. He quickly rescued the shoes from the floor before they had been trodden on and started lining them up in pairs, though the young people kept clawing through the stack, finding likely pairs and fitting them on.

"What's this?" said one of the young men, holding up a slip of colored paper with some printing on it. He obviously was illiterate, for he passed it to Marco.

"Something printed? Where's Toño? I don't know my right hand or the letter *C*."[5] He waited with pride while Antonio studied the paper.

"It's funny," said Antonio, his voice breaking with embarrassment. "Something religious—*Four Things God Wants You to Know.*"

"Hah! There's about four things I'd rather God didn't know!" retorted Marco lightly, patently enjoying the flicker of laughter he had elicited. "Well, we're not going to break up this party to study religion."

By the energetic way he was sorting the shoes, Rosa saw he was wishing he did not have to delay his own pleasure by tending to customers. He was making some sales, of course, that he might not have made if the customers had been in a more deliberative mood. He nodded approvingly when Rosa began packing the merchandise onto the narrow crowded shelves behind the counter.

"Here's another of them papers," said another youth. "Say, this looks queer. It says—" The voice changed sharply. "Could this be some of that devilish propaganda of the *evangélicos?*"

"Could be. There's a few of them in Ocaña. How would they slip anything like this into my packs, though?"

"Where'd you buy the shoes?"

"In Ocaña, of course. Where else?"

"Who from?"

"Well, the leather ones—the men's shoes—all come from Francisco Velásquez. He makes them."

---

[5]Idiom: *Ni C ni mano derecha*—an inability either to recognize a letter of the alphabet or to write it.

"Well, that's where the papers are—in the men's shoes. There's one in every pair. Look, here's a couple more."

"I don't think Velásquez did it. He doesn't look to me like an *evangélico*. He's a good man—wouldn't even drive a crooked bargain."

"Could be just a sly way to take you unawares. He thought you could read, maybe, and that you'd start reading his propaganda without guessing anything."

"I'd be inclined to read anything he gave me. Maybe we ought to find out what the papers say."

"I don't think we should," exclaimed one of the young women, shrilly. "I've heard enough about *them* to know that, whatever it is, it's evil and dangerous. I think I'm going home."

"Now, now, Clarita," said Rosa soothingly. "Don't pay any attention to Marco. He just said that to hear himself talking."

Marco brushed the tracts from the counter to the floor. "You came here for a good time, and we're going to have a good time," he declared and took the lamp out to the veranda, where the momentary distraction was forgotten. It was near dawn when, to Rosa's relief, the party finally broke up.

Next day, however, perhaps because of the innate curiosity of his nature or because an illiterate has a deep respect for anything printed, Marco gathered up the crumpled papers from the floor, straightened them as best he could between his fingers, and slid them onto a shelf under the counter.

The farm on which the Marco Franco family lived belonged to Agustín Plata, Rosa's brother-in-law, who—though they all evaded the subject—had contracted leprosy some years previously and had been forced to move to the government *lazaretto* at Agua de Dios. Silvia, Rosa's sister, and her six children, lived in nearby Bogotá. It was only natural that Agustín should send his sons, occasionally, to visit the Francos. When José and Carlos came some weeks later, Rosa welcomed them eagerly.

Having been served *tinto,* the syrupy black coffee which is the cup of Colombian hospitality, the young men wandered about, relaxing from their long ride.

"What's this?" exclaimed Carlos, the younger Plata, holding up the small sheaf of tracts. "Where'd you get these?"

"Oh, those—" said Marco. He narrowed his eyes. "Say, can you fellows read?"

"Yes, we learned at the *lazaretto* school."

"Well then, maybe you can tell me what the papers are about."

"They're tracts, Don Marco," said José, looking over his younger brother's shoulder. "They tell of God's love."

"God's love?"

"I told you, José, that it was a good idea to bring it," said Carlos, almost triumphantly. "Don Marco, we've brought a book that tells lots plainer than that small tract about the love of God."

"Well, bring it out. Bring it out!"

José brought the book from his saddlebag, brushed a few crumbs from the table in the patio and sat down. The family, children and all, crowded about as he opened the book to read. Rosa, always busy with so many mouths to feed, sat on the veranda's edge, peeling yuca with a machete, holding the long heavy knife by the center of the blade and slashing at the bark-like covering to peel it away in large sections.

While José read the beautiful story of the birth of Jesus, Marco nodded his head occasionally and admonished the children to listen. This story was not new.

"Yes, listen well, *niños*," said José, "because I'm going to ask you again what it was the angels said."

"Well, read it again," said Alicia.

" 'Fear not:' " read José, " 'for, behold, I bring you good tidings of great joy, which shall be to all people. For unto you is born this day in the city of David a Saviour, which is Christ the Lord.' "[6] Then with his finger in the book, José asked,

[6]Luke 2:10-11.

"Would you like to have me tell you another word for good tidings?"

Marco nodded, leaning forward with avid concentration.

"Evangelio."

The word dropped like a grenade into their midst. The older children gasped, almost in fear. Marco had jerked up to even more rigid attention.

"Then what's this book you're reading from?"

"It is the Sacred Scriptures of God."

"Do you mean it's one of those—those *evangélico* Bibles?"

"It's a Bible, but the good news—the *evangelio*—is for everyone."

Marco frowned and looked at Rosa. She voiced his half-formed thought. "Should we let the children listen?"

A wail of protest rose from the children, who wanted to hear especially now that a note of excitement, of forbidden wickedness, had been added. Marco wavered, but only for a moment.

"Read on," he said sternly. "I can't see anything evil in this—so far."

"Well, this is the time for my question." José turned toward Antonio, probably because he dared not face his uncle with the question. "Do you think the angels were sent from God?"

"Sure. Why, sure."

"Then you think they told the truth?"

"Sure."

"Then tell me, what did they say?"

"Well, they said they brought the—the *evangelio*—that the Christ-Child was born."

"That's not what the angels said," barked Marco. "You young people who think you're so smart and can read!" He snorted indignantly, then drew on his prodigious memory. " 'To you is born this day in the city of David a Saviour, which is Christ the Lord.' " He turned triumphantly to José. "Right?"

"Right, Uncle. Now tell us again just who it is they said would be the Saviour."

"Christ, the Lord."

"Exactly, Don Marco. And when you really believe that in your heart, you're an *evangélico.*"

Marco looked in disbelief from one clear, earnest face to the other. Nothing in the steady eyes of his nephews even faintly suggested deceit or trickery.

"You're kidding."

José shook his head. "We've all heard misleading things about the *evangelio,* but we've read you the Sacred Scriptures. They're God's own words. When you receive forgiveness of sins, you get a new peace of heart. After I found this . . ."

Marco bristled visibly. "Then you—*you* are *evangélicos?*"

"Imagine something like that happening in our family!" exclaimed Alicia.

Marco scraped his chair back from the table and got up. "Come on, Toño," he said. "It's time to go and fix that fence." As far as he was concerned, the subject had been closed.

After Antonio had left with Marco, José continued to leaf through his Bible dejectedly, as though he were trying to understand where he had made a mistake. Rosa felt sorry for him. Whatever religious trap he'd fallen into, she could see José was sincere in his desire to share it.

"Marco didn't give you a chance to finish what you were saying. What were you going to tell us about your peace of heart?"

Carlos spoke up, "Auntie, if you knew that right now you had eternal life and that you would be with Jesus the second your soul left your body—would that give you peace of heart?"

"To know?" Rosa pondered his question. "But that's impossible."

"Do you believe that Jesus spoke the truth while He was here on earth?" interjected José. They both seemed so eager for her to understand this strange doctrine.

"Why, yes. Could the words of Jesus be false?"

"Listen!" José leafed earnestly until he found the place. "It says here, 'Verily, verily, I say unto you,'—this is Jesus talking—'He that heareth my word, and believeth on him that sent me, *hath* everlasting life, and *shall not come into condemnation;* but is passed from death unto life.' "

"Yes," added Carlos, "and Saint Paul said that dying is 'to be absent from the body and present with the Lord.' "

"Has my sister—has Silvia accepted this doctrine?" asked Rosa timidly. The boys nodded.

"It's for you too, Aunt Rosita," said José. "Mamá said for us to be sure we told you how different things are with her now."

"Why don't you do as she did?" urged Carlos. "Confess your sins to God and receive forgiveness—God's everlasting forgiveness that Jesus bought on the cross when He died."

If Silvia, her older sister, in whom Rosa had the highest confidence, had believed these beautiful words and received this blessed peace of mind the boys spoke of, then Rosa was inclined to take this *evangelio* seriously. More, she began to have a deep sense of emptiness—a conviction that in this way of life lay a fulfillment she had never dreamed of before.

As she asked questions and was given answers right from the Bible, she realized that she had never heard a more comforting message in her life. Yet a deep turmoil was stirred up by the same Sacred Scriptures. This forgiveness of God's, though He erased the memory of wrongs as though they were buried in the deepest sea, seemed to come with a stipulation.

" 'Forgive us our wrong-doings,' " Carlos had read, " 'as we have forgiven those who have wronged us.' " And what was just as disturbing, " 'For, if you forgive others their offences, your heavenly Father will forgive you also; but, if you do not forgive others their offences, not even your Father will forgive your offences.' "[7]

If God were only in some sort of cubicle where He could not see her face, she might ask for this forgiveness of Him. But José had assured her that He looked right past her face and into her soul. So God would know that she hated Efigenia with

[7]Matthew 6:12, 14-15, 20th Cent. N. T.

every ounce of her being and that she could never forgive her. Never!

Rosa's concept of religious doctrine had never been anything but vague. One gathered one's views about God and the life beyond from what others said. One usually believed the reasonings one heard most often or heard from people known to be level-headed. Who had ever spoken before with such positive assurance?

The forgiveness of the confessional was easier, because she needed say only what she wanted to reveal. But was it efficacious, now that she compared it with the promises in this evangelical Bible? Didn't one have to burn in purgatory for terrifying ages to be rid of those same sins? Then this was the way of absolution, but it was a hard way. If the forgiveness was reality, God demanded also that the confession be real. It was a hard way, but oh, how her soul wanted that way!

"If I forgive everybody but one person," Rosa asked, tremulously, "do you think God would forgive me?"

José met her eyes in sympathetic comprehension, but he shook his head. "Hating is not the *evangélico* way, Doña Rosa. It is not Jesus' way. I will read you His own teaching about it."

But to you who hear I say—Love your enemies, show kindness to those who hate you, bless those who curse you, pray for those who insult you. When a man gives one of you a blow on the cheek, offer the other cheek as well; and, when any one takes away your cloak, do not keep back your coat either. Give to every one who asks of you; and, when any one takes away what is yours, do not demand its return. Do to others as you wish them to do to you. If you love only those who love you, what thanks will be due you? Why, even the outcast love those who love them! For, if you show kindness only to those who show kindness to you, what thanks will be due to you? Even the outcast do that! If you lend only to those from whom you expect to get something, what thanks will be due to you? Even the outcast lend to the outcast in the hope of getting as much in return! But love your enemies, and show them kindness, and lend to them, never despairing. Then your reward shall be great, and you shall be Sons of the Most High,

for he is kind to the thankless and the bad. Learn to be merciful—even as your Father is merciful. Do not judge, and you
will not be judged; do not condemn, and you will not be con-
demned. Forgive and you will be forgiven. Give, and others
will give to you. A generous measure, pressed and shaken
down, and running over, will they pour into your lap; for the
measure that you mete will be meted out to you in return.

Luke 6:27-38
Twentieth Century New Testament

"I have a promise to El Cristo Rey," muttered Rosa, after her
nephew had finished reading. It was true, too. Many of the
older and wiser women had assured her that she should try
making a vow to the gigantic statue of Christ that stood outside
and above Ocaña. True, they could promise her nothing, but it
was said that some divine or magic influence would emanate
from the cool stone to bring healing to her crippled child.

José, however, thought she was just quibbling. "Aunt Rosa,
the Lord gives us strength when we don't have it. God can help
you to forgive . . ."

Rosa lifted the apron that she had thrown across her sleeping son and picked up the eighteen-month-old's little clubfoot,
so twisted that Santander was not using any part of the sole.
His ankle had been bruised by his attempts at walking. Recently he had even developed ulcerating sores over the prominent
ankle bone.

"I made a vow—for Santo's foot."

"Aunt Rosa," said José gently, "you don't have to go through
with that vow."

"But I must. If there's any chance for Santo to have a good
straight foot, I must do everything possible to get it for him."

"But El Cristo Rey is nothing but a stone statue," exclaimed
Carlos, with the tactlessness of youth.

"You're wrong," retorted his brother. "The statue outside
Ocaña is an image of the true Cristo Rey who not only forgives
sins but hears prayer. The living Christ rose out of a grave and
now waits in heaven to answer your prayer for Santo's foot."

When Rosa hesitated, he pressed his argument. "The statue,

the image of Christ, has stone ears, but he'll never hear your prayers. Can his stone eyes see Santo's twisted foot?"

"But we know the Saviour in heaven does answer prayer," Carlos interrupted, eagerly. "For real. Like Santo's foot."

"Believe in the *living* Cristo Rey, Auntie Rosita," urged José. "He will heal Santo."

In that case, she didn't dare miss out on the *evangelio*. Beyond the great yearning that haunted her each waking hour was this added promise of a child made whole. The boys even read her stories of Jesus' miracles and His promises to answer prayer. Because they would be leaving Aspasica, she asked them to teach her a prayer. She would pray for a strong straight foot for Santo, even if she knew she could hardly hope that God would hear her cry for forgiveness, for could even God answer José's carefully included petition that God would grant her a forgiving heart? Rosa knew that, though she might desire it, and even if her eternal destiny depended on it, she could never stop hating Efigenia Castilla.

Because of this knowledge, Rosa wavered between faith and fear during the days that followed. What if God wouldn't hear her prayer for Santo's foot either, if she could not meet His conditions? Once she rode to the plateau, carrying the deformed child before her in the saddle. She knelt as she had at other times, placing her offering before the statue, but now acutely aware of the cold and immobile stone under her clasped hands. Her pleas sounded ineffectual and hollow to her own ears. Did they reach any others? Her tears splashed down against its unresponsive hardness, but El Cristo Rey stood towering above her, aloof from her tearing grief. She returned home more distraught than ever.

"Believe in the *living* Christ," Carlos had admonished. "He will heal Santo."

If the living Christ healed Santo, she vowed, she would become an evangelical, whatever it involved. If He showed her so great a mercy, she could do no less, even though she knew she could never attain forgiveness nor the salvation of her soul.

2

Marco's Decision

WAS EVERYBODY STONE BLIND?

The inevitable incident that would spontaneously open the subject and make it easy for Rosa to declare her faith *had* to come soon. As weeks passed, her urge to talk to Marco—to get him to listen when he was in a good mood—was maddening. Still, dreading his violent disapproval, she procrastinated, though she felt she must burst with excitement. Even after her nephews returned to help with the seasonal farm work, she had not found opportunity or courage to break her news. Every day she told herself she had to wait until she was absolutely sure, but deep inside she knew. She already knew!

Her nephews, José and Carlos, had not come without their Bible. Almost every evening they brought it out to the patio, snatching at any comment that might result in friendly discussion. Although Marco was not particularly receptive to what they read out of the Bible to bolster their remarks, his own argumentative nature forced him often to introduce the subject of their new faith. He was astounded when Rosa spoke up, one evening, to defend her nephews' point of view.

"The *evangelio* is the true way," she said. "And the living Christ answers prayer. He really does!"

"Mamá!" cried Alicia, in a tone of shocked reproof.

Rosa had been cuddling Santander fondly in her lap. "Look!" she said, beaming. "Look what has happened to little Santo's foot. I thought that you all would have noticed him walking, long before this. It's a miracle. The bones are going back into

28

place, just like the other foot. It's the Christ that's healing Santo."

"What makes you think it's this *evangélico* Christ?" retorted Marco, obviously amused.

"I've never finished paying my vow to El Christo Rey. And I don't intend to."

Marco glared at Rosa silently for a moment, then snapped, "Does that mean then that you're going to strike out for yourself—as an *evangélica?*"

Rosa gasped at the cruel import of Marco's thinly veiled threat. Never, in all these years, had it ever occurred to her that Marco might not only desert her, but that he could even leave her children unprovided for.

"Well, no," she said tremulously, "I wouldn't go that far."

Everyone on the patio, except the smallest children, read Marco's meaning. He was Rosa's husband only by common-law union; and, although the community had long accepted Rosa as Marco's wife, she had no more legal claim on him than did his other mistress. Rosa, who had borne Marco eight children, seven of whom were living, occupied a status of extreme insecurity.

Rosa realized with sickening certainty that, if Marco left her unprovided for, her home would be shattered. She would have no way of supporting the smaller children; and, if she took the unpopular stand of becoming an evangelical, the older ones also might go their own way. Alicia had already indicated her disapproval.

Antonio looked thoughtfully at his mother, then at the foot of the toddler. There could be no doubt. Santo's twisted foot had changed miraculously, and the ulcerated areas were healing.

"I'm convinced," he said, meeting his father's furious stare without flinching. "I think you fellows have brought us the truth."

"Oh, no!" wailed Alicia. "Not you! What will our friends think?"

"Well, why should they find out?"

"They'll know," said Carlos. "There's no hiding an *evangéli-co*—a real one. You'll give a public witness, and you'll give up the things that are displeasing to God."

"Such as?"

"Such as smoking and dancing and—" Carlos hesitated a second, glancing uncertainly toward Marco, then plunged on. "And liquor."

Marco snorted in disdain and marched from the room. Moments later he stepped from the patio veranda, his hat at a rakish angle, his machete swinging jauntily from his belt. Rosa picked up the sleeping Santo and turned to take him into the bedroom. Though she tried to move away in a matter-of-fact manner, she had not been able to hide the spasm of fear and grief that blanched her face.

Rosa, rigid in her own dismay, was only dimly aware that for a long silent moment the group of young people seemed to be frozen by their own individual reactions. Then she heard Alicia's voice raised in withering scorn.

"I suppose you thought you were taking her part?"

For a long while all that was audible was Antonio's quick pacing back and forth in the room. Rosa thought she heard him groan.

"I guess I wasn't thinking at all, Licha."

José and Carlos left early the next morning for Agua de Dios. Bound together by a tragic possibility too frightening to contemplate—for every one of them adored their father—the children tried to maintain the pretense that nothing unusual had occurred. They followed the busy pattern of their long, hard days in the fields without a word from Rosa. When they returned to the house, they evaded each other's eyes and spoke in hushed tones as though they were in the presence of a great sorrow or in a house of death. Even the smaller children sensed that something serious was amiss.

On the second afternoon after Marco so dramatically left the house, Carmelo tiptoed into the house with a strange secretive air.

"Papá's at the rock," he whispered with unnecessary caution. "And so is Emalina. She's got Santo up there, marching him around."

"Yes?" Even that one word caught in Rosa's throat, which was constricted with panic and a hope so wild it left her voiceless.

"He felt him, Mamá. Papá felt Santo's foot."

Tears long restrained filled Rosa's eyes and splashed down her cheeks. Now he would know! She would not need to persuade him. He would know that his little son truly would walk. But would Marco be too proud to admit that she had been right?

"He knows it's a miracle," declared Carmelo emphatically. "You should have heard Emalina!"

"Let's pray for another miracle, then," cried Rosa. "Let's pray he'll come home to us very soon."

For the first time in her life, Rosa knew the comfort of kneeling in prayer with one of her children, really hoping that God would hear them. A few minutes later she heard Marco's long, energetic stride as he crossed the patio and entered the house.

"Have I got a clean shirt, Rosa?"

Rosa had anticipated just such a question as this with dread, and she had prepared for it. She had washed all of Marco's clothes, lest he should demand to take them away to the evil-tongued Efigenia in whatever condition they were. That morning she had checked all of them for buttons missing and for any mending that needed to be done. Though every stitch had seemed like a long thread of pain drawn through her heart or like the sewing of her own shroud, she had mended them all and folded them neatly into a paper carton. If Marco was going to come back to remove his belongings, she wanted it to be over quickly. She could not trust herself to maintain her poise, but she was also too proud to permit him to see the depth of her desolation.

Marco, who had followed her into the bedroom, took in the entire situation at a glance, divining even her motives. She saw it all in the swift flush of his swarthy face.

"Getting ready to boot me out?" he remarked lightly. When Rosa didn't reply, he forced her to meet his quizzical scrutiny. "You know you'll need a shotgun to make it permanent, don't you?"

Later, when he had slipped into a clean shirt, Marco spoke with studied nonchalance. "The boy walks, you know. The foot is turning straight—just as you said."

Rosa knew this was as close as Marco would ever come to an apology, and when she turned he was waiting for her to walk into his arms. Characteristically, Marco never mentioned the incident again, and Rosa as carefully refrained from any reference to the painful crisis.

A few weeks later, Marco suddenly decided they needed a new and better home. Since it pertained to the Plata property, he notified Agustín of his intention. The latter sent José and Carlos to help with the work. It became a regular habit, during those days, for José and Carlos to take out their Bibles at night to read to the whole family.

Instead of arguing at any wild tangent just for the sake of argument, as he previously had done, Marco began asking searching questions regarding their faith. Being who he was, Marco did not explain the reason for his change of attitude; but Rosa was certain it could be linked to the fact that little Santo was walking without much of a limp on a foot marvelously becoming normal.

Telmo Castilla, who had come to whitewash the walls, and other people who had come to pass the time or to get a drink in the country *tienda,* would join the group around the one good lamp in the patio. Some of the listeners openly ridiculed.

"You shouldn't listen to that drivel. It's stupid nonsense."

Antonio was equally outspoken. "I wonder who's being stupid."

"You are, if you think you're going to be an *evangélico,*" Telmo asserted. "Why, those people are a bunch of queers."

"Queers?" broke in another skeptic. "They're cursed infidels."

But Antonio listened more and more carefully to the reading

of the Scriptures and to the explanations his cousins gave. Marco too was paying sharp attention, though he still was living his gay double life. However, Rosa guessed that the building of this new home was a gesture of appeasement—a reassurance of a measure of fidelity that he was too arrogant to put into so many words.

When the house was finished, Telmo surveyed his work with satisfaction and announced that he had passed word around the countryside for a housewarming fiesta.

"They're coming to sing you a good *serenata*," he declared, "and they're bringing their own liquor. So you haven't a thing to do but show them around."

"Well," remarked Marco jocosely, "if the whole neighborhood is coming, we'll see if they can raise the new roof." Then to please Telmo or with deliberate intent to needle his nephews, he added, "We'll dance. You can read your Bibles. That'll be the liveliest crowd, and biggest, you've ever had a chance to preach to. Maybe you can make a bunch of converts."

José grinned good-naturedly. "It doesn't strike me as the best occasion to read the Sacred Scriptures."

"What's wrong with taking a few drinks with my neighbors?" Marco asked testily, not really expecting an answer. "And how am I going to get my girls married off if I don't show them off to the young bucks in the neighborhood?"

"Oh, Papá," laughed his eldest. Alicia had just turned sixteen.

José was serious, as he had been when he promised Rosa that Santo's foot would be straightened. Almost in prophetic solemnity, he said, "I believe God is going to show you tonight what is wrong with this kind of entertainment. Mark my words, everything is going to go wrong."

Marco's brother, Miguel, who lived not too far from Aspasica, brought his whole family to the housewarming. Among the merrymakers from the surrounding community were many acquaintances who had come from long distances, so that the new house was crowded with guests.

As the evening became noisier and tongues became at once

thicker and sharper, someone started a dispute with Don Miguel Franco. Marco stepped in to set things straight. Unfortunately, Marco had had as much to drink as the men who were at odds with each other. Hot-tempered at any time, he became furious when they paid no attention to their host and continued shouting insults.

Later, nobody could tell Rosa just what had happened or who had struck the first blow, but soon Marco was fighting with his own brother—the host with his guest. Miguel's sons joined the fracas on their father's side. In a moment it developed into a free-for-all of flashing fists, and soon machetes were flashing as well. Finally, somebody shot off a gun.

Now thoroughly aroused and blazing with wrath, Marco knocked against the table with the flat of his machete blade.

"Que en seguida me desocupen la casa!"

Though Marco was conspicuously slender of build, not one of the other men had any desire to tangle with a person so beside himself with fury. His eyes blazed from one to another in the room. The amateur musicians let their music die in midmeasure. Couples that had not been involved in the brawl spun to instant attention. Marco repeated his peremptory order.

"Telmo," he roared, addressing the man whose idea the party had been, as though he were responsible for this eventuality as well. "Get these people out of my house. Immediately!"

While Marco stood rigidly watching, the crowd of guests—people who had been invited as his best friends and well-wishers—left sullenly and aloof and melted quickly away into the night. His new house, in scandalous disorder, mocked him silently for his breach of hospitality.

Sobered by what he had done and by the stricken faces of Antonio, Alicia, and Natividad, who stood staring at him wordlessly, Marco walked woodenly to the older house, where Rosa was putting the children to bed. Without a word to her, Marco jerked open the door of the storeroom where the Plata boys slept. He almost stumbled over José, who had come to the darkened room to pray. José got up from his knees.

"All right," snapped Marco irascibly, glaring at the young man's face, which was wet with tears, "you might as well say it. You were right. The whole thing ended in a fiasco. Everything went wrong, as you said. But I'm in no mood to hear you repeat it."

"Uncle Marco—"

"If you say one word to me, I'll beat you to the floor!"

Knowing Marco's explosive temper, the boys left early the next morning. José pressed his own Bible into Antonio's hands. "It will be your responsibility now, Toño. Alicia has no use for the *evangelio,* and Aunt Rosa can't read. Keep reading the Word of God. It will show you the way of a good life."

Marco had other views, however. Mortified and angry at the outcome of his housewarming, he now seemed to connect it with José's prediction of disaster.

"Give me that book!" he barked on the first evening that Antonio brought it out to the patio. "It's this book that's jinxed us. I'm going to throw it into the fire."

"Marco," Rosa protested, "the book belongs to José. You can't just destroy it like that."

"I can't?" He swung on Rosa with an oath, but she stood her ground.

"They spent weeks working for us, building the house, without a peso of pay, and you let them go without thanking them. Is this how you demonstrate your gratitude?"

His belligerence ebbed slightly under logic. "Then get the blasted thing out of my sight," he ordered. "I don't want to see that *evangélico* Bible again!"

Rosa packed the Bible into a trunk into which Marco would in all likelihood never look, but she did it with real regret. The healing of her son was not a gift to be accepted without a great yearning to know more about the Giver—this One who had listened to her prayers. Even if the Bible's assurances of a richer, an eternal life, could never be hers because of the rancor in her soul, she would miss the evening sessions over the Sacred Scriptures very deeply.

Rosa had not forgotten her vow to this living *Cristo*. She intended to become openly an evangelical and tell others of this eternal hope, even if she herself could never attain to ·it. She began to long for God to help her find forgiveness—to work in her the miracle of a forgiving heart.

She had allowed Marco to intimidate her into denying her wholehearted allegiance to the gospel on the day she had declared her faith in Christ's healing power. She had backed down then, and she had confessed her ingratitude and cowardice with tears. She promised the *Cristo* that she would begin to tell others and that she would lead her children into this faith.

She told herself this and repeated it in her prayers, but she wondered if she really would ever have the courage to say so in Marco's hearing. Would God expect her to pay such a high price for her faith? Day by day she battled this question in her heart.

One day, in the middle of June, a couple of men came into the Aspasica neighborhood to sell patent medicines, spices and other household odds and ends. Marco invited them into the patio and offered them *tinto*. When Rosa brought the coffee, one of the men, José Elías Rico, led the conversation around to the Sacred Scriptures.

"Oh, we've got one of those books around somewhere," exclaimed Marco, congenially. He turned to Antonio, then to Rosa. "Where'd you put it?"

Her hands trembling with eagerness and some trepidation, Rosa fumbled at the bottom of the trunk for the Bible and took it out to the patio. Antonio was there as well as Alicia and Natividad.

Alicia glanced at Antonio with upraised eyebrows and a slight gesture of surprise. Antonio, however, ignored his sister's attempt at covert impudence and leaned forward eagerly while Señor Rico found his place and began to read. His exposition of what the Scriptures said answered many of the questions that had been puzzling Rosa during these days. She was stung by his declaration that any man who believed these truths would proclaim them to everyone he knew, not matter what the cost.

Antonio got up and paced back and forth on the veranda, and Rosa guessed at his agitation, for her own heart was pounding like that of a captured bird. In a few minutes Antonio swung around and crushed out his cigarette decisively.

"No more cigarettes for me. I'm taking a stand as an *evangélico.*"

Alicia hooted derisively, "Well, give your cigarettes to me. I'll smoke them!"

More quietly, Rosa also made known her commitment to Christ. Pale and apprehensive of Marco's reaction, she nevertheless declared her faith in Jesus Christ, telling of Santo's crippled foot and its miraculous healing. Even as she spoke, she realized that she had irrevocably announced her allegiance, and now that it was out she was no longer afraid.

Surprisingly, Marco did not make the wild scene she had anticipated. He seemed to be deeply preoccupied the rest of the day, and when Antonio asked him, before his next trip to Ocaña, to buy him a hymn book and his own Bible, Marco merely nodded. The purchase, Rosa knew, meant contacting Rico or another of the evangelicals in Ocaña. She now knew that Francisco Velásquez, the cobbler, was indeed one of them.

That his family had become interested in what he called their heresy did not appear to concern Marco too deeply at this time, for he actually had no genuine religious convictions of his own. The evidences of spiritual reality and the bold purposefulness he had seen in Rosa and in his son were upsetting his tranquillity. Until now, when he had roared, his family had trembled. In the present novel state of affairs he seemed to have lost his power. It was as though a greater than he had assumed authority in his home.

Not much later, when Pedro Castilla came to pass the time of day with him, Marco nodded absentmindedly as his guest recounted his experiences in preparing a batch of home brew. Pedro asked for a couple of glasses, and Marco sampled his product.

"Want to buy it?"

"Why don't you peddle it yourself at the fiesta?"

"How about selling me some of the empty pop bottles from your store, then?"

"Help yourself. It's too much bother to lug them all the way back to Ocaña anyway. If you want to, you can stay here and sell it from the store."

Pedro laughed. "Here? When tomorrow is the twenty-fourth of November? Anybody knows you can get more for liquor on the plaza."

Because she was the patron saint of Aspasica, the fiesta of Saint Catalina would draw nearly the whole populace to mill about the plaza all day and to dance almost all night. The festivities would start that evening. Pedro would have two good nights of business, and would probably run out of home brew before it was over.

Marco had reminded his family of the fiesta, but their unaccustomed lack of enthusiasm, he discovered, did not stem from forgetfulness. Neither Antonio nor Alicia were planning to go with him that evening. Their decision angered him, and the thought of riding into town alone brought on a black mood of resentment.

"Killjoys!" Rosa heard him mutter angrily under his breath when he went to the bedroom to dress. She realized he was ready to fly into a rage if these evangelicals in his family had connived some means of keeping him from the hilarity of which they seemingly no longer approved. She held her breath, fearful that he would find fault with anything.

Marco slammed the door, fully expecting evidences of some obstructive attempt to thwart his own enjoyment; but Rosa had put out his shirt, clean and beautifully ironed. Instead of feeling relieved, however, he seemed strangely disturbed. Rosa smiled when she heard him rumble, "What's come into her?"

In times past, Rosa admitted, Marco had had to go to a party with a ruined disposition and a soiled shirt because of her neglect or perversity. Tonight, without a word from him, she had served supper earlier than usual. Her thoughtfulness perplexed him.

Rosa knew very well that her consideration was unusual as it was deliberate. Many changes had come into her life since she had made that declaration of commitment to Christ. A joy and peace of mind far beyond her expectations had quietly flooded her life and seemed to have little relationship to circumstances. Much of her work, because of her primitive housekeeping equipment, was still drudgery, but even she herself had noticed a lilt of sheer happiness in her voice. Did Marco notice these things? Hadn't she caught him a time or two looking almost wistful, as though he was being left out of something she was enjoying?

He must be glad, however, that she didn't nag anymore. She didn't feel like it, for *things* had become less important. Antonio's attitudes had changed, too. She might merely be noticing that, of course, because they understood each other better since they had started praying together.

Antonio now came to where she was sitting out in the patio. He nodded in the direction of the bedroom. "What's he doing so long in there? It never takes him that long to get dressed."

"He's just sitting—not doing anything," offered el Chico.

A few minutes later Marco came out into the patio and sat down on the veranda step. He was wearing his work clothes. Rosa was puzzled with his silence and at his delay.

"Didn't you find your shirt, Marco? It's on the bed."

"Well, do *evangélicos* go to fiestas?" he retorted somewhat testily and stared out into the sky where the evening star had made its appearance.

"But you'll be late, Marco." A born extrovert and naturally gregarious, Marco never missed a fiesta.

He shrugged, half angrily, as though somehow she was to blame for his decision. Could he possibly mean that he was considering becoming an evangelical? Certainly they had prayed that this would happen, but wouldn't he have to stop his relations with his mistress before he adopted the evangelical way of life?

Surely, even if Marco was convinced that this was the true way, wouldn't Efigenia effectively block any inclination he had toward entering it? Marco loved Efi. At the beginning Efigenia might have been nothing but a diversion, but Rosa had faced the fact long ago that Marco loved her. Men are polygamous. Marco loved Efi as deeply as he loved her. He could no more stop loving Efi than Rosa could stop hating her. For them both, Efigenia was like a great barrier that closed off their entrance into this life, into this eternal life.

Rosa saw Alicia shrug. Was the girl thinking, with some resentment, of the violent end of his own party not too long before? Could Marco be remembering how often his drinking resulted in unpleasantness? Liquor at tonight's festival was inevitable. Rosa breathed a sigh of relief. Tomorrow he might go, but tonight he would be sober. She always dreaded the sequels to these bouts on the bottle.

Later, after the family had gone to bed, Marco got up in response to a pounding at the door.

"It's me, Telmo Castilla." There had been an argument, he explained, and Pedro had been shot. "They've got him in the tavern storeroom, Marco. He's bad. I don't want to stay with him alone."

"I'll come in the morning," said Marco brusquely, without even opening the door for Telmo, who struck at it with some object a few times to vent his displeasure at Marco's indifference. Marco came back to bed.

"Sounds like he's whacking at the door with his machete," growled Marco. "He's drunk, of course." He drew the covers up over his head as if to shut out the thought of Pedro's need of him, or his imminent death. Was Marco thinking also of the hope of the gospel? of life after death? He tossed in bed with sudden, angry movements. Once he spoke out aloud, somewhat defensively.

"There's no question of Telmo being alone. You know how it is. There'll be a roomful, all of them soaked."

Yes, Rosa knew how it would be—how it always was. To keep from thinking they—these men who were watching someone die—would keep drinking. Often there was more fighting because of their excess. These vigils were an old story, and Marco had taken part in many of them.

Neither of them slept, and Marco got dressed a long while before dawn. Rosa got the fire started to get his breakfast.

"Just *tinto*," Marco said, pacing the veranda.

"I'm heating an *arepa*," urged Rosa. "It won't take any longer than heating water for *tinto*."

Marco went on with his silent, intense pacing, oblivious that she had spoken. When she served him, he shoved the food from him with a gesture of repugnance.

"Well, that's life," he said cryptically as he reached for his coat. "Who knows? Maybe his own home brew was the death of him."

Pedro was still alive that morning but unconscious. Marco remained at Telmo Castilla's home throughout the day and most of the following night. When Rosa responded to his familiar knock at the door and let him in, Marco was grim but, surprisingly, he was sober.

"He's gone?"

Marco grunted assent. "Never regained consciousness. He's dead."

Marco spoke as though he still could not believe his own words. A day before the fiesta Pedro had been here, joking with him and talking trivialities. Now he was dead. There would be a wake for Pedro, but could its solemnity effect the finality of death? Wasn't it too late?

"I don't need God," Pedro had proclaimed to all and sundry in the very tavern where he had been shot. Marco had laughed at his tipsy braggadocio. And they had laughed, too—these defeated men who now had held vigil over Pedro's last hours. Pedro, thus encouraged, had blustered further about being free—master of his own fate. Marco had joked about it when he came home that day. Did Marco feel the heavy sickness that dragged at Rosa's being as she pondered his sudden confrontation with eternity? He knew that Pedro had gone out to meet the fate he had chosen.

Marco had lived as had Pedro—hilariously ignoring the thought of death and the reality of eternity. "Living it up" they had called it. Now Pedro had lived it up; he'd lived up all the life that there would ever be for him. Marco knew just how empty such a life really was. Would eternity offer more? Pedro had had no time to repent, to make reparation.

"Are you going to the wake?" Rosa spoke into the darkness, knowing that Marco was not asleep.

"No."

Marco turned over, pulling the cover up over his head in a gesture precluding further conversation. In the morning he astonished the whole family with the declaration that he would never take another drink.

"It was liquor that did it for Pedro," he said decisively. Then, clearing his throat and glaring about at each of them as though to challenge their right to ridicule or disbelieve him, he spoke again with fierce resolve, "And from today, I'm following the Lord."

Before any of them had recovered from their surprise he had swung out of the house. A moment later they saw him striding out toward his farm with a hoe over his shoulder.

"I'd better get out there," muttered Antonio into their stunned silence.

Now that Rosa's prayers had been answered so abruptly, Rosa found that she could not believe Marco's assertion. She found too many obstacles between his statement and any possibility of Marco's being able to live up to it.

"Do you think he's serious about it?" Alicia asked, some time during the morning. She did not need to elucidate. Nobody had been thinking about anything else since Marco had spoken. All of them knew how very much was involved in such a decision on Marco's part—cataclysmic changes for him and a strange and wonderful new life for them as a family.

"Of course, Alicia," replied Rosa. "He wasn't joking."

"I know that, Mamá," returned Alicia, probably thinking of the same difficulties that were in Rosa's own mind. "What about—" Alicia flushed and retreated from that thought to propound another almost as hard to answer. "Can an alcoholic stop? I mean—" she stammered to cover what seemed an accusation of someone she truly loved. "Hasn't Papá got to the place where he *has* to keep drinking when he starts?"

And could he refrain from taking that first drink? When something angered or worried Marco or a drink was offered him as a gesture of conviviality, could Marco really adhere to the rigid standards of the gospel as Señor Rico had very forcibly outlined for them from the Scriptures? Her nephews, too, had said that evangelicals do not even smoke. Surely Marco had not seriously intended them to believe that all that Rosa was thinking of would be ended?

When Marco returned from the field, Rosa sensed a strained wariness in the attitude of the children. She herself was at a loss for words of either a casual or serious nature. Marco did not seem in a mood for conversation of any kind, so he was providing no indication of what was going on in his own mind.

Instead of bringing the Bible to the patio and commandeering the one lamp as he had been doing nightly for the past few weeks, Antonio glanced at Rosa uncertainly. When Marco lost his natural garrulity, they had all learned to expect him also to become irascible, flying into an unreasonable rage over trifles. If Antonio should appear to be putting pressure on his father or testing whether his earlier statement was just an avowal evoked in a passing mood, the boy could not be sure that his father would not react violently.

Marco brought the lamp out himself and began examining his thumb, mumbling something about a thorn. Rosa silently went for a needle which Marco took without comment and began to poke exploratively into his calloused hand. The whole family's activities were somehow suspended with all their attention focused on him. When he gave up on the thorn, Tive was waiting at his elbow with the iodine and a small bit of cotton. The children were standing by solemnly as though he were performing major surgery.

Suddenly Marco looked around, aware of the tension. "Why all this fuss over nothing? Haven't I ever had a sliver before?" Then he added peremptorily, "Get the Bible."

Marco remained uncommunicative and aloof during the days that followed. Perhaps, thought Rosa, the death of his friend had been an unusually great shock. She did not for a moment entertain the delusion that Marco was restrained through embarrassment over a hasty avowal he was far from carrying out. Marco had never been bothered by so scrupulous an adherence to his word. If Marco changed his mind that was his own business, and no one ever had the effrontery to remind him of a previous pronouncement.

Once, during the customary wake for the dead, Marco went into Aspasica, but he returned a few hours later.

"It's a good thing Pedro can't hear their jabbering," he muttered as he came into the patio. "All those guys are staggering drunk. Who wants to think about what's next for any of them?"

Saturday night he made another announcement. "If I'm going to get to the church services, I've got to get going before sunup."

It was his first statement of any kind to indicate what had been going on in his mind during the past few days. Rosa could see that Antonio was dying to accompany his father, but he seemed to sense that this Sunday was peculiarly Marco's.

He left at dawn, taking the long, hard trail to Ocaña, where he joined the handful of evangelicals in their morning service. Sometime during that meeting, Marco declared himself a recruit to their faith, though he confessed that he did not know much about it except that he sensed its reality. He knew, of course, that one did not become an evangelical by permitting his name to be added to a church membership list.

Entregarse al evangelio—the term invariably used by the sturdy-hearted Colombians who had taken their stand in this new Christian movement—meant total commitment to the gospel, to Christ. Inseparable from faith in Jesus Christ was the gospel—the proclamation of His reality and of the change that God and man expect of one who is rightly related to Him. An evangelical was a witness.

Witnessing did not necessarily mean much talking, though Marco had never been a man to mince words. One of his first acts as an avowed evangelical was to clear out his stock of liquor and tobacco from the store. The fact that Marco did not even try to make some profit from these rejected wares, but destroyed the entire stock, struck the neighborhood as outrageous waste. Marco Franco's astounding adoption of evangelical standards provided a juicy tidbit of gossip such as is not allowed to hang unplucked on a mountain village grapevine.

When challenged to account for his seeming madness, Marco pointed a calloused finger at an arresting and colorful poster that he had tacked up on the sala wall even before he had started clearing his shelves. The poster provided a detailed pictorial declaration of his present beliefs. His neighbors and customers, young and old, soon were studying the scenes that probably had been inspired by Bunyan's *Pilgrim's Progress.*

To the left of the graphic picture, a voluptuous statue of Venus and the squat figure of Bacchus straddling a wooden keg were mounted on high pedestals on either side of a wide gateway. Crowds wandered in, indifferent to warning signs along the broad street that led, at the end, to a toppling city in lurid flames. Dark, bat-winged demonic beings darted through the smoke, above which hung a luminous balance, the symbol of judgment. However, the eyes of people who stood before the poster were caught in the detail of the foreground where were pictured empty pleasure, lust, cruelty and other vices of which most of them were guilty.

On the right, a man in clerical attire was pointing burdened pilgrims to an inconspicuous and narrow gate that opened on a path toward the cross. On the most difficult part of the precipitous trail that led upward toward the glory of the celestial city, lurked a lion crouched for a spring upon any who would pass to climb onward. Above the entire scene was painted an all-seeing eye.

This awesome spectacle hung on a wall of nearly every evangelical church of that area, and most evangelicals had a copy prominently displayed in their homes. For Rosa and Marco, who could not read the Scriptures for themselves, this poster formulated the doctrinal positions they were to follow with all diligence to the end of their days, as indeed it did for most of the believers in rural districts.

As Marco had foreseen, the poster immediately became a conversation piece. Reactions varied according to the temperament of those who studied it.

"Look!" exclaimed one of a group of giggling girls. "It's the women with umbrellas that go in here. If you carry an umbrella, you'll never make it to heaven!"

"Is it wrong to borrow money, do you think? Or just to go with it into the Casino?"

"You know, we'd better send one of these pictures to the government. *They* run the lottery. Do they know they're all on their way to hell?"

"It's a good thing I've never gone anywhere on a train. This one's going right into hellfire!"

"What about buses? Don Marco, they don't have any buses on this picture. Where do buses go?"

"Don't you worry yourself about buses, señorita," Marco replied. "What you can see, that's enough to make you repent."

Others, more thoughtful, did not pick out the trivia of the poster. It illustrated the trend of their own lives all too clearly. Some walked away silently thoughtful; others stalked out scowling with resentment over what seemed a personal affront.

"So war is sin," said one of Marco's customers, studying the picture. "Does this mean that, if the Liberals start fighting, you won't join us in shooting it out with them?"

"The Liberals won't make any trouble," said Marco. "Gaitán's a good man, and he's not going to lead any fighting."

"Gaitán?" The questioner swung toward Marco and eyed him sharply. "The election is over, Marco. And Gaitán lost it." "So he lost the election!" retorted Marco. "He still leads the Liberals. It's what's going on down in Caldas that'll make Gaitán president the next time we vote, and decent Conservatives will help him get in next time. Nobody likes to see his neighbor murdered and his home set afire. And that's the kind of government Ospina is giving us."

Jorge Eliécer Gaitán, idol of the Colombian masses, had raised himself, by sheer eloquence and the gift of leadership, from poverty and obscurity to the top of Colombia's powerful Liberal party. Gaitán had lost the last presidential election, in June, 1946, only because the Liberals had split into right- and left-wing factions. Conservative party leader, Laureano Gómez had obtained the election for Mariano Ospina Pérez—a weak and pliable tool to be manipulated at will. That Gómez was behind the sadistic police attacks on Colombian citizens was generally acknowledged. Another of Marco's customers, who had come in at the end of the conversation, voiced that fact.

"President Ospina isn't to blame. It's Laureano Gómez that's behind that bloody business up there around the capital."

A man strode in breathing heavily as though he had ridden hard. He asked for liquor and looked at Marco in openmouthed amazement when the latter stated that he'd given up the sale of hard drinks. "I still carry *gaseosas*," said Marco, reaching for a bottle of the pink, over-sweet soda beverage. The man took it, still speechless with unspoken wonder which one of the other customers attempted to satisfy.

"Don Marco's become an infidel. He's started up the narrow way."

When the traveler still looked utterly bewildered, he was drawn toward the poster, where he was given a vivid—if inaccurate—idea of what it means to be an evangelical. Marco was by no means abashed and stated his beliefs firmly. With the poster as his point of reference, he spoke of repentance and salvation by way of the cross.

3

God's Hand on the Gun

THE POSTER depicting Pilgrim's progress toward the Celestial City continued to draw the attention of Marco's customers. While they were making captious comments about the picture, they were eyeing even more closely his clean break with the illustrated vices. Nor did Marco leave the matter up to their keenness of observation. Where Rosa waited for a propitious opening to introduce the subject of her miraculously answered prayer and her ensuing faith, Marco barged into a declaration of his reversal of viewpoint and life. With no encouragement whatsoever, he witnessed of his new faith and exhorted earnestly to repentance. What he lacked in doctrine, he made up in enthusiasm.

How complete Marco's reversal had been, Rosa was to discover from some of her Aspasica neighbors when she accompanied Marco to a christening in Miguel Franco's home some weeks after Marco's conversion. At the feast following the ceremony, an acquaintance of Rosa's withdrew, with a nod and a significant smirk, from a tight cluster of women who had been engaged in excitedly animated but sotto voce chatter. She drew Rosa—as well as the undivided attention of many more than the simpering and abruptly hushed group of women—into a corner of the crowded patio with an air of great mystery.

"Is it true," she whispered, patently bursting to wring from Rosa the story she would waste no time in sharing with her friends, "is it true that Marco has had a row with Efigenia?"

"So that's what all this commotion is about!" exclaimed Rosa, bursting into a hearty laugh. "Why don't you ask Marco—or Efi? Do you think they take me into their confidence about their private goings on?"

"You mean he hasn't said a word—even to tell you what he thinks of her?"

"I only hope he doesn't talk any more to her about me than he lets me know about her," said Rosa, more seriously.

"Well, if you want to know," retorted her inquisitor turned informant, "Efi's been going all over town telling what a skunk Marco is. Everybody knows they must have had a knock-down-and-drag-out brawl!"

"Everybody," corrected Rosa with some amusement, "but me."

"I don't believe it," exclaimed the other. "Marco's not the sort to get into a fight like that and not show he's mad, even if he won't talk about it. When did it happen?"

Rosa happened to look up to find Marco's quizzical glance on her. From across the patio he had been observing the easily interpreted pantomime with secret enjoyment. Then the obvious solution struck Rosa with a sudden impact.

"I think I know when it happened," said Rosa. "I didn't know that he had made any move toward it, but to be a proper *evangélico* he'd have to break off that affair. Well, he's become an *evangélico*—and so have I."

"And you mean, after all that to-do of Efi's, that's all it amounts to?"

"The *evangelio* amounts to a great deal," replied Rosa. "Still I'd hate to be in Efi's place!" She was amused at the talemonger's expression of disappointment over what had promised to be such a magnificent scandal. Suddenly Rosa found herself feeling genuinely sorry for Efigenia—the woman she had never wished anything but ill.

Her amusement was swept away by a mighty wave of exultation that obliterated all consciousness of her surroundings. The fettering shroud of her hatred had fallen from her soul so gently she had not known when the bitterness had gone. God had worked in her the forgiveness she could never have gained by striving, and even now she knew that she, too, had been forgiven. Like Marco, she'd become a true evangelical! She had been accepted by God, and she knew it as surely as though God had given her a document of proof with His signature and seal.

Only gradually did Rosa become aware that Marco, on the other side of the patio, had been drawn into the center of a ring of bantering friends of his own. Offered a drink, Marco had refused politely but firmly. For Marco to be sober at a fiesta of any sort was completely out of character, and it was not long before he was being twitted about his unsociable attitude.

"Liquor killed Pedro Castilla. I've not had a drink since," Marco declared.

"Well, all of us have quit one time or another," said one of the men, "but we all get back to it."

"Sure, and today's as good a time for it as any."

Marco, delighted with such a good opportunity and so large an audience, began to tell about Santander's foot, of Rosa's declaration of her faith in the promises of the Sacred Scriptures, and of both their acceptance of the evangelical doctrines.

"I wasn't sure just how it would go here," he added. "I've never been able to stand around while someone else had a drink. But I know it and can say it now. I don't even *want* a drink. And if you ask me, that's a bigger miracle than what happened to Santo's crippled foot. Have you seen the little fellow walk?"

Duly informed, the priest who had christened Miguel's child approached Marco a few minutes later. "Is it true," he asked, "that you've forsaken the church?"

"Are you telling me," retorted Marco with a chuckle, "that you've considered me a good Catholic all these years? I'm not forsaking the church but my own evil ways."

"You were baptized into the Catholic church."

"And that's about where it ended, padre," Marco confessed.

"Whatever profession of piety I ever made in church was humbug. Now I know I have the real thing."

"The real thing?"

"Well, like I was telling the men here. I've lost my thirst for liquor—and you know what a soak I've been. Then there's our crippled boy. He's walking now. God hears evangelical prayers, and that's something that never happened to us before."

"I doubt whether it was the power of *your* faith that made the difference. If there's a change—"

"No, it wasn't my faith," replied Marco. "As for change in the boy's foot—there's no doubt about it. That's what made me start to listen. It was Rosa's nephew—"

"Stop arguing with the padre," snapped one of the bystanders.

"Who's arguing?" retorted Marco. "I was just telling him..."

"Shut up!" growled the guest, who had imbibed a bit too freely. Obviously he felt inclined to make more of the situation than it warranted.

"Come over and take a look," invited Marco. "Then I won't have to do any talking."

"I'll knock your teeth out, so you won't *feel* like talking," the man cried, quickly belligerent. His fist drove home his last words with two quick punches to Marco's mouth.

Marco stepped backward with cut, bleeding lips. He reached into his pocket for a handkerchief. Judging from Marco's past reactions or from what his own would be in the circumstances, the ruffian yelled, "Grab him, he's pulling a gun."

Someone pinned down Marco's arms, informing the quickly gathering crowd that Marco had started the fight, arguing with the priest. Asking no questions, several men began belaboring Marco with their fists, knocking him down to the patio cobblestones. One of the children dashed into the house to find Miguel Franco.

Don Miguel strode out quickly to find his brother with his back to a wall. His assailant and two other men had drawn their guns, and one of them was decidedly unsteady. The situation had developed beyond the point of questions or remonstrance, Miguel knew, so he pulled Marco brusquely from his guests' clutches and stepped between him and the guns.

"Out of the way," growled one of the men. "He's a heretic."

"So that's what it is!" exclaimed Miguel. "Well, now, you listen to me. I'm not in sympathy with Marco's new religious views, but whoever shoots my brother will have to kill me first!"

The man who started the trouble edged over to the side, still fingering his trigger menacingly. When Miguel drew his own gun, he shrugged and muttered sourly that shooting is too good for infidels, anyway. "Just wait," he added, glowering at his host.

"Let it be a long wait," snapped Miguel. "And don't try anything here on my premises." He drew Marco into the house with no great gentleness. "What's the matter with you? You don't have to start preaching your propaganda at my fiesta," he growled.

"I wasn't preaching. I just said—"

"You haven't stopped preaching since you took up this nonsense. Just keep your mouth shut about it."

"Miguel, if you'd only listen! It's so—"

"I said, keep quiet about it. You've caused enough of a brawl."

On the way home, Marco casually opened the subject that Rosa would not have trusted herself to introduce. "So they told you about Efigenia, did they?"

"Yes," said Rosa. "They say that you've had a spat."

"That may be Efi's viewpoint. I just had a talk with her about the *evangelio* and how it affects our relationship."

"You know, Marco, I'm going to have to talk with her, too. The *evangelio* has changed my feelings toward her, and I want her to forgive me. We've had words—mine have not always been kind."

"Have you noticed that when you do something hard, that you end up feeling better? Is it a cleaner conscience—or what?"

"I think it's recognizing that God has done something we

couldn't possibly have done. Like, for instance, your not drinking today. It's a wonder and awe that God is involving Himself with us. Or just knowing that He's *living*—and real!"

"You may have something there, Rosa. I'm sure obedience has something to do with it, but what gave me a real jolt was that I didn't grimly fight the liquor today. I even told the fellows it's a miracle. And it sure is."

Antonio enthusiastically joined his parents in an earnest testimony of God's goodness and power, and the peace of heart that the message of the gospel brings. Even the older girls, though not committed, did everything they could to vindicate their parents' faith to critical friends. They spoke more of the transformation of their father and the wonderful change in their home.

Rosa had been watching for an opportunity to visit her old rival. One Sunday afternoon she accompanied little Leonilde home after the child had had a tumble. Seeing Rosa, Efigenia became agitated, thinking the child had been more seriously hurt than was apparent. Rosa reassured her and spoke of the gospel and the joy it can give. When she asked Efi's forgiveness for unpleasantness she had caused, Efi lashed out in harsh and bitter anger against Rosa, against Marco, against this same gospel that was spoiling her life. Rudely, she ordered Rosa from the house.

As the months passed, a few curious adults and neighborhood children ventured in for the family's Sunday *cultos*[1] in response to their frequent invitations, though Marco usually rode in to attend Sunday services in Ocaña.

On one Sunday, when Marco was gone, the family had begun their service as usual with a hymn. Even Emalina and el Chico sang, lustily and almost in tune. Suddenly a man appeared in front of the house shouting abuse and profanity. When he threw stones through the open door, Antonio went over to close it.

"It's just el *chiflado*," Antonio mumbled, recognizing a harm-

[1]Meeting for worship.

less village idiot. "They must have put him up to it. He wouldn't have thought of coming here like this—not by himself."

The following Sunday, the mentally defective man returned; but, when the Francos did not retaliate, other youths joined him, even battering at the barred doors. Finally a barrage of stones and shouted insults that terrified the children ended the service.

Marco, earnestly desirous of learning more about his new faith, ignored these harassments and continued to attend the Ocaña services. His absence Sunday after Sunday emboldened the vandals still farther. They hacked at anything accessible to them or carried it with them. A cane mill was demolished on one of these Sunday raids, and a cow was stolen.

That week, Marco hastily erected a lean-to stable of cane stalks adjoining the house, so that he could keep an eye on his livestock. He had been inclined to make light of their personal danger, though Rosa had described the moblike quality of the attacks. To her relief, he gave up his weekly trips to Ocaña.

After Marco stayed home for the family *cultos,* the molestations stopped. Still regretting that the family's safety forced him to miss the Ocaña meetings, Marco announced that when Christmas came, the entire family would ride down for the program. His proposal met with instant and jubilant approval, especially from the younger children, who had never been to the city.

With the Christmas buying season approaching, Marco needed to replenish his stock of supplies for the store. The distance and the shopping necessitated an overnight trip to Ocaña. Antonio, in his late teens, was responsible for the family's safety during his father's absences. He was always careful, of course, to bring in all their cattle and livestock before nightfall. This time he was especially uneasy.

"Well, they've left us alone," he sighed, when the evening advanced and nothing had happened.

"Maybe nobody saw Papá leave. That would account for it."

"And why do they only bother us when Papá's away?" said Tive.

"They haven't forgotten that Papá was as quick with a trigger as he was with his temper," retorted Antonio, grinning.

"I'm glad you say *was,* Toño," said Rosa. "And I'm glad all of you can see how much he's changed."

"In a way," replied Antonio, "I'm glad the other people haven't seen it. They might lose their respect for his shotgun."

Later, after they had gone to bed, Rosa was wakened by a strange sound in the stable. She lay listening for a moment. An iguana on the thatched roof that had been extended to cover the stable could make a disturbing rustle. But this crackling?

Convinced that something was wrong, she called Antonio, who ran outside for a look.

"The stable's on fire," he yelled.

Already up, Rosa shook the girls awake. The urgency in her voice brought Carmelo out of bed as well. Between them, they picked up the smaller children and carried them outside.

Antonio had plunged into the flaming stable and, with a machete, cut the ropes by which the cattle had been tied. He had nearly finished driving out the bewildered animals when Rosa had her family safely out of the house. The fire quickly spread across the entire roof.

At great risk and hurrying feverishly, they were able to save most of their clothes, some bedding and a few other valuables. Had the house, too, been built of cane, Rosa thought gratefully, some of the family might have perished in the blaze. The stable was a total loss.

Rosa put the sleeping children down on the bedding they had managed to bring out. Antonio, the girls and even Carmelo helped her fling buckets of water across the burning thatch in a vain attempt to save more of their belongings. Even after the roof collapsed down within the walls, they kept carrying more water and throwing it on the burning framework.

Soon after dawn, Rosa and the girls took the smoke-blackened bedding and clothing to the river to wash, after they had cooked yuca from the field for their breakfast. When Marco returned, she was helping the girls spread out the clothes to dry on bushes not far from the house.

Marco had reined his galloping horse to a halt near the ruins of his house. Carmelo was helping Antonio gather the charred remains of the roof supports from among the furniture on which the water-sodden ashes had caked in caustic lumps.

"Where's Mamá?" Marco shouted in quick anxiety. "Where are the others?"

"At the river, washing stuff," said Antonio, brushing ashes off on his pants. "They burned the barn, Papá."

"I was beginning to suspect as much," retorted Marco, his sense of humor coming to his rescue.

As Rosa came around the corner of what had been their home, she saw a reluctant grin appear on Antonio's dejected face.

"I mean that's where they set the fire."

Marco's eyes flashed as they told him about the night attack. An attempt to destroy animals by fire is brutal, but to set fire to a thatched roof under which a whole family is asleep is an act to make the blood boil.

Marco took a deep angry breath, then set his lips tightly against the outbreak of his wrath. Rosa knew how Marco would have settled this matter a few months previously. Could Marco be blamed if he reverted to the only tactics these merciless scoundrels would understand? What, actually, would Marco do?

"We'll replace the roof with tile," he said quietly. Then, his rare humor breaking through, he added, "They've burned my picture, so I can't look up what to do. So we better pray."

Standing in the debris of their home, they prayed for the neighbors who did not understand.

"We'll need backbone, Lord, to keep witnessing to them even if they resent it. Help us to really forgive them, so we can mean it when we tell them how to get peace of heart."

Such a complete reversal of attitude in a man with Marco's

temperament substantiated the power and reality of his faith more forcefully than all his verbal witnessing. Later that evening at *culto* Alicia and Natividad both declared that they were joining their parents in their faith. On hearing them speak, Carmelo, now nine, said simply, "That goes for me, too."

That *culto* was held within the walls of their damaged home, which, with great industry of large and small, they had freed of debris and swept out, washing the cement floor of soot and grime. Within the week the walls were whitewashed again, and the framework for the tile roof was up. When the roof was finished, Marco built a high wall around their back patio for their greater security.

Marco still continued peppering his friends with a barrage of scriptural darts that he kept in the ready shaft of his phenomenal memory. Since the trouble at Miguel's, several of them seemed to be embarrassed in his presence, ostensibly evading him in public, though they listened to what he had to say when they were alone together. Some engaged Marco in inane arguments, others curtly refused to listen to any mention of this new *evangelio*. They spat out the word as though merely uttering its syllables could involve them in its heresy or bring a curse on them. Some old friends seemed to approve outspokenly of the harassment, even of the cold-blooded arson that might have brought their death.

So hostile was their attitude that Marco reluctantly announced that it would not be wise to go to the Christmas program after all, since their absence might invite serious vandalism. As both Marco and Rosa had foreseen, cancellation of this trip brought loud and tearful protests from the younger children. Rosa shared the less effusive disappointment of Antonio and the girls.

Don Francisco Velásquez, the cobbler who inserted tracts into shoes he sold, and who was to have been their host, must have understood the disappointment of the whole family. He sent back a message that turned the children's tears into excited anticipation.

"Missionaries are making a visit of Colombian congregations at Christmas time—four of them. I'll bring them up to visit you." Two of the guests would be women.

"What will we give them to eat—the *Americanos?*" worried Rosa.

"Just what we eat," retorted Marco briskly. "Maybe they don't eat like we do, but we'll feed them better than they know how to cook!"

"And the way I look!" exclaimed Rosa.

Marco followed her glance to her cumbersome figure and grinned. "The gringas have babies, too. Do you suppose they have a different way of carrying them?"

In spite of his bluster, Marco rearranged his store in the sala to make things more presentable for the visiting evangelicals and provide more room for the meeting. Anyone who came into the store was eagerly invited to attend this rare Christmas service.

With real missionaries coming, exulted Marco, all Aspasica would have an opportunity to hear the gospel and be convinced. It did not even occur to him that he must not share the good fortune of this unprecedented visit because of the neighbors' hostility. Though Marco had taken precautions to protect his family and property against abuse, he had not yielded one inch in his outspoken stand for the evangelical faith.

"Now you can ask *them!*" he challenged the men whose captious arguments he had been unable to refute. Marco had many questions of his own that he wanted to ask.

The momentous day arrived, and Rosa and the girls were feverishly preparing for their overnight guests as well as the Christmas meal. Marco puttered excitedly. He would have gone to meet them if they had given him any indication when they would be arriving. As the afternoon advanced, the children began watching the trail from their favorite lookout. Surely their guests would come well in time for their evening meal.

"Who's doing the shooting down there?" Marco demanded of Carmelo, who had come into the house.

"Some sort of *parranda*,[2] Papá," replied the boy. "There were some people on the trail, coming this way. We thought it could be the *evangélicos*. They were almost here—up to that big sharp turn—and then they met these others, and they all went back down, hollering and shooting off guns."

"Why didn't you tell me?" cried Marco. "That sounds like an ambush!"

"No, Marco," cried Rosa. "Surely they wouldn't attack *Americanos!*"

Marco did not even answer her. He called sharply to Antonio. The youth had to run to catch up with his father, who was already hurrying down the trail.

Could the men of Aspasica have dared ambush such important men as the missionaries? These men who had burned the Franco house while the family slept, would they stop at anything? During this season when most of them were drinking more freely than ordinarily, it would not have been hard to organize a mob.

For more than an hour they waited tensely. Each heavy minute dragged roughshod heels across their taut nerves. Then the children dashed into the house.

"Papá is coming . And the men are on the trail!"

Moments later, Marco burst breathlessly in through the double doors. Alicia slammed them after him, seizing the heavy poles with which they had been propping them shut for added security at night.

"Never mind," gasped Marco, still out of breath. "I don't think any of them saw me. I came up by the cow trail from below."

"Was it the *evangélicos?*" asked Rosa. Then before Marco had time to answer, she cried, "Where's Toño?"

"Toño's following them down. They must be past La Playa by now."

"So they're not coming here!"

[2]Revel, carousal.

"No chance. There must be two hundred people in that mob."

"What did they do? Did anybody get hurt? Is Toño back in Ocaña with the missionaries?"

"We hadn't come to the *evangélicos* yet, but we met that little Pepe Arango. He said that's who they were, and that the men had gone after them with guns and machetes. And the kids were throwing stones, he said. So we knew it was the *evangélicos*."

"And you let Toño go on alone?"

"It was Toño that made me come back here, Rosa. When we saw that Aspasica crowd coming back up the trail, Toño said they might head up here and try to clean up on you here in the house. So I said for him to come back here, but he was scared. He said he couldn't hold off that mob alone."

"But what's happening to the boy out there? And our company!"

"Like Toño said, Rosa. Whatever they've done to the *evangélicos* is finished. He just went to see what happened and if there was something we could do for them."

"Did Pepe say anyone was hurt?"

"One, he said, was hurt bad. He didn't know if he was shot, or whether they knocked him out with a *palo*."

"So they were beating them with poles!"

"They must have come right up into the ambush. Around that point they couldn't see even that big crowd until they were there."

Marco began to pace back and forth, back and forth, the full length of the sala. Rosa shared his anxiety. What had happened to their guests, the North Americans? Don Francisco had been with them. Who else had come? Who was it that was hurt? Or had they all been killed down there somewhere along the trail?

"I wish you would have stayed with Antonio until the mob had gone by. One boy alone—"

"If I was going to be any use to you, I had to get here first," replied Marco, without pausing in his steady striding to and fro.

Murder on the trails was no longer an uncommon occurrence. The political climate of Colombia was conducive to senseless violence. Again and again, during the past year, they had been appalled by reports of gruesome crimes committed along mountain trails just like these. The stonings and burning of their home, committed without fear of judicial investigation, represented a dreadful lawlessness that had descended on Colombia after the last election.

"We're forgetting something," said Rosa at length. She placed a hand gently on Marco's arm. "If God could straighten Santander's foot, He can protect His missionaries."

"It's pretty late to ask Him," worried Marco. "The damage was done before we thought to pray."

Nevertheless he kneeled with Rosa, and they poured out their anxiety to God. Sometime after midnight Antonio rapped sharply on the bolted door. Neither Rosa nor Marco had gone to bed; so, after they had deluged Antonio with questions and been reassured that their visitors had not been massacred, Rosa set out food for the three of them. Antonio started from the beginning of his story.

Because of the steepness and danger of the trail, the Ocaña men had deemed it expedient to come on foot. Some Aspasica men had passed the evangelicals, apparently on their way home from Ocaña.

"They started cursing the gringos and the three men from Ocaña—Don Isaias, Don Francisco, and another man I don't know. Then they threatened them and rode off. The *evangélicos* nearly got here, when they were ambushed by the big mob. The men from up here had guns and machetes, and right away they began throwing stones.

"They beat Don Isaias down with *palos*. He fell down on his knees and started praying, because he thought the end had come for him. They couldn't see any escape for any of them; they were being stoned. The missionaries were praying aloud—

the other *evangélicos,* too. Then Don Enrique Castilla aimed his shotgun right at one of the missionaries and pulled the trigger."

Rosa gasped in dismay. "Oh, no!"

Antonio grinned. "Nothing happened, Mamá. The gun didn't go off." He set down his mug and turned toward his parents as he continued. "He shot in the air, and the gun worked. That scared him."

"Is that when they came back?"

"No, but that gave the *evangélicos* a chance to get away, because it scared the others a little, too. They ran down the trail, but Don Isaias was pretty bad hurt. They had to go slow and help him. And the Aspasica men were right after them, throwing stones and swinging their machetes. They shot off their guns some more, but I guess they just did that to scare them, after what happened to Don Enrique.

"When they got down to the canyon, there was a bunch of drunks out on this side of La Playa, just where that ridge facing south goes straight down—in front of Don Alvaro's place there. Well, there they were, between two mobs and with no place to run to. So they stood still to die, thankful that they were ready to go and that they could give their lives to God and for the *evangelio.* That's when Don Alvaro came out of his house and hollered for them to get up on his veranda. And Don Alvaro faced that whole crowd and stopped them."

"But he's an old man!" cried Rosa.

"And he's not an *evangélico!*"

"Don Francisco says he has no explanation for the way the old man acted unless it was God's only way of saving them, so he used one of *them* to protect the *evangélicos.* Anyway, Don Alvaro said, 'You've done enough to these people. They have a right to live, even if they have a religion that's different from ours.' Then he took out his machete. 'Anyone who touches one of these *evangélicos* I personally will kill.'

"Well, they respected him; and Don Francisco and the

others went along home, praising God for saving their lives two times on that trip. I guess by now they're safe in Ocaña."

Not long after Christmas, Gregoria Peñaranda, a midwife, came to stay with Rosa to take care of the delivery of another son, whom they named Jonas. Some Aspasica women came in to see the new baby and to wish Rosa well. It seemed that the neighborhood's ire had spent itself and they would have normal relationships again.

Pablo Peñaranda was also staying with the Francos as long as his sister remained; and, since it seemed unthinkable that the neighbors would cause a disturbance when they were aware of the baby, just eight days old, Marco decided to take the opportunity to restock his store again. Naturally, the family did not advertise the fact that he had gone to Ocaña.

As they had hoped, the day passed without incident. Pablo, interested in the gospel through much that Marco had explained to him, helped Antonio light the gasoline pressure lantern in preparation for their usual family *culto*. The younger children scrambled to get the hymnal, though they had learned many songs by heart by that time. They loved this part of the family devotional time and sang the songs with childish gusto.

Hardly had they begun to sing when a stone, well-aimed, came through the open door and struck the gasoline lantern, breaking the chimney. Other stones sprayed into the room. Little Santander screamed suddenly. A rock had struck a boil and broken it open. He ran from the room shrieking with pain.

Alicia, nearest the double door, slammed it shut. Antonio quickly brought the heavy poles to prop against it. The other children did the same for the back door, though that one was now protected by the high wall that encircled the patio.

A shower of stones pounded on their new tile roof, bouncing down together with fragments of broken tile. By the commotion, it seemed that the whole community had united to destroy them at one stroke. Shouted threats corroborated the impression.

"Kill the infidels!"

"Chop these *evangélicos* into mincemeat."

"Batter them to death."

Men began hacking at the unyielding doors with machetes. Alicia rushed to join Pablo and Antonio as they leaned against the door to keep it from bursting open as heavy men shoved it from outside. They kept pushing, even when machetes began coming through the damaged door.

Alicia gasped when a blade barely missed her cheek. "We can't stand here and let them chop our heads off."

"We can't let them in, either," said Antonio through gritted teeth, his shoulder still against the door though a machete was flashing near his face.

"We'll have to run for it through the pasture," suggested Pablo.

"But Mamá! How can she run? And the baby—"

"If the light were out, we'd at least have a chance to get away, if they get the door open. They wouldn't be able to see us. It can't hold much longer, Antonio."

"They'll have flashlights," replied Antonio. He did turn out the lantern, but that made it more dangerous than ever to lean against the door. They could not see where the machetes were coming through.

Almost immediately, however, the battering lessened. One last rock landed with a heavy crash, and the sound of shattered tile sliding from the roof faded into silence. They could feel an easing of pressure against the door.

"Maybe they just didn't want us to have a *culto,*" Alicia whispered in the uncanny hush. "They've quieted down."

"That's what bothers me," muttered Pablo. "If they were going off, you'd hear them talking. It's *too* quiet."

The suspense of the stillness became more frightening and oppressive than the visible blades of machetes coming through the weakened door or the feel of bodies shoving at it for entrance. It bore a more sinister menace than the shouted threats. Antonio went into the bedroom where Rosa was praying and trying to calm the younger children, who clung to her in frenzied terror.

"Mamá," he said, "Pablo says we should go out to the patio."

"But if we go out into the patio," protested Gregoria, "they'll hear us."

"We'll have to be quiet."

They formed a tight cluster in the patio. The children were too terrified to be a problem. They whimpered softly against Rosa's body, trembling with fear and from the chilling drizzle that was falling. Gregoria gathered the toddlers into the circle of her arms as she knelt with Rosa, praying just as earnestly for God's protection on them all. The children were praying, too, for they all had learned to pray in their daily family *cultos.*

"I think I'm going out there to see what they're doing," whispered Antonio after some time had passed.

"Don't, son," said Rosa. "It's a mob, and they're in a mood to kill. You heard what they were shouting."

"Well, you can't stay out here all night, Rosa," said Gregoria. "Or the baby. Maybe they've gone home."

Antonio slipped out of the patio by way of a gate in the wall. In a moment he was back, his teeth chattering.

"They've got a mountain of rocks ready to throw, Mamá. But they seem to be waiting for something."

"Could they have set a bomb?" said Pablo. "Then we'd better get out of here. But maybe that's just what they're waiting for."

Pablo's suggestion was not altogether improbable. Rosa knew he was thinking of the kegs of gunpowder stored in a dusty alcove of the church together with various other paraphernalia for fiesta celebrating. Almost every man and youth in Aspasica had helped fashion a rocket from that powder. Anyone who could make a rocket could also make a bomb.

After some discussion, the adults each picked up one of the toddlers. Pressing the faces of the smallest against their shoulders as they ran, they sought a sheltered spot beyond the pasture where the babies' crying could not reach the mob crouched near the front of the house. There they prayed for God's intervention to protect their home.

Moments later they were glad they had come away. Small fires springing up along the ground soon began to merge, and their cattle stampeded in all directions.

"They're burning the pasture," growled Pablo, "but I can't figure out what that bunch of scoundrels up near the corral are doing."

Jorge spoke up. "I think they caught one of the cows. They're cutting it up for meat."

"What vicious people!" exclaimed Gregoria. "You can't stay here in this town. It's not safe."

At last they saw that the mob had withdrawn, and they crept back, shaking with cold, damp to the skin. When dawn broke, Antonio discovered that their remaining cows had escaped from the pasture or had been stolen. He took Jorge and Carmelo to help him scour the mountainside for them.

On Marco's return, Pablo described the terror that the family had experienced, while he took Marco out to survey the ravages of the night's attack. The new tile roof had been seriously damaged; the splintered door would have to be replaced.

"It looks as though you've lost most of your livestock, Marco. You'd better get out of here while your family's still alive."

Instead of putting his newly purchased stocks on the shelves, Marco decided to take Pablo's advice. Pablo took Gregoria home, intending to come back the following day with two pack mules. Marco went off to get other pack animals in Aspasica.

Rosa was plunged into the harassing details of organizing household belongings to be moved by pack mule, feeding her large family and taking care of her new baby. Antonio and the boys did not return until almost noon to report gloomily that they had found no trace of the cows. Informed of their plans, Antonio set to with a will, binding into secure packs the bundles the girls had already prepared. The children's lighthearted banter demonstrated, Rosa thought, that they did not realize that the loss of their home and property left the family practically destitute. Momentarily they had chattered about the boys' fruitless search and a recounting of their dangerous stand at the splintering door, but now they were talking excitedly about the world outside of Aspasica that they had only rarely glimpsed.

Their youthful optimism and eagerness was contagious. Soon Rosa could even see that the tragedy that had befallen them might have agreeable compensations. She found herself looking forward to a quieter life, the opportunity to attend church services, and friendships among evangelicals.

Rosa's glance happened to fall on Jorge, his tongue between his teeth in earnest intensity as he helped Antonio pull the ropes tight for knotting.

His serious concentration amused Alicia. "Don't let Jorge get his tongue into the knot," she called. "Then we'll have to tie him onto the pack."

Jorge grinned and withdrew his tongue from public comment, though he used it to make one of his own. "One way of being sure of going."

Jorge! Jorge was Efigenia's son. Now that Marco was leaving Aspasica, who would take care of the farm that now supported her and Marco's other children? Jorge was Efi's oldest son! Jorge obviously had been thinking of it, but had Marco?

Without a word, Rosa inconspicuously rummaged through their personal effects and removed Jorge's clothes. The decision would be Marco's, of course, but she knew what he would have to do. She felt a pang of regret, for the genial lad had become as dear to her as one of her own.

Efigenia—the woman who had embittered her past and imperiled her future—would be left behind in Aspasica. No longer would Rosa need to face, every day, that other household that had divided her own. Yet now her triumph lacked the exultation she might have expected to feel. She felt sorry for the woman.

Rosa paused in her activity to look up toward heaven with reverent gratitude. She had asked God that some day—some vague future day —she might find the grace to forgive. So impossible had it seemed—while her heart burned with hatred—that the prayer had sounded hypocritical in her own ears. Yet her heart now confirmed that her rancor had never returned. God had worked that miracle!

Marco's face was grave when he reached home. Not only had he failed to get the loan of one animal, but men standing in the village square had accosted him with insults and threats, some of them brutal and explicit. Among these men, Rosa felt sure, had been the very ones who—just a week after their attack on the missionaries—had decapitated the mayor's secretary with a machete. Telmo Castilla had lost an eye in that brawl. No one could tell what they might do, spurring each other on as they were doing.

"Don Guillermo said he wouldn't let us pass his hacienda alive. And everybody knows we're getting ready to leave."

"Don Guillermo!" exclaimed Rosa. The man had been a close friend.

"I don't want to worry you, but they mean us harm. The man with Guillermo said it would be like stamping out a nest of rats." Marco decided to leave before morning, and that meant leaving before Pablo returned with the mules. "It's more important to get you away safe—and the children. They won't expect us to leave during the night. I can come back for the other things."

Miguel was allowing Marco to take his donkey, and all the baggage they could take with them would have to be rearranged into a pack for that one animal. Marco insisted Rosa ride his mule, since her condition would not permit her to make that strenuous hike on foot.

Jorge picked his way through the disordered room where all the children were noisily unearthing small treasures they could not bear to leave behind. Jorge's cheeks were smudged with the secret tears he had been ashamed to shed before the others. Unknown to Rosa, he had even found his own bundle. So, Marco

had talked with the boy, as she had foreseen he must do; and
Jorge had come to tell her goodbye.

"Doña Rosa," he began earnestly, making tracings on the
floor with the great toe of his left foot. He was trying so hard
to be brave, but he couldn't go on. Throwing himself at her
feet, he buried his wet face in her lap, sobbing in wild, naked
grief.

Marco came in, shaking his head. "I could bawl, too," he
said, not noticing that Rosa was also crying. "Why couldn't
they leave us alone?"

Later Marco took the boy's hand and walked with him and
his pathetic little bundle across the trail. He still had to make
arrangements for this other family to survive the troubles
brought on by his faith, even though they did not share it.
Rosa busied herself quickly so that she would not have to think
of the scene that was probably taking place at this moment in
the other house.

They ate late that evening—Marco moodily silent, the toddlers nodding, Emalina giggling with Carmelo, Antonio and
the girls exaggeratedly hilarious. Rosa ate hurriedly. She had
to suckle little Jonas before they got away.

After all the lights had been put out in the houses around
them, they silently left their home, slipping out into the dead of
night. Rosa left last, struggling with her memories of the house,
built recently to make things easier for her. What hardness lay
ahead? Almost angrily she brushed away tears that had sprung
into her eyes. Hadn't she set her heart to suffer for the gospel,
even unto death?

Still, worries crowded in on her mind against her wishes.
Would any of these things be left to them? Wouldn't the mad-
dened crowd, missing them, destroy everything that was left?
With what was she to keep house for all her family. What
would they eat? A thought insinuated itself—*sometimes it's
easier to die!*

What about Marco? She was losing only things and was
moping about it. What he had just done would have been no

less painful than cutting out part of his heart. Rosa firmly drew the door outward and snapped the padlock on it.

Astride the donkey, she held out her arms for Jonas. Marco placed Santo, now just over two years old, on the rump of the mule. The toddler clung to Rosa's waist, silent and round-eyed with wonder. Silently Marco picked up his own heavy pack.

Santander, still a baby, began whimpering almost inaudibly into his mother's back, which he had been clutching with the tightness of mute terror ever since the mule had ambled off down the trail. His chubby little arms would tire soon. Rosa drew him forward to ride in the circle of her free arm for greater security.

Almost at once the donkey, which had gone ahead of Rosa's mule, began to slither head foremost down the cliff path, a route so steep that the Ocaña evangelicals had hesitated to bring their North American guests, unencumbered, along the trail on donkeys. Now, hurrying downward through the blackness of night, a misstep of the mule could mean a fearsome fall or sudden death.

Rosa held her baby tightly to herself to absorb the jarring gait of the animal. With her other arm she steadied little Santander and clutched the reins and the pommel of the saddle to steady them all in the steep descent. The trail was strewn with rocks and wound in and out narrowly among heavy boulders that could crush an exposed foot even in daylight riding.

The flight was no less trying for the children who were trudging along on foot. El Chico was less than five years old; Emalina was seven. Carmelo, just turned ten, fairly staggered under the small odds and ends that had been heaped on him one by one. Alicia and Natividad were loaded with as much as they could carry, and both Marco and Antonio had strapped heavy packs to their shoulders and could not carry the youngsters no matter how tired they became.

Day was dawning through a haze of clouds when the weary procession entered the tiny, irregular dead-end street where lived Francisco Velásquez, the cobbler. The children were crying with fatigue. They were footsore and hungry. Doña Emma busied herself with a hearty breakfast for all of them and then found bedding for the children to spread on the floor. Rosa, pale and utterly exhausted, was tucked into the large homemade wooden bed with her infant and the two smallest boys.

Don Francisco and Marco went off at once to find other evangelicals who would return with them to salvage, if possible, the Franco's remaining goods. Antonio and Carmelo left with them.

Marco looked in on Rosa before he left for the mountains. At her unspoken question, he said, "We'll have to report to your brother-in-law about the farm. Will you get Doña Emma to write? Tell them to look us up a place near Agua de Dios, where nobody knows us."

Agua de Dios? The leper colony was in Cundinamarca Province, beyond the capital, Bogotá, and over five hundred kilometers away.

4

Whatever Price We Pay

DONA EMMA SLID the heavy wooden bar from its solid moorings across the double doors which opened on the street. Carmelo, with Emalina and Chico in tow, slipped out to view this unfamiliar aspect of their world grown suddenly larger. Rosa realized that even Carmelo had never been this far from Aspasica. To her amazement, they were back, knocking excitedly on the door, only seconds later.

"What? So soon? Or were you afraid you'd get lost?"

"We found the *tienda!*" cried Emalina, excitedly. "And that's where Papá always could buy us some candy in Ocaña." She exclaimed shrilly about how many more things there were to buy in Ocaña than they had had in their own store. "Oh, you should see it, Mamá! And how many *centavos* will I need for some candy?"

Actually, the shop the children had found was one much like their own, a counter and shelves in the sala of a private home.

"There are a dozen like it in the next two blocks," remarked Doña Emma, amused. "But why doesn't Alicia take them to the market? I'd like to send her for some meat—if she doesn't mind."

"Mind!" cried Alicia eagerly. "I've been wishing I dared go out, but I wanted to stay here to help if you needed me."

Emalina was tapping her mother with a sharp little finger. "How many *centavos* do we need—"

Rosa wished that she need not deny the child the pleasure of

72

making a small purchase on this first wonderful venture into the city. But, with their staggering losses and with more expenses still to come, they could afford nothing but direst necessities. She kissed the excited little girl's slightly grubby cheek.

"You'd better wash your face, Emalina. And take Chico out to the patio and wash him, too."

Natividad came in, looking wistful. Her wish Rosa could grant. "Do you think Alicia will be able to control those live-wires? Why don't we go along, too? Santo and the baby are asleep."

Natividad kissed her mother hurriedly before she skipped off to join the others in the patio around the *pila,* a rectangular cement tank in which water was stored for doing the family laundry. Lacking the convenience of stones by a mountain stream—such as Rosa had enjoyed—Doña Emma pounded her clothes clean on a gently sloping slab built against the *pila.* City people had one great advantage. A twist of the faucet over the *pila* supplied all the water the whole household needed.

Doña Emma gave Alicia a small blue enameled kettle with a lid and a few frayed *peso* notes. "Let the children have a few *centavos* apiece," she instructed.

"I didn't promise them anything," said Rosa.

"And I admired your adroit evasion of what I expected to turn into a tearful tantrum. I'll admit I'm inclined to be more generous because it didn't happen."

The children were excited and awed by this visit to Ocaña. They chattered delightedly about everything they saw.

Aspasica and the other *caseríos* they had passed on the way down were mere huddles of houses set at random near a convenient trail. The houses in Ocaña formed a solid front along the full length of a block. The narrow, raised strip of concrete or brick along which they walked led right along the walls, as though it were meant for a long, communal doorstep.

The closed, double doors were almost identical—taciturn, noncommittal, like masks employed to disguise the character of the home sequestered behind the high walls.

Once a door opened on shining tiled floors, beautiful both in design and color. The children stopped to gaze at this grandeur, their eyes widening even further as they glimpsed a tiled patio beyond the sala. A riot of flowering shrubs and trees, rustling in the breeze, demonstrated the reason why families lived in the enchanting patios around which their dwellings were built.

Another open door on the same street disclosed a home of destitution and shiftless neglect. Dirty and half-naked children were playing on a gouged and unswept earthen floor in a room completely devoid of any furniture. In the patio beyond—a junk-littered patch of weedy yard—scrawny chickens scratched forlornly for insects, and a pig ambled over the veranda to nudge at a listless baby. Another was pushing its snout into an unwashed kettle that stood on the edge of the veranda floor.

Only a few heavily barred and shuttered windows punctuated the contiguous line of house fronts. In a building or two, windows seemed to have been bricked in rather recently. Massive double doors were conspicuously closed and locked. On some, heavy chains were drawn through holes bored right into the wooden frames of both doors and then fastened with one, two, or even three formidable padlocks. Seven- to ten-foot adobe walls, often crowned with spears of broken glass, circled both business quarters and private patios at the rear of each home.

Most open doors led into small shops. A short distance farther on, the dirt street was practically paved with bottle caps. In a country that still did little of its own manufacturing, but which charged exorbitant duty on electrical appliances, a refrigerator was not considered equipment for a private home, but was becoming popular as a means of chilling the pink, oversweet *gaseosas* and the less popular Coca Cola.

"Who's that, on the horse?" demanded Carmelo, pointing to the statue in the center of the town plaza.

"That," retorted Alicia sagely, "is General Francisco de Paula Santander, and Santo's named after him. So is this province Ocaña's in. He was something in government."

Alicia was quite correct. Santander had fought for the establishment of honor and justice in the early beginnings of Colombian government and had served as its first vice president in 1821.

A score of steps extended along the entire far end of the plaza, leading up to a magnificent church. Passersby who approached from the business houses crossed themselves as they walked by the open door or entered to add one more to the dozens of lighted tapers at the altar.

"Look!" shrieked Emalina. "Look at all the *tiendas!*"

Parque Santander was, indeed, surrounded on three sides by shops of every kind, specializing in shoes or hardware or cloth. The storefronts were open, like great, roofed stalls, with merchandise casually piled on counters or arranged in careful displays. Some of the stores around the park even boasted plate-glass windows, well protected with formidable steel bars, behind which more modern means of displaying ready-made clothing were employed to tempt Ocaña's comparatively prosperous customers.

"Who would have money to buy such clothes?" Natividad wondered without covetousness. So far beyond her experience were these frocks that she viewed them merely as a part of the city sights.

Nor did the younger children seem to comprehend that all the wonders under their awed gaze were items for sale. Such overwhelming quantities of desirable objects precluded the idea of choosing or possessing.

Carmelo exclaimed at how many cars were parked around the plaza—more than he had thought there were in all Colombia. There were twenty-three. He had counted them. Many of them were taxis, since Colombians for the most part did not own private automobiles.

Beyond the plaza, both sides of the narrow rutted street were lined with general stores, exalted forms of their own *tienda* in Aspasica. Garden hose and buckets, crackers and dishes, rope and rat traps, and tooth paste and jelly could be seen stacked in heterogeneous disarray over counters, shelves and floor. So much was new that even Chico forgot to ask questions.

A truck thundered by, overloaded with people perched high on top of bags and baskets of farm produce. They passed carts drawn by donkeys or pushed by barefoot men. *Campesinos,* peasants from the little farms on the mountains, who might have walked for hours to reach town, padded barefoot along the thoroughfare leading to the market. Business girls in short, tight-skirted frocks clicked by on high heels. Shabby and drunken derelicts, bleary-eyed and bloated-of-face, rubbed shoulders on the narrow sidewalk with nuns whose white starched skirts swung gently just above the filth on the pavement. Men in well-pressed business suits, priests in white robes or black, beggars in deliberately heart-moving tatters, Indian men whose straight dark braids hung over their homespun ponchos, neglected children without a stitch to cover their emaciated bodies and swollen abdomens—they were all there in the crowded street.

As they neared the market area, *campesinos* were hawking papayas, pineapples, plantains, potatoes or onions, selling them right from the two huge baskets that balanced all that they had been able to load on their abused and tired burros. Others, women as well as men, had bound the same great baskets to their shoulders, supporting part of the weight by a leather band across their foreheads. Some had begun to spread mats on the sidewalk to display their fruits and other produce, and people stepped over or around them.

They passed open stalls selling notions—looking-glasses, scissors, saddles, combs, and machetes—all lined up along the curb or set down in the open market area wherever fancy had dictated. For the equivalent of two dollars, a person might buy a chair, handmade and covered with cowhide, hairy side up.

"It's just like ours at home that Papá made," said Emalina, still not realizing that her father was having to sell all their furniture at a great loss because it would be impossible to bring anything down here to sell except what could be packed easily on the donkeys. The evangelicals were even then loading up the pack animals near the home the children possibly would never see again.

One could fit shoes right at the curb or buy a shirt, a hat, or a gun. For a peso, one could get two dozen finger bananas or a large pineapple. Surprising wares were offered. A cat yowling in a bag represented good merchandise where rats were a nationally recognized health menace and a perpetual nuisance. A blue and yellow macaw pecked irritably at the slender reeds of which its cage had been built. A diminutive monkey chirped like an overgrown cricket at the end of a leather leash. Here they almost lost four-year-old Chico.

A boy offered lengths of sugar cane. "You *sell* it?" asked Carmelo. "Up near Aspasica, a person just goes into a field and cuts himself a good juicy length if he feels like it."

"Sure I sell it. Who has a cane field around here?" retorted the boy, grinning. He recognized in Carmelo another *campesino*. He seemed to have been doing a flourishing business, for several people were standing around, crunching into the succulent stems and spitting the cellulose onto the littered pavement.

Just ahead of them someone had just bought a mouth-watering slice of pineapple, dripping with goodness, right from the grimy hands of the man who was wiping his machete clean on his ragged shirt tail. For thirty *centavos* they could get two slices; and, if they bargained well, they could buy four for the equivalent of a U.S. nickel.

A blind beggar in the burned-out stage of leprosy brushed by, holding out a small enamel dish with blunt stumps of fingers. The man who had just finished his pineapple dropped in a couple of *centavos*. The beggar would have been amazed to receive as much as a peso—something under a dime—from one individual. He mumbled a morose blessing toward his benefactor and shambled off on swollen, bandaged feet.

Meat and such household supplies as come in cartons or tins were sold in an enclosed, roofed market of immense proportions.

It was clear that they had come very near the meat market. People who had not brought covered kettles to hold their meat came along the street swinging their purchase at the end of a string, which is regularly supplied in meat markets. Anyone who desired beans, salt, rice, or corn came prepared, of course, to carry them home. Only a gringo would come to market without a bag.

The children returned to the Velásquez home fairly bursting with questions and comment. Then they discovered that they had forgotten to buy anything for their own *centavos*. So the smaller three, with little Santo, boiled back out onto the pitted street toward the nearest *tienda* where Emalina had spied candy earlier.

Though Don Francisco had returned late the first evening, driving a couple of pack mules with some of the family's more immediate personal belongings, Marco and some of the other evangelicals had remained in Aspasica. Marco had been having a hard time selling his furniture. But for the fact that everything was going too cheaply to pass up, people were not inclined to buy.

Even when Marco returned to Ocaña, he spent his energies to the point of exhaustion trying to realize enough from the sale of his chattels to get his family to Cundinamarca Province. In the meantime, a letter came from Rosa's brother-in-law, Augustín Plata. She was completely unprepared for its inhospitable tone.

"You say you are coming this way because of persecution. If you want a safer place to live, you must not come to Cundinamarca Province or anywhere near the capital. There have been many lockouts of workers and strikes. The workers are out on the streets making trouble. There is much political unrest."

"The political unrest we have here, too," muttered Marco. "Well, that's the way it is with writing things on paper. The boys haven't been up this way since things got rough, so they think we're just restless or something. We'll have to go and talk with him face to face. He might want to sell the land. Or he has to get somebody to work it."

"Are we still going—all of us?" asked Rosa. Doña Emma's offer of hospitality until Marco found a place to settle appealed to her. She longed to go to a few evangelical services, to find out more about the teachings and to get acquainted with these warm-hearted people she had begun to meet since they had come to Ocaña.

"Too many people know us here, Rosa."

What was on Marco's mind? Had he decided that, wherever they would start anew, they would avoid the harassments and loss their open witness of faith had brought them in Aspasica? Could she agree to it? Was there such a thing as a secret evangelical?

"If we don't say anything about being *evangélicos*—"

Marco swung on Rosa, his eyes flashing. "Is that your way of thanking God for Santo's foot and for the hope we have in eternal life—to keep it to yourself so we can keep out of trouble?"

Rosa laughed at Marco's expression of indignant injury. "Well, you had me scared. I thought, from what you said, you'd had enough. And I didn't like any part of such an idea. After all, how can I keep from telling about Santo's foot? And that God answers prayer? And that he's made you a steady, sober man? I couldn't keep still, Marco, even where we're strangers."

"Nor me. Whatever price we pay for sharing our faith, Rosa, somehow I don't feel poorer, but as though we're getting something back to make up for it. In here." He gestured toward his breast and laughed somewhat self-consciously. "I know it doesn't feed the kids, Rosa, or buy them clothes, but maybe God will help me on that part of the deal, too."

Though Rosa still wished they might remain, she did not press Marco for his reason in moving so far away. A man must provide for his family, so it's the man who must make the decisions.

At ten o'clock one morning Marco knocked brusquely on the heavy door. He looked gaunt and tired as he strode back toward the patio where Rosa was bathing the two babies.

"I've been able to get us on a truck going to Bucaramanga. It's much cheaper than bus, and the driver says we can get there in time to catch a bus out of there for Cundinamarca."

"Then we're leaving today, Marco? If you could give us a day to get ready—with a family the size of ours—"

"I left Toño in the plaza to hold our places on the truck. As soon as we've got things tied into bundles here, I'll go on with them and send Toño back for you. He wants to leave by noon."

The usually quiet Velásquez home was quickly in a pandemonium of activity as each member of the Franco clan tried hurriedly to organize the personal belongings they would need on a trip of several days. When Marco stalked off with an armload of luggage, Doña Emma stopped him purposefully.

"You haven't slept a full night since you left Aspasica. Now, you're not leaving here without anything to eat!"

She served him at the plank table in the patio. He ate hastily, with no apparent knowledge of what he was eating. Don Francisco came to the table and read a Psalm, while Marco gulped the last of the food that had been piled on his plate. All activity ceased then, as this journey was committed to the God they all had learned to trust. Marco grasped his benefactor's hand in a hard firm grip after they had prayed.

"Thank you, Don Francisco. Somehow the pressure seems to have lifted. The Lord will see us through this trouble."

"We here in Ocaña will not forget to pray for you."

More time than Marco had allowed Rosa had passed before the children had been fed, and everybody rushed around finding their trifling or important belongings. Alicia had been scolded for thinking more about how she looked than whether the children's clothing had been packed, Emalina had got the whole front of her dress thoroughly wet washing with unwonted diligence for the dusty trip, and Santo had gotten his feet and clothes spattered with the mud near the *pila*. Tive was in tears because she had misplaced her only jacket; and Antonio, back from the plaza, was roaring at them all to hurry or they would be late, and the man would go along without them. They were twenty minutes late getting to the plaza, where they found Marco pacing back and forth.

"He's gone to the market to load some things to sell in Aguachica," he said.

"Will he find us here?"

"I don't trust that man. If he finds other fares, he won't bother to come back. We'd better look him up."

"But it's such a great big market," exclaimed Alicia. "Will we find him?"

"If he hasn't already gone," snapped Antonio.

Though they reached the truck half an hour late, they were forced to wait another hour, always hovering right near the truck, since the driver kept assuring them he would be leaving in a minute or two. Rosa did slip away to bargain sharply for two of the large hand-braided baskets that were being taken home empty. The baskets were large enough to hold almost everything they were taking with them.

"There," she exclaimed with a sigh of relief. "Now we won't be losing half our belongings." She organized their bundles in such a way that the most needed articles would be readily accessible.

At last they were off—Rosa, Marco, and the babies in the front with the driver, the rest of the family together with a growing number of passengers on a shifting cargo of edibles and freight. At a bakery, the last of many stops on the way to the edge of town, the driver tossed a gunny sackful of bread onto the cabbages and onions also bound for some *tienda* along the way. Soon they rounded the brow of the mountain on which stood the high statue of El Cristo Rey and began roaring along a road that wound in incredibly sharp turns along the mountain flank.

Soon Alicia was fumbling among the bundles to pull out additional clothing for the children and, as the road led higher, for herself and Natividad as well. Antonio shrugged at the cold, disdaining even to roll down his sleeves, though the cool wind raised gooseflesh along his muscular brown arms.

Three ranges of the Andes extend along Colombia from north to south. The western range, widest of the three, holds on its shoulders a charming valley in which Ocaña—with its pleasant, temperature climate—nestles like a nest of eagle eggs. Now, as the truck climbed to the top of a ridge, the passengers in the back of the truck had a dramatic view of the plateau, perhaps thirty miles across. Green hills in the foreground were etched against a wide deep-blue ribbon of peaks framing the other side of the elevated valley. Five distinct chains appeared along the skyline, and the mountains in the far distance blended with clouds in the sky.

Farms plastered to the mountains' almost perpendicular sides were no novelty to any member of the Franco family, though Toño remarked that this area seemed not to be high enough to be good coffee country. Bananas, plantains, corn, yuca—these were the crops they saw along the highway. Houses, though isolated, were unwalled. Many were built of adobe, some of logs, though the mountains were not heavily wooded.

Poorer homes had been constructed around sturdy vertical corner posts. Sticks or cane from the farms had been bound to the outer as well as the inner surfaces of these heavy stakes, and the hollow wall thus formed had been filled with mud, a solid barrier against the mountain wind. Roofs were coarsely thatched with banana or plantain leaves, which the wind had ripped into ribbons and the rains had turned a dirty brown. Where the mountain fell sharply from the highway, a few of these flimsy pole shacks, propped against the edge of the roadside to offer soft drinks or other merchandise to travelers, seemed to be balancing precariously on stilts.

The road snaked down abruptly into a valley, and they came suddenly upon a village of tile-roofed houses set neatly along a mountain stream, withdrawn a few rods from the routes of traffic. A prim little bridge led from the highway to the town, and the inhabitants turned to stare at the travelers who had turned off the road to cross their bridge.

More than anywhere else in the world, perhaps, Colombian towns each have a personality of their own. Just as topographical character and climate change suddenly within an hour's jarring drive along roads still dangerously inadequate, so also the towns present differing faces to people who pass through.

In Rio de Oro, no ramshackle huts were propped to the edge of the road to do business with outsiders. The double line of houses of which the village consisted were orderly, substantial structures in which people watched their children and grandchildren grow to maturity and taught them to build their own sturdy homes. The high-spired church that faced the central plaza was properly at one of the highest elevations of the decorous village.

Their driver stopped his truck on the narrow cobblestone street to transact some business, taking off some of his cargo and bargaining closely and at length over the price of delivery. When the truck started again, they were quickly out of the village, passing over another narrow, solidly constructed bridge, to resume the road westward and over the summit of the pass.

La Brisa stood high over a valley that had narrowed there to form a vast, deep gorge. The mountains on either side fell at an awesome angle straight into this canyon. Looking ahead along this widening rift, they could see the Magdalena Valley, still hazy with the sweltering humidity that would seem unbelievable after the cold they were suffering on the open truck, even with coats buttoned against the wind. At La Brisa, a high, cold, windy widening of the road, a lone tavern offered beer and *gaseosas* for travelers, and water for overheated motors.

Though the slanting rays of the sun betrayed the lateness of the hour, incredible, stifling heat settled over them heavily, as they descended into the vale. On the road that now stretched out before them without interest, someone identified a clump of huts as Totumal. The children, hot and tired, had become fret-

ful and quarrelsome. At last Antonio said, "We're just about
there. There's Aguachica."

Aguachica, a town of less than five thousand inhabitants,
sprawled out as though reaching for breathing space. And well
it might, situated eight degrees above the equator in the steam-
ing Magdalena River basin where heat prevails at all seasons.

According to the accepted Colombian pattern, Aguachica's
solid blocks of houses followed the contours and irregularities
of the haphazard streets. Perhaps because of the suffocating
heat, or because the population had been debilitated by malaria,
an air of impermanence hung over the town. Here, where the
equatorial sun beats down in torrid intensity, half the roofs were
made of corrugated metal, often with no ceiling, as though the
owner had quickly put up a shelter of the simplest and cheapest
construction just to provide shade until he could move on. Or
he had put up a metal roof because it was quicker to do, and
the climate is not conducive to undue expenditure of energy.

People were pouring out of the ovenlike houses to sit on the
communal doorstep that stretched past their homes. Women as
well as men had hitched chairs back to the wall or against a
tree, or sat on the edge of the concrete step with the children.
Pedestrians walked in the dirt street, which householders were
watering down with hoses against the choking dust. Neighbors
were drifting into clusters, drawing their chairs into a common
circle to trade the latest gossip or just to relax after a hot day.

Emalina poked Antonio with her sharp little index finger,
then used it for pointing. She had noticed the wide stripes of
paint along the base of buildings. In Aguachica they were all of
one color—blue—and on some houses the paint was clearly
new, though the upper walls had been neglected.

"They paint their houses just at the bottom," she remarked.
"If they could go to Ocaña, they could buy other colors."

"Well," retorted a man who had been sitting on a sack of
cabbage near the little girl. "If you would paint *your* house,
what color would you use?"

Emalina considered this question, but Chico had an instant answer. "I'd paint it red—all the way around!"

Several of the male passengers sat up in rigid alertness and glanced at the Franco's baggage on the truck.

"So that's why you're on the move!"

Alicia laughed easily. "No, we're Conservatives, but in Aspasica, where we come from, nobody pays much attention to paint. The children don't even know what the paint means."

Emalina's next question was ready immediately. "Do Conservatives paint the bottoms of their houses?"

"Conservatives paint the baseline of their houses *blue.*"

"Why?" she returned, round-eyed with interest.

"Because, *chiquita,*" answered the stranger, "blue is the Conservative color. If you'd paint your house red, like your little brother said, they'd come and burn it down. They've got no use for Liberals around here."

Antonio pointed toward newly painted bands of paint. "In Aguachica, it looks like people are making sure everybody knows where they stand politically."

"You don't allow for guesswork in this place. It's not healthy."

The truck jolted to a stop on the rutted main street of the town. The driver waved toward the door of what appeared to be a tavern. A faded sign over the entrance identified it as Hotel Imperial. "You can get something to eat here, and then you can take a taxi out to Bucaramanga."

"A *taxi?*" exclaimed Marco. "You said you were taking us to Bucaramanga!"

The man shrugged. "This is where I stop."

"I knew there was something shifty about him," groaned Marco. "He wanted our ten fares, but he never meant to go to Bucaramanga."

"Will there be room for us in a taxi—and our things?"

"A taxi's out of the question. It costs sixty *pesos* just to Ocaña from here. It's four times as far from here to Bucaramanga. We'll have to stay here for the night and take the bus we should have taken right from Ocaña." Marco shook his head disconsolately. "It will cost us more now, because of the hotel."

"Rooms" in Hotel Imperial were mere cubicles of wire screen, five or six feet wide and just long enough to place a bit of baggage at the foot of sagging wooden beds. Ceilings were also of screen. The arrangement offered more ventilation than privacy, though a curtain of flimsy cretonne could be drawn against prying eyes, provided no light was used inside.

As they inspected the accommodations, one of the employees dashed toward them, exclaiming with urgency, *"La plaga,*[1] *señor! La plaga!"* She shoved Marco aside almost roughly and closed the screen door, which he had held ajar while they discussed the proportions of the rooms and the dire necessity for economy.

"You're filling the room with mosquitoes," the woman cried indignantly. "Then you'll spend the night swatting."

They crowded into two of the narrow compartments, Marco taking the boys, Rosa sharing her bed with the girls and the babies.

"Six in a bed!" cried Emalina. "What fun!"

Between the stifling heat and the crowding, even the children slept restlessly, especially so since it had been impossible to watch the youngsters' comings and goings. They had admitted enough mosquitoes to make it seem that the high, uninterrupted humming was all right inside the screen. The children cried fretfully in their sleep, and in the morning scratched at red wheals all over their bodies.

Food was served on a veranda facing a cluttered patio. Seven or eight men were eating at tables over which limp cloths of dubious color had been draped in slovenly carelessness. Each meal would cost nearly ten *pesos.* Marco ordered six breakfasts to divide between the nine of them. But for the baby's sake, Rosa would have given el Chico more of what was on her plate. The boy watched the others in wistful silence after he had hungrily devoured his share.

[1]The plague (malaria).

"Eat up good," Marco admonished. "It's going to be a long day."

Geographically they were no nearer Bucaramanga than they had been while in Ocaña, but the only route to the larger city made this detour to avoid the mountains. Most of the trip would be made in the choking valley heat; and the bouncing, rattling, top-heavy bus onto which they crowded as soon as it arrived offered less comfort than riding in the back of a laden truck.

Rosa found the ride very fatiguing, and her ingenuity was strained to the limit in finding ways of coping with the small personal emergencies for which the bus would not stop. Traveling with eight children, three of whom were under five, was proving an almost overwhelming undertaking. Even the children greeted the sight of the city with almost tearful relief. Rosa realized, better than they, that Bucaramanga was really only the beginning of their long trip into an unknown future.

5

Sermon on the Shuddering Skeleton

BUCARAMANGA, its clean whitewash gleaming against the cool
blue of the Andes among which it nestled at an altitude much
like that of Ocaña, provided a welcome break from the valley
heat. The bus station faced the town plaza, so while Marco and
Antonio remained to see what arrangements they must make to
proceed further, Rosa led the children to the small park. With a
sigh of relief, she sank down on one of the stone benches scattered through the square. Now the children could release some
of the pent-up energy that had made the last miles a restless
turmoil.

Emalina discovered a public drinking fountain, having observed its use, and was off, closely followed by Chico. Tive took
Santo who was fussy with fatigue and thirst. After they had all
drunk long and eagerly, she washed their hot dusty faces, bringing a soaked cloth back to Rosa for the baby. Alicia fumbled
through one of the parcels they had stacked near the park bench
until she found a mug. She brought it back full of water for
Rosa.

Santo had been crying intermittently for a long while. Now
Chico began to whine and hang onto Rosa's skirt, refusing either
comfort or diversion. A sad-faced young woman on a bench not
far away was having a hard time coping with a similar problem.

"They're hungry, poor things," she called sympathetically to
Rosa. "The children miss home more than we do."

"I suppose you're right," replied Rosa. "I myself am so tired from the jolting and heat, I'm not the least bit hungry."

The food Doña Emma had pressed upon them when they left had provided their lunch at noon, and the smaller children had been munching occasionally whenever their cramped confinement to the uncomfortable bus had made them restless. Now, even Carmelo edged closer to his mother as she brought out the basket.

"Do you want *arepas?*" she asked. "That's all that's left."

She allowed the older children to help themselves and divided a cake between Santo and Chico. "Now see that you don't just crumble it up and waste it," she admonished.

The toddlers from the other bench had joined the ring pressing around Rosa and her basket. The older of the two stood by in large-eyed wistfulness, but the smaller held out his hand for food. Rosa gave them each an *arepa.* So hungrily did the children cram the food into their mouths that Rosa looked wonderingly toward their mother and was startled to see tears streaming down the woman's cheeks.

"They shouldn't have begged," she sobbed, "but the poor dears were so hungry. It has all been such a terrible shock to them."

"But they didn't really beg," Rosa protested. "And the *arepas* would have spoiled if I had kept them overnight. Come," she invited, holding out another to the oldest of the children. Then quickly adding another one, she said, "Take it to your mother. If you're that hungry, I'm sure she hasn't had anything to eat."

When the woman had gained control of her emotions and had eaten as hungrily as the children, Rosa turned toward her again.

"You spoke of a shock. Have you been in trouble, something that brings you here—" She gestured to the public square. Hardly conscious of the fact that she herself was homeless and that her family was almost destitute, Rosa reached out in sympathy toward this sad-faced woman.

"We're from Román," she replied. She seemed to feel that

the bare statement would explain everything. When she saw Rosa's perplexity, she added, "Surely you know what has been happening up there to the northeast?"

Rosa shook her head. "We live up in the mountains and get little news up there. I haven't heard of any trouble in Román."

"In my life I didn't think I would see such trouble," cried the other, and she seemed to become almost hysterical. Was it anxiety or memory of some great sadness? She spoke on, rapidly and in a high-pitched voice. "It was a massacre, do you hear? The men and even the children—the young boys—had guns and were shooting each other."

"What was it about—the shooting?"

"How does one know? They say it was because some from Román burned bridges. Some say it's because of the elections. Why should the people in San José de la Montaña want to kill us? And why should we have to shoot them—the people who used to come to our weddings and fiestas—to protect ourselves? The men say they understand it, but they don't agree."

"They came to Román to fight with your men?"

"They were fighting from doors and windows, and then, when we left the houses, from rock to rock and bush to bush. The whole day they were fighting as though we are having war. And we were running along the roads—the women and the little ones—to get away alive. But then we didn't know what had happened to our husbands, so we stopped and hid in the underbrush and went back when it was dark. But they didn't leave. And we didn't have anything to eat."

"You lost your husband?"

The woman shook her head. "No, but we lost everything else. Everything. We came away with just the clothes we had on."

"Then you still can thank God," Alicia said, too glibly, but with good intent. "It's not as if you were alone."

"*Thank* God?" ejaculated the dejected woman bitterly. "What has God ever done for any of us that we should thank Him? or the church? The church is for the Conservatives.

That's where the men meet in San José before they come to murder and plunder Román."

"I don't think God cares who gets to rule in Bogotá," said Rosa, "but I've learned that He wants us to trust Him. He can bring us happiness and peace of mind in any circumstances, señora."

"It still depends on our politics, doesn't it? We can't eat unless my husband finds work. Umberto says this town is full of Communists, and they want strikes. He says that even strong men who aren't weak with hunger can't find work. So we sit here in the plaza and starve. Or we steal. Will God help us with that? What good is God to us?" She gestured angrily toward other family groups huddled together in the plaza. "Or to them?"

Rosa began to comprehend her brother-in-law's brief letter. Here in Bucaramanga plaza was an example of what must be going on all over southern Colombia. What chance would Marco have to find work? With all these other men seeking land, would he find a farm? And when hungry men grew desperate, wouldn't the political violence change into lootings and personal vengefulness? She should have known that Augustín, usually so hospitable, had had good reason for advising them not to come to Cundinamarca. She decided to ask Marco to make further inquiries before he took them down into greater trouble.

When Marco appeared, however, he patted the tickets in his pocket triumphantly. "We're all set. With our tribe of ten, we might not have got on the early bus, the man said, if I hadn't got the tickets now."

"You couldn't turn those tickets back," ventured Rosa, "and get the money again?"

"Whatever for?" retorted Marco in amazement.

"Have you heard about the violence—I mean the serious character of the violence in some districts? Marco, it's far worse than I dreamed from what we were hearing in Aspasica."

"All you hear anywhere is about this violence, Rosa. But

we can contribute to this rash of stories ourselves, remember? It just sounds worse when it's in a strange place, Rosa."

"But, Marco, in some places whole villages are involved. There must be two hundred people in this plaza, and they say most of them are refugees from places where people are fighting with guns."

"Now don't you worry yourself," said Marco, briskly. "We're all set to get out of this plaza, and then we won't be hearing all this scary talk. We'd better make up our minds how to feed this family without spending all our money, though. I'm hungry."

Antonio had a suggestion. "Did you notice all those venders near where the buses stop? You can buy pineapple slices and roasted corn and some funny white lumps the man said was corn—popcorn. I'd sure like to find out what that corn's like."

Rosa patted her tall son's muscular arm. "Some day we'll have popcorn for all of us. Right now we just can't be interested in that kind of delicacy. We can buy filling food here as well; but, in my opinion, it would be cheaper in the market."

Marco nodded energetically. "Good idea. I was thinking how much it would take to buy another meal in a restaurant—with enough to eat for everybody for a change. Do you know where the market—"

Marco stopped talking, and Rosa realized that he had seen that her attention had wandered to that other family, desperate in their need. In fact his glance had followed hers to the nearby bench where the husband, of slight build and shabby appearance, was standing in dejected helplessness over his wife, who was silently sobbing against the back of the stone park bench.

"These people—they're all the way from Román. They've nowhere to go for help, and they haven't anything to eat."

"Now Rosa, my dear. We're in a city, not in Aspasica. We can't feed everyone who is hungry. The park is full of people."

"My supper—what I would eat—may I give it to them, Marco?"

"You need your food, Rosa, for the baby if not for yourself."

Rosa nodded sadly. Even now, perhaps because of the fatigue of travel or the irregular and inadequate meals, the baby was increasingly fussy. She knew that he was not getting enough to satisfy him, even though she was nursing him more frequently than usual. Marco was right, of course. Still, she knew she would not enjoy her own food when this other family must go to bed hungry.

"Well, take mine then," said Alicia. "It won't hurt me to go without supper."

Natividad moaned audibly, then murmured, "I'm hungry, but—yes, my share, too."

Marco, knowing his daughters' healthy appetites, looked from one to the other sharply, then chuckled as he often did when his children had wheedled something from him against his better judgment.

"You mean it, don't you? Well, let's see you wring the extra food out of this money. Solid food, mind. No fancy stuff!"

Typically Latin, Marco put the money into Antonio's hands, though he depended on Alicia's greater discretion. Then he stalked off toward the other park bench.

"My name's Franco, Marco Franco," he said, holding out his hand. "I hear you're in something of a bind, so I've sent my girls off to buy us some supper. How about having something to eat with us? It won't be fancy food."

Marco was interrupted with a deluge of gratitude. "I was getting pretty shaky," admitted the man, who introduced himself as Umberto Rojas. "You can't hope for work unless you're strong enough to do it. I've been looking all day, but I'm a farmer. I don't seem to know how to go about finding where the jobs are in a city."

"I'm a farmer, too," said Marco. "From east of Ocaña. What's this I hear of trouble near Román?"

"You might say we're having a civil war out there—and right on up to the border. The guns are coming from Venezuela."

"You mean they're actually giving the people guns?"

"Are you joking?" barked Umberto. "Guns like I've never seen before. They shoot like a woodpecker gone crazy; and the ammunition, they say, is better than what the army has. And they're shooting it up as though somebody's bringing it in as fast as they can use it. It's that way in Pamplonita and Ragonvalia. Even in Chinacota they're fighting like that."

"Who's furnishing the guns?"

"It's the Communists, if I have my guess. They're arming both sides. What they want is a full-sized revolution, so they can take over the country. And who's worse—Laureano or the Reds?"

"Well," said Marco, "we can always hope the country holds together until Gaitán gets in. That'll take care of the Communists and Laureano Gómez at one time."

Umberto shrugged his shoulders dispiritedly. "It's an awful long time till 1950 and the elections. And if Laureano has his way, there won't be any Liberals left to vote for Gaitán by that time. Else why has Laureano got his police spread out all through the mountains? What have they got to do with law and order? If a man is Liberal, Laureano's police wipe out the family and burn his house."

Umberto pointed to a group of women sprawled on the far side of the plaza.

"See those women up there? For four days they've been hiding, running from one bunch of those cursed *bandoleros,* then almost getting caught by another. Kids, too. Finally the Conservative beasts had them corraled—I don't know how many—someplace between Cucutilla and Arboledas. The army shot it out with Laureano's police to get them out. They're catching up on sleep now, but not one of them knows where her man is or if he's alive by now."

"One arm of the government fighting the other! That's a hard one to figure out."

"Well, the army won't go along with Laureano in killing off the Liberals. The army, they say, still protects all citizens—or tries to. But how are we going to live? Our cattle are still in the mountains. I turned them out to pasture before we left. Some tried to drive their cattle out, so they'd have something to sell or to live on. It was a good thought, but they abandoned them along the trails. Chickens, goats, cows—we saw them along the trails where people had left them. It's better to come out alive, señor, than to die rich!"

Antonio and the girls had returned while the men talked, and Rosa spread a cloth over the grass, exclaiming with approval over the food they had been able to purchase in the city's large market. Alicia had shopped astutely and with imagination. The fresh roasted yuca burst from its crisp skins in appetizing flaky whiteness.

Antonio had located a man who sold huge pieces of beef strung onto a wooden skewer and roasted in the marketplace. "We all get to eat a whole hunk," he whispered, boasting of his adroit bargaining. "This beats dividing up plates in a restaurant, and I'm hungry enough to eat a porcupine, quills and all."

Neither children nor adults needed two invitations to collect for the meal, which was spreading a mouth-watering aroma into the park air.

Marco stepped forward before they sat down on the grass. "As a family, we have a custom of asking God to bless our food and to thank Him for it. The food tonight isn't what either of our families are used to. We've suffered, too, and we've lost much that we had. But we have our lives. When I listen to these stories, I know how much we have to thank Him for.

Before Rosa bowed her own head in thanksgiving, she saw their guests exchange startled glances as Marco began to pray. At Rosa's side, Alicia moved nervously and nudged Tive. The girls, hypersensitive to nonconformity as teenagers always are, were acutely aware that these strangers probably had never heard anyone offer extemporaneous prayer. And Marco, seizing his opportunity for witness, not only thanked God for the food but prayed for Umberto and Rita Rojas by name. To their further embarrassment, he prayed for both factions who had been battling—the Conservatives as well as the Liberals.

An awkward silence had fallen at Marco's first suggestion of prayer, and it held them in disconcerting restraint until the children, eager for food, stirred impatiently and began a soft chattering. Rosa, turning toward Rita, saw her blinking away a tear.

"That was a beautiful prayer," Rita murmured, addressing Marco. "If we could all pray like that—" She choked. Obviously she was thinking of the hatred, the cursing and the threats she had been hearing during these past days.

"We all *can* pray like that," answered Rosa, gently. "But first we have to know that the Lord to whom we pray is reliable and that He is kind."

Rita studied Rosa's face. "You really mean that, don't you?" Tears again filled Rita's eyes as she took from Rosa's hand the food that would permit them to sleep without the gnawing of hunger.

"I think God had it planned that you should eat with us," said Rosa. "If we hadn't met you, we might have gone to a restaurant to eat, spending more money, and the food would not have been better."

"Not as good," said Natividad, "if restaurants are alike. And Alicia even bought a pineapple—a huge one—for a *peso.*"

"Well, that's what we'll do from now on," said Marco decisively. "Tomorrow, before we get started, we'll see that we have enough in the basket for noon."

"Before you get started?" repeated Umberto, somewhat puzzled. "Are you going on from here, then?"

Marco nodded, breaking open another tuber of yuca. He handed a piece to Emalina, then one to the Rojas boy nearly her age. "To Cundinamarca. Rosa's sister lives near Bogotá."

"But man! That whole area around the capital is worse than it is up here," exclaimed Rojas. "That's Conservative country."

"Then we may have no trouble at all down there," replied Marco, his eyes twinkling. "I'm a Conservative."

Umberto, who had been wolfing his food hungrily, had just taken a large mouthful of meat. He sputtered, and his eyes started from their sockets as though he had choked on his food.

"A Conservative—*you?*" he gasped, when he could get his breath. "I can't believe that."

"You can believe it," Marco said quietly. "I'm a Conservative."

"But you are feeding us," stammered Umberto, and then he flushed deep red. "I called them *bandoleros!* You didn't say a thing. And after that—*after that* you said we should eat with you. How is this, señor?"

"Before I am a Conservative," said Marco softly, "I'm an *evangélico.* Would Jesus Christ have refused a fellow human being a share of His food just because the man belonged to another political party? That's what it is to be an *evangélico.*"

For one startled moment, Umberto's mouth fell open, then he swung around to his wife. "Did you hear that, Rita?" He turned back slowly, as though still stunned by this new discovery. He faced Marco. "I've always been told that *evangélicos* were—" He paused, fumbling for a satisfactory word lacking open insult.

"Worse than anything you called the Conservatives," Rita said, finishing for Umberto.

Marco began to laugh. "Just wait," he chuckled, "until you meet some Liberal *evangélicos!*"

Rosa, in her turn, corrected her husband. "You should rather have said, 'Now we'll see what kind of people you, as Liberal *evangélicos*, will be.' Because, you see, we want to share with you the most wonderful thing that's ever happened to our family."

Forgetting their own misfortunes and their fatigue, the Francos eagerly shared with these strangers what their relationship with Jesus Christ had come to mean to them.

The children had long since fallen asleep on blankets that had been spread out for them, and the Francos decided to sleep out on the plaza also, since so many others had been forced into this extremity through troubles similar to theirs. Before the two families separated for the night, Antonio fumbled through his own belongings until he found his New Testament, a very precious possession. He pressed it earnestly into Umberto Rojas' hand.

"Read this. If what we have told you has not convinced you, then the Holy Scriptures will lead you into the truth and into a life so wonderful that you may yet bless God your trouble brought you to Bucaramanga."

Like people in a dream, Umberto and Rita Rojas went back to their own park bench. Marco nodded confidently to Rosa. Their own wonder at the gospel message was far too new for them to forget the almost unbearable hope that it may be true and the conflict of prejudice and self-will against the convicting power of God's Spirit.

They had no opportunity to talk with the other family again. Early the next morning they boarded the conveyance that would take them as far as Bogotá. It was the same kind of top-heavy, lumbering bus that jarred the passengers until their teeth rattled in their heads. For Chico, the vibration provided a fascinating diversion, and Rosa was relieved not to have him tumbling about on the seat and hanging on her shoulders.

Their chauffeur had fastened to a ledge above his dashboard two plastic donkeys, not more than three inches high, which nodded entertainingly with long-eared, solemn heads, as soon as the bus had gone into shuddering motion. A skeleton, slightly taller, also responded to the rutted road and the vibration of the roaring motor with great agitation—a violent trembling in every loose jointed bone supported by hidden springs.

"Is it a person?" Chico asked, wide eyed, when the chauffeur's smile indicated he might venture a question.

"I guess it is. It's a skeleton—just the bones of a person."

The youngster studied the jiggling skeleton solemnly for a little time. Soon he was ready with his second question.

"Is that how people grow—the bones first and then the meat?"

The chauffeur took his eyes off the road for a few seconds to study the boy, his grin growing wider as the sincerity of the interrogator became quite obvious. He shook his head, answering with his eyes back on the road. "*Al contrario.* This is how people end up. It's all that's left after a person dies."

Chico digested that for a moment. "Then he wasn't an *evangélico.*"

The bus driver roared with mirth. He turned around to share his joke with all and sundry. "Listen to the kid," he called. "He says this skeleton wasn't an *evangélico.*" He turned back to Chico. "Now tell me, *niño,* how you can tell from the bones if this wasn't an *evangélico?*"

"An *evangélico,*" retorted Chico solemnly, remembering what his little ears had seemed too small to understand, "goes right bang up to heaven." Then he added his own interpretation to the doctrine. "He doesn't stop to leave his bones."

Though the driver burst out with another loud guffaw, Chico stood his ground. "Honest. Ask Papá. *He'll* tell you it's so."

"That I want to hear," returned the driver. "An *evangélico!*" he added, as though the full implication of Chico's statement had just penetrated. He glanced around at Marco sharply but then continued to be amused at the little boy, who had begun to study the donkeys with the same interest.

Rosa, however, had become instantly aware of an atmosphere of suspicion and antagonism against them. It was in exchanged glances, in averted faces. A chill crept over her. In Aspasica, where they were known, where they had been among former friends, their lives had been in danger. Could Chico's innocent statement have endangered their lives? Rosa glanced up at Marco's serious face, but it broke into a smile.

"We've counted the cost of being witnesses, remember?" he murmured. "No man lights a light and sets it under a bushel."

After awhile, the passengers were offered another diversion, and they appeared to forget the Franco family, although Rosa continued to wonder, in the midst of the excitement, what lay before them in a land aflame with political violence and religious bigotry.

A new passenger had presented, as part of his baggage, a squealing, half-grown pig which protested energetically against being tied to the luggage carrier on the top. Mile after mile it squealed and flopped about overhead. When at last it grew quiet, the driver stopped the bus, and he and the owner got out to see if they'd lost their lively cargo.

Apparently it had given up the battle. More likely, it was succumbing to the heat and its own agitation. This, the owner explained excitedly, could be fatal. The bus driver agreed that this was so, but he bluntly refused the owner's next proposal.

"No, the pig cannot be brought into the bus. It's your baggage, like you said. It stays on the baggage rack."

"Then you can give me back what's left of my ticket, and I'll go the rest of the way on a truck."

"You think your pig will enjoy truck travel more?"

"Well, I don't want to lose that pig. It shouldn't be in the sun."

The driver shrugged. "Get into the bus."

"If I hold it?"

"No! Chickens I have permitted inside. Pigs, no."

"I will pay its ticket. To save its life I will pay fare for it to go inside."

The proposal gave the driver pause, especially since this arrangement meant money in his own pocket. "All right. But mind you don't let it loose in there."

For awhile the pig merely lay on its owner's knees, panting. Marco suggested that a rag soaked in water would help keep it alive.

"In the heat, pigs have to wallow. I've poured water on them to keep them alive if they're overheated from chasing."

Having no rag or even a towel, the man took off his shirt. Someone else had a canteen of water. Soon the pig was grunting occasionally, and finally it began to squeal dolefully, though it was still panting.

A truck tore by with a sharp blast of horn; and the pig, now fully revived, freed himself from his owner's restraining grasp with a sudden, unexpected lunge. It shot forward toward the freedom suggested by the front windshield, quite oblivious to obstacles, among which were the driver's legs.

Santo bounced excitedly on the seat beside Rosa, and Chico shrilled that the pig would get away. The driver struggled heroically to retain control of the bus, while the owner plunged under a seat after the pig, which had dashed off in a new direction. He missed, and the pig, now thoroughly frightened, darted below the seats as though people's feet were merely loose boards in a pen and not to be taken into account.

The driver roared at the unfortunate owner. Women cried out in irritation, and children shrieked in fear or gleeful encouragement. Men who felt inclined to be helpful joined the mad melee, plunging over and across passengers' knees or skirts, and grabbing for the elusive porker. Santo thought it a delightful game, and Rosa was fully occupied keeping him from wriggling from her grasp to join the fun. Marco was similarly employed with Chico.

Due to the generous distribution of large and small parcels under seats and around the passengers' feet, and the pig's complete disregard for property, the latter always managed to bolt off in another direction before pursuers had more than touched his dampened hide.

The driver pulled the bus to a stop at the side of the road to concentrate on the pig's capture. By kicking under the seats and waving odds and ends around the skirts of the women, the men were slowly but surely getting the pig cornered. The driver stood over the proceeding, yelling directions and imprecations. At last the owner stood up, triumphantly hugging his squealing charge.

"The cursed hog goes off."

"It's a passenger," barked the man, bristling. "I paid full fare."

The driver digested this fact and the belligerent stance of his passenger, his face growing redder as he studied his dilemma. He got back into his seat, and the bus roared into shuddering motion with the angry sound of stripping gears.

"All right," he shouted over his shoulder. "But you get your tickets refunded at the next stop. And you tie your hog and keep him tied until we get there!"

The unhappy man darted a questioning glance about the bus, then settled back in his seat, dejectedly clutching his pig by its feet. To Chico's disappointment, the noon stop gave the man time to sell his well-fed pig, and he completed his journey in morose retrospection, solitary on his two seats.

On the following day, exhausted from the long hours of traveling and the strain of trying to keep the restless children from irritating other passengers, Rosa had been dozing heavily. She was wakened abruptly by a banging noise. The shouts of a group of men running along beside the bus and motioning for the driver to stop startled her to full wakefulness. The driver halted the bus and stepped outside to collect their fares.

A small village spread out along the roadside, with a few clumps of scraggly trees breaking the monotony of the dry terrain. "Where did all these men come from?" wondered Marco, watching the angry and vociferous gesticulating of the men for a moment. "Something's going on out there. I think I'll step out to see what."

The men looked like day laborers, shirts out over faded jeans, sombreros dark with a peculiar oily filth. Rosa heard somebody speak about nearby oil fields. Marco confirmed the conjecture when he slid back into his seat near her.

"They're from La Tropical Oil Company at Cantimplora, about a hundred kilometers west of here, near the Magdalena River," he said. "They're all out of work and so upset about the strike that they'd as soon go to Bogotá and tear it apart. Wherever they land, there's bound to be real trouble."

"It's dreadful," whispered Rosa. "No matter where we go in Colombia, we can't seem to get away from this violence. The people seem to be pushed into it. They're desperate."

A man with a blue checked shirt sat directly across from them. Marco motioned out the window at the arid scene.

"What's this place?"

"This? Barbosa. This is where we cross over into Boyaca Province. We think we might find work in Tunja, the capital."

"I wager we don't get work in Tunja," growled his seatmate. "The strike at the Esso plants started before ours did. Duitama's closer to Tunja than we are right this minute."

"I thought I heard someone say it was the Esso plant across the river from yours, at Puerto Berrío, that was on strike."

"Señor, the strikes are everywhere—Berranca Bermeja, Petroléa, El Banco, Puerto Wilches. You came from up north, didn't you? Weren't they striking in Bucaramanga?"

"That I didn't hear," replied Marco. "But the plaza was full of families from the direction of Cucutá. They've been fighting up there, one town against another. People leaving home. Hungry."

"Well, the whole oil industry is going to be paralyzed. We'll all be hungry if we keep looking for a job on the oil fields."

"On January the sixth," said a man called Chepe, "the public works in Bogotá went on strike, too."

Another of the men spoke up from farther back. "This country is going to blow up—like a volcano. In Antioquia they assassinated Roberto Rojas, and that was a good man. In Chichinquirá, just a few miles south of here, they began fighting—the two factions—and fourteen were shot. Hurt bad."

"In Moniquirá, right on this road, six are dead. We'll pass it or stop there in maybe twenty minutes. Twelve more hurt. The Liberals were having a bazaar in the plaza. The police shot into the crowd. Women, children—what do they care?"

"In Villanueva, they say, it was a massacre. Twenty-two dead. In Arauca more than thirty. The police are Conservative. The dead and wounded are almost all Liberals. I don't like it."

"Well, Juan," rasped a man behind them, "it's not going to stay that way. If I don't get work, I join the guerrillas. We'll put a stop to some of this bloody business."

"They tell us to strike," growled another, "and shoot us if we don't. But who goes hungry? Not them!"

"We're not the only ones going hungry. What about the Liberals on farms? They crowd them off, make them sell dirt cheap. And the Conservatives buy it up. They're getting rich on this blood."

"That's what happened to us," commented Carmelo. "We were in Aspasica. And we're not even Liberal."

"Aspasica? I thought all that territory near Ocaña was Conservative."

"Well, they ran us off our farm up there."

"And you Conservatives? Who did it?"

Carmelo shrugged. "The people up there."

"It wasn't political." Marco was always bluntly frank. "We're *evangélicos*."

"Well, why did you let them find it out?" retorted Chepe. "You don't paint your house blue or red if you're one of *those*."

Marco grinned. "No, it's not the color of paint. But nobody sees his son healed and his whole family changed, and gets peace in his soul, and still keeps his mouth shut. At least I don't."

"You say your son was healed? What of?"

"Show them, Rosa."

Santo was sleeping on a seat opposite. "This foot," she said, holding it up for them to see. "He was born a clubfoot, twisted to the inside so that he didn't walk on any part of his sole. See the scars on this ankle? He learned to walk on that."

"And most of the time he crawled," Alicia added.

"How long ago is that?"

Antonio spoke up. "A year ago. It happened early in 1947. And that's what made me know it was the truth."

Juan clicked his tongue softly. "I've heard of miracles, but I've never taken much stock on it. This is the first one—"

"And you're not sure of this one. How do you know these *evangélicos* don't cook up some kind of a story that—"

"But we all saw it," ejaculated Tive indignantly. "Do you think we'd all lie about it?"

"It was like this," spoke up Emalina, trying to turn her own foot sideways. "Only worse. Ask Mamá. She'll tell you how it was."

"All our neighbors could tell you the same," said Rosa. "But it's not only the child. Our whole life has been changed." She recalled the perpetual anxiety of losing Marco altogether. She glanced at him, grateful to God for the miracle of a family secure in a mutual affection. Her eyes were brimming when she turned back toward Chepe and Juan. "I can't tell you—"

But Marco could and did. Marco never lacked for words, and for the next ninety minutes he told them, speaking earnestly to the men of what the gospel could do for them as well. The rest of the tiresome journey toward Tunja seemed to slip by in a few minutes; and, before they knew it, they had again entered the pleasant coolness and scenic splendor of the western Andean range. People in the full length of the bus had been listening.

The bus would have a long stop in Tunja. As they stepped out of the door, Rosa saw the driver tap Marco on the shoulder.

"There's some in our vehicle who don't like *evangélicos*. A word to the wise—" He saw Marco was getting ready to start on him, so he turned toward Rosa. "Tell him. In Colombia it is not the time to make enemies."

6

Villa Rica

"THIS——" Marco announced jocosely, with an exaggerated, pompous gesture encompassing the whole dismal clutter of houses along the highway—"This is Villa Rica!"

From Marco's false flourish of bravado, Rosa realized that he, too, had felt the depressing effects of the Tolima flatland's sweltering heat settling down upon them even before they had left the bus. Her heart sank at the cheerless aspect of the village.

Alicia, insensitive to the hollow note of despondency in her father's voice, reacted with outspoken asperity. "Villa *Rica?* If this town is *rich,* I'm glad we didn't land in Villa Pobre!"

"Is this really where we're going to live, Papá?" asked Carmelo.

Marco's thin veneer of forced pleasantry fell before the cruel slash of his daughter's bluntness. He lashed back at them all out of his own deep discouragement.

"Moving from Aspasica may have been a holiday for you kids, but you might as well find out, now as later, that if this is a *villa pobre* to you, then we've found the place where we fit. We are poor people!"

He evaded Rosa's glance as he picked up one of the huge baskets and strapped it to his shoulders.

"*Caramba!*" muttered Carmelo to Antonio in an undertone. "What have we done to deserve this?"

Rosa was sure that Marco heard the boy's insolent remark,

though he did not deign to respond. He stalked on ahead of Rosa, and the discontented children straggled behind, far enough away for their heated discussion to be unintelligible to her ears.

Fatigued from the long journey and not a little discouraged herself, Rosa fumbled numbly for something to say that might relieve Marco's wretchedness and convey her assurance that the burden of this poverty was not his alone. She knew that Marco, as head of a family, was assuming sole responsibility for their present evil circumstances. His was the role of provider; his was now this disgrace.

"The children don't understand," she murmured. "They're young."

"They understand all too well," Marco retorted curtly.

Rosa, struggling under clumsy parcels and the weight of the fretting baby, did not speak again.

Stooped with his own knowledge of the inadequacy of their future home as much as by the huge load of baggage he had lashed to his back, Marco stopped at last before a squalid hut shallowly roofed with battered sheets of corrugated tin.

Marco thrust almost angrily at the unpainted door that sagged heavily on one rusted hinge. As he let his heavy load slide to the pitted earthen floor which was littered with worthless articles abandoned by the previous tenants, Rosa stepped over the high doorsill to his side. Though she had steeled herself for makeshift housekeeping, she had not been prepared for this one-room hovel to which Marco had led her. They looked at their new home wordlessly, then at each other.

Rosa let him take her parcels. For the life of her, she could not speak, but she took one of his hands and pressed it to her quivering lips.

Marco, too, must be thinking of the new home he had built her, of its lovely mountain setting, of their prosperous farm and the additional income they had received from their *tienda.* They had not been rich, but among their neighbors they had been considered well off. Now they were impoverished, destitute, hardly knowing where the next meal would come from. Marco would be working as a day laborer, his work subject to the vicissitudes of the season or the whims of his employer.

Suddenly this hardship came into sharp focus as Rosa recalled the reason for their change of fortune. Hadn't she had to face the loss of home and livelihood—without Marco, without his love, and perhaps without her children—when she had made her decision to take her stand as an evangelical? Though the commitment had torn her soul, she had deemed her faith worthy of that price. And at that time she had not even foreseen the peace and joy and companionship that would follow—that she now possessed! If the gospel had been worth her sacrificing everything then, how much more certain she should be that it was worth it now. *Christ was worthy!* The living Christ who had enriched them all—He was worthy.

"We have more now, Marco," she murmured, "than if we had not heard or had not accepted the *evangélio* that has set us free. And I have you." Her voice broke.

Wordlessly Marco crushed her to himself. "Let's pray," he said at last, "that we'll have courage to be better witnesses here than we ever were in Aspasica."

They had no more time for sentimentality than they had for self-pity. The children, who had lagged with their own burdens momentarily, now rushed noisily toward the house. Rosa met them at the door, before they could begin stacking a jumble of parcels onto the debris on the floor.

"Set everything down in the shade outside. We're moving the last renters out of here first!"

She met the anticipated gust of questions and comment with a smile, putting them all to such a flurry of work that they had no breath left for complaining. While Marco scraped together the rubbish, Alicia sprinkled down the dirt floor so that her energetic sweeping would stir up a minimum of dust. Natividad had been sent to the stream for water; Antonio went to scour the area for something that would burn with enough heat to cook their plantains. Carmelo and Chico had gone off to search for suitable stones on which Rosa could balance her kettles to cook their noon meal.

Emalina was poking Rosa for attention, bursting with something she felt was very important. "They're Liberals, Mamá, and brown."

Rosa glanced at her eager little daughter, thin and brown as a ripe coffee berry. "What do you mean, Nina?" she asked, reverting to the name of endearment that Emalina had provided—as had each of the other children in their turn by the first childish lispings of their own names. "Browner than you? Are they Indians?"

"Brown on the houses, at the bottom, Mamá. What is it, when it's brown all around the house?"

"She's talking about politics, Mamá," explained Alicia. "She heard about that border of paint in Aguachica."

"Brown's the same as red," said Marco. "What's ours?"

"I think ours has rubbed off," said Emalina, dashing out to make sure. "There's no paint left."

"I hope the little twirp doesn't get us into trouble with this fancy for the borders of people's houses," worried Alicia. "It's bad enough being strangers here, without being Conservatives."

"What are you grumbling about?" questioned Antonio, who had returned with an armload of combustible trash. "Where do you want this junk?"

"Not in here," retorted his sister. "We'll cook on the lee of the house today, if not from now on."

"What about us being Conservatives?" Antonio persisted.

"Well, Emalina's got this enthusiasm for the color of paint. Before we know it, she'll have it all over the country that we're Conservatives. Then just leave it to the busybodies to add to it." Alicia made an angry swish at a heavy mesh of spider web in a corner near the ceiling. "Why can't Papá just go and register as a Liberal? He won't vote anyway, so—"

"Don't talk nonsense," barked Marco.

"Can you change the shape of your nose or the color of your eyes by signing a paper?" Antonio asked.

Alicia voiced Rosa's own incomprehension of Colombian politics when she cried, "Is it hereditary—being a Conservative? Isn't politics an opinion? Does Papá agree with these massacres? He's even said that if *evangélicos* could vote, he'd vote for Gaitán!"

Emalina had had the solution for some time and had been shrilling, "Papá, Papá!" Her insistent little index finger gained Marco's attention at last. "If we paint the house red at the bottom, we'll be Liberals. The man in Aguachica said so."

Marco brushed a lock of dark hair back from the child's forehead. "First we have to eat, Nina, before we start painting."

"Well," said Rosa briskly, "I think that takes care of our politics. The house is neutral; so are we. We do nothing about politics—we do nothing about the paint."

"You hear that, Nina?" said Toño. "We're neutral. That means we don't have politics. Stop worrying about this paint business."

Politics, however, became the crux of the family's problem during the hard days to come. When a potential employer demanded Marco's political affiliation, he did not evade the issue. Soon, in spite of the unpainted condition of their house, the entire community knew that Marco was a Conservative by family tradition.

Agustín Plata had foreseen this trouble. In fact, he had exploded almost before the Franco family had entered his house, declaring that their coming to Agua de Dios in spite of his definite advice was not only embarrassing but it could be extremely dangerous.

"For us," he said, "but most of all for you. Not only are you Conservative, but you've complicated it by taking up with this *evangélio.*"

Rosa had looked quickly at her sister. Silvia had shaken her head silently. Agustín had not shared her faith. Marco, who had not seen her, had taken it for granted, however.

"Danger?" he retorted. "Why, your boys kept telling us that

we should be prepared for persecution! Fact is, that's why we're here."

"Persecution, eh? You came *this* way because of persecution?"

Rosa had soon seen that Agustín hardly knew what to do with them. After all, she was Silvia's sister, and Agustín's sons had been her guests weeks on end. His deep agitation was not due to reluctance to provide hospitality.

"If you wanted a safer place to live, you should not have come to Cundinamarca or anywhere near the capital. I wrote you about the labor lock-outs in Bogotá. The workers have begun rioting. It's spreading to the country."

"It's not just drunken brawls with occasional fights like we're all used to," interrupted Carlos. "They're gunning for each other. There's looting and rape and murder."

"Every man looks at his neighbor with suspicion, Marco. What chance have you got—a stranger that they'll call a heretic?"

"Now that they're here, Agustín, the boys will help Marco and Antonio find a farm," Silvia interposed.

"That's a whole lot easier said than done," retorted Agustín. "Nobody wants trouble. They're leery of strangers."

Agustín's keen observation of the political situation had been confirmed by Marco's experience. Day after day he had come back, worn out and increasingly discouraged.

"The trouble is," he confided to Rosa, "we haven't enough money to get back to Ocaña. Not even for the trip. I have to find work."

After an absence of several days, Marco and the boys returned, exhausted and hungry. Marco had found work in Tolima, the province bordering Cundinamarca to the west. He said it would be a bus trip of fifty or sixty miles. They had been walking steadily for the past two days. Carmelo had a huge, angry blister on his heel.

Agustín resented Marco's ignoring of his advice, and his morose silence had been increasingly hard for Rosa to bear.

That night, a little giddy with the relief of getting settled soon in her own home, Rosa felt that nothing could vex her. Usually the prospect of getting her family ready for a journey dismayed her.

"It's like trying to count a hive of bees," she had told Marco, when they started away from Ocaña. "By the time you get one settled, the next one's gone off or fallen into something or is in some kind of scrape that makes you have to start all over."

That evening in Agua de Dios, Marco had reminded her of her earlier remark. "Ready to move the hive again?"

"With a home to go to, Marco, I'm ready for anything," she had replied lightheartedly. "We'll just scrape them up and put them in a bag."

Rosa had noted, but with only a fleeting awareness, that Marco's grin had seemed forced. She had not asked him that night or afterward what sort of accommodations he had found for them. In the first place, it did not matter. In the second place, she had sensed that he did not want to talk about it.

On their arrival in Villa Rica, though shocked with the grim reality, Rosa had determined to demonstrate that the peace and mutual understanding they had found would make any kind of home one to be envied. In spite of her brave resolve, her soul quaked at the monumental project of keeping house for ten in this one bare room without a stick of furniture.

She had had enough foresight to bring with her their emptied feather ticks; and, as soon as they had eaten their first meal, she dispatched the boys to find good clean straw. While she tried to assort the baggage that had been piled in a corner on a piece of torn brown paper, she began to make plans.

Fruit was transported in roughly sawed wooden crates. A few of them, piled one upon another, would make a passable cupboard. It would not keep out the rats, and by all evidences the house was overrun with them; but it would raise their food and dishes up off the floor, providing her a means of battling the inevitable hordes of ants and cockroaches. Similarly the crates, if she could find enough, would help her keep the family's clothes organized. To nails already in the scarred walls, she fastened cord upon which she hung some of their clothing.

The vermin, which Rosa had foreseen with her first glance at the unsavory interior, lurked in every crack. Though she had swept down the walls before they moved in, and brushed them with a broom dipped in kerosene, ravenous armies of bedbugs descended on the family at nightfall. Rosa found it impossible to cope with the vermin, since everybody slept on the floor.

Far worse were the rats that swarmed in from their hideouts as soon as the light was out. They scampered across the floor and the sleeping family, burrowing through the loose straw upon which the children slept. Emboldened by their very numbers, the rats hardly paused in their bustle of gnawing, digging, searching, though one shouted at them or threw a shoe.

During the first weeks, Rosa slept little. Time and again she sprang from her pallet to recheck the weighted lid of the huge crock in which she stored food. At the first whimper of one of the children, Rosa would toss a heavy garment in that direction, even before she rushed over to see if the child had been bitten. Eventually, tired beyond endurance, she slept in spite of the rustlings and exploratory nudgings of the relentless rodents.

Though Rosa did not know it, the mosquitoes that swarmed in dark corners during the day and settled on them in stinging voracity at night were more dangerous to her children than the rats. Reared on the mountains, she did not understand the insects' connection with the fever and chills of malaria.

Rising long before dawn and working until late, Marco and Antonio had little time to spend building needed furniture. They were peons now, and their time was not their own. When bad weather released them from plantation work, both the men tirelessly searched for a piece of land they could rent and so regain a measure of independence, even if they would work no less strenuously.

The children tumbled off their straw pallets in the dark to join the family's predawn devotions. Though it was too dark for them to share the song book, they sang the hymns and choruses they knew. Antonio read from the Bible by the light of a sputtering tallow candle. They had brought their gasoline pressure lantern, but they could not yet afford gasoline to use in it.

Each Sunday they had their own service, scheduled on occasion to fit the chance or prearranged visit of a neighbor. Few of the people in Villa Rica condescended to have much to do with the poorest family in the dismal settlement.

Weeks went by, each one much like its predecessor. Each day began long before dawn and ended in abject weariness. At last, on an evening in early April, Antonio brought news of a piece of property that they might be able to acquire as their own. A part of each year's crop would be taken as payment, and during the time of indebtedness they would also be required to help the owner on his own adjoining hectares of farmland.

"They say Don Mauricio is a fair-minded man," said Antonio. "He'll pay current wages for work we'll do on the farm. He's Conservative, and I guess he's in a bind to get help. That's why he's making us a good deal, I think."

Marco, who had been trying vainly to refasten the loose sole of his shoe with tacks he had straightened on the ax head, nodded in frowning silence. On the section of log that served as chair or table, as circumstances demanded, Marco had fastened a squat, homemade candle. By its flickering light, Rosa watched the lines in his face deepen. She knew he was weighing the years of peonage against the hope of reestablishing himself financially.

"It may be our only chance. It looks like no Liberal wants to risk selling to a Conservative—afraid his neighbors will draw false conclusions about his own politics."

"And Liberals won't work for a Conservative, either. That's the reason this land is open now. The family that lived there has moved to Venezuela. That farm is next to the one where the police—"

Antonio's voice trailed off when Marco gave him a sharp look. The story of the brutal massacre of a family not far along the valley had been kept from the younger children. Even now Chico was having frightening nightmares.

Emalina, who had been playing with the squirming baby on the parental straw pallet, twisted about to face the narrow circle of light in which her father's serious face was the only one clearly visible. "What?" she piped, her perennial curiosity aroused. "What did the police do?"

"Don't you think it's time for the *culto,* Papá?" Rosa said quickly. "El Chico's almost asleep."

Marco grunted assent with a tack between his lips. "I'll have this shoe fixed—if it's possible—in a minute."

Emalina, Rosa saw, was not to be distracted so easily. She advanced on Antonio, poking her sharp finger into him for attention. "Toño," she said shrilly. "Toño!"

"Nina," Rosa said sharply. "Stop pestering Toño and help Tive unroll the quilts so you can sit down for *culto.*"

"Licha can do it," said Emalina, still poking. "Tell me, Toño, what did the police do?"

"What police?" asked Antonio coolly. He had been squatting on the bare floor. Now he unfolded his thin legs wearily and walked to the box where he kept his clothes and other personal belongings. He fumbled in the darkness until he found the Bible.

Carmelo followed him, lowering his voice. "Tell me!" he demanded.

"Melo!" Marco spoke sternly. "Help Tive make up the beds."

"There aren't any beds," muttered the boy, petulantly. "I wish we were back in—"

Marco struck a final blow without much hope of success and brushed the worn shoe to the floor. He got up from his knees. "Do I have to tell you again?"

"I'll help Tive, Papá," said Alicia. "All Carmelo wants is for someone to tell him a story—any kind of story. It's time he learns to read for himself."

"That's a good idea, Alicia!" exclaimed Rosa. "Carmelo should learn to read. So should Emalina."

Like many other rural communities, Villa Rica had no public school. A woman was tutoring a few children in her home some three miles away, but from reports of the pupils' accomplishments Rosa knew Alicia was far better qualified to teach the children right at home. Possibly other families, hearing of their lessons, might want their children to come, too. It could mean added income. Furthermore, it might be a way of getting more of their neighbors to come to their Sunday worship as well.

The preparation of the bed on which Rosa and Marco slept, and the girls' bed, though they had the two straw-filled ticks, had been a skill somewhat hard to acquire. Alicia and Tive now accomplished it very quickly, with Carmelo's reluctant aid.

Since their day had begun early and the single candle did not offer much inducement for evening pastimes, the children fell asleep soon after the devotional time.

"What do you think of this Don Mauricio's proposition?" Rosa asked Marco. Almost anything, she felt, would be better than their present circumstances. "Is there a house?"

"The house may be as good as the one we left. With our passel of boys, we should be able to keep up our land and the other. It won't be ours at once, but we'll live in it. The farm is good land."

Lest Marco be offended, Rosa restrained a wild, delirious impulse to dance and sing all over the cluttered hovel. Surely Marco realized how trying it was to keep house for ten in one room —the bedbugs, the rats, the crowding. The delightful prospect of getting into a proper house was coupled with the tormenting thought that someone else would get to the man before Marco did. The hour was still early. Why didn't Marco go *now?*

Her glance happened to drop to where Marco's shoe lay. Could this be the reason that Marco was delaying? Marco was not usually deterred by a matter as small as the state of his shoes. Still, a buyer probably must not appear too destitute.

Marco, noting her questioning look, laughed. "It's not my shoes that kept me, Rosa. Don Mauricio has gone to Bogotá on some kind of business. Toño says he'll be back next Friday night. Saturday for sure. I'll not let any grass grow under my feet, *querida*. Don't worry, I want to get us settled as much as you do."

The hours crept like a sated slug across the long suspense of the intervening days. Antonio went back to Don Mauricio's home on Friday evening and again on Saturday. His wife, a pleasant woman, promised to send word when her husband returned. Doña Elena seemed delighted that the Franco family might be moving next door.

"There's safety in numbers," she had told Antonio, when she learned that he was from a Conservative family.

"She seems to be nervous, Papá," said Antonio, who repeated the remark to him.

"That's not surprising. It was police that did the looting and burning of that other home. But Don Mauricio is Conservative, and in the minds of some ignorant people that puts him right with them. The family may fear retaliation."

"Don Mauricio had nothing to do with it."

"You don't talk sense to a man with a grudge. Or to a mob."

Antonio took the short stub of candle from the log, scraped the wax off with his calloused hand, then turned to fix the candle to a small prominence in the uneven, pitted wall. He picked up the Bible and held it so as to get full benefit of the flickering light.

"You're going to burn a hole in that good hat, and then you'll have learned your lesson," Alicia warned.

"It's only *gentlemen* who take their hats off in the house," chided Tive, shrugging her shoulders expressively.

"All right, all right, smarty," retorted Antonio, looking at the corner draped with drying diapers. "Every time I get a place that's safe from the kids—"

Rosa put the baby down. She took down some clothes spread on a saddle. "It's been raining all day, Toño. The diapers are almost dry. I'll double them somewhere else." She took the hat from Antonio and placed it carefully on the saddle.

"I could have done it, Mamá," said Antonio apologetically.

"You're tired, son," said Rosa. "And it's time to start *culto*."

The children squatted on quilts spread on the straw for the night. Alicia leaned against one of the walls, and Tive lolled on her shoulder. The baby had begun crying again. Rosa picked him up.

"What's the matter with the baby?"

"The same fever, Marco. He's been fussy all day."

Marco placed his horny hand gently on the baby's head. "Poor tyke! He's been having this fever on and off ever since we came." He bowed his head in an attitude of prayer, but said, "Read, son. We have to get through before the children fall asleep."

After they had prayed, each one in turn, and the younger children had fallen asleep, Marco put the heavy pole against the door as he did every night. The door sagged wearily on its rusted hinge. He repeated the words of Psalm 121 to fix them in mind. "He that keepeth thee will not slumber. . . . The Lord shall preserve thy going out and thy coming in from this time forth." He gave the unsteady door one more shove with the pole. "And He can do it even if the door decides to fall off its hinge!"

He fumbled his way back to their own pallet on the floor where Rosa was cuddling the restless baby. The candle had burned itself out. Chico, who had been sleeping between Tive and Alicia since he had begun to have nightmares, whimpered softly. Rosa could hear Alicia patting him and crooning sleepily. Then by their regular breathing she knew they had all dropped off to sleep. The baby, however, felt even more feverish than before and was beginning to cry. To keep him from disturbing the others, Rosa got up to rock him against her shoulder. A hurried knock drew her to the door.

"Yes?" she murmured. "Who is it?"

A man's voice, choked by fear or excitement, answered, "Is Antonio here? Or Don Marco Franco? I'm from the house of Don Mauricio."

Though the man's statement held no clue as to why he had

arrived so late at night, his voice carried its own message of urgency. This was not a matter of contracts or business propositions. She slipped across the dark room and shook both Antonio and Marco awake. It had stopped raining, so they all slipped out into the moonlight to speak where the children could not hear.

"Is there trouble?"

"There's trouble. Gaitán is dead—assassinated. Bogotá is burning. And—"

"Burning? The capital? Then there's fighting between Liberals and Conservatives in Bogotá. Is it civil war?"

"That's what I had to see you about. The retaliation is not restricted to Bogotá. It's here—with us."

"What do you mean—*with us?*"

"They got Don Mauricio. He'd been to Bogotá, he and his son."

"Yes," interrupted Marco anxiously. "I knew he went to Bogotá."

"They got off the bus here and were coming up the trail toward the hacienda. They beat him to death with their mule's harness. We need help. The boy got away from them alive, but he's so scared that he's no good to anybody. And the woman —" The man shuffled his feet. "I don't blame her. Don Mauricio Aguilar was a good man. She can't think of anything else but that he's dead and how they killed him."

"Sure," said Marco, at once. "We'll both come over to the house and guard them. We'll sleep there after this, if she wants, until we're sure they don't mean to do her any harm."

"There's no house to guard, Don Marco. They burned it and the one on the other farm. They're hiding in the brush on the estate, she and the boy, but we have to get them away before morning."

Only after the men had hurried off into the night did the implications of this tragedy in regard to her own future dawn on Rosa. Again their hope of improving their lot had been thwarted. Refusing to dwell on her own interests, Rosa prayed for the woman hiding in a daze of bereavement and terror, and

for the men who were hoping to help her to safety. Still, her
own sickening disappointment kept beating in her mind with
brutal insistence. She lay awake, tense with a renewed fear that
the trouble might not be over and that her own menfolk were in
danger.

Night had begun to dissolve into the gray of dawn when a
sharp rap at the door startled Rosa. Marco identified himself
in response to her cautious challenge. Antonio pushed open the
creaky door as soon as she removed the supporting pole. While
she prepared their early breakfast, they told her the whole dreadful story.

To the boy, Roberto, the opportunity to accompany his father
to Bogotá for a few days had provided a new and appealing diversion from rural monotony. They had reached the city during
a time when political party spirit was running high. Students
had assaulted the Ministry of Education, and a week later a
bomb had been installed in the Ministry of Government building. Earlier, in February, an attempt had been made to dyna-
mite the office of La Tropical Oil Company, and the oil pipe-
lines of Cantimplora were damaged by explosives. Telegraph
lines were destroyed, and railway tracks leading to oil fields were
sabotaged. A plot to set fire to the large storage tanks of gasoline aborted, preventing fires of unimaginable proportions.

Acts of violence committed by Conservative President Ospina and his reactionary supporters, and by Conservative-con-
trolled police, had been increasing. In the provinces most strongly Conservative, police had begun a campaign of terror against
Liberal citizens. Many had fled the country.

Dr. Jorge Eliécer Gaitán, forty-five year old lawyer, Liberal
idol of the masses, had published lists of these atrocities, calling
on the government to stop its criminal activities. He had joined
in a demonstration of citizens bearing banners of black crepe
through the streets of Bogotá as though in mourning procession.
In the plaza, Gaitán made his celebrated oration on peace, in
which he demanded first of all a cessation of persecution by government authorities.

"Stop this violence, Señor Presidente. We only ask you to defend human life. That's the least a people can ask!"

The nation had taken it for granted that their hero would represent Colombia at the IX Panamerican Conference as one of the delegates, but President Ospina was determined to recoup political power. He had maneuvered to get Liberals so disgruntled that they withdrew from his cabinet. He promptly replaced them with Conservatives. The last straw was the appointment of Laureano Gómez, arch reactionary and the Liberals' bitterest enemy, as Foreign Minister and Colombia's delegate to the Panamerican Conference.

Gaitán was put under repeated pressures to collaborate in sabotaging the conference, which began March 30. He not only dismissed each inducement peremptorily but, in order to prevent distortion of his views, distributed to all news agencies a statement in which he declared himself incapable of contributing to the discrediting of his country. "Nor do I desire to obstruct the task upon which all the countries of our hemisphere have determined to act." He urged the public to abstain from every action that could result in prejudicing the labors of the conference.

Gaitán's unalterable stand for peaceful settlement further endeared him to the public. The people concurred that he would win the national presidential election scheduled for June, 1950, and he had been set up as Liberal presidential candidate when the election was still more than two years away.

For Don Mauricio and his son, the Panamerican Conference had minimal meaning, though they had heard that reactionaries had ignored Gaitán's pleas, and a bomb had been discovered in the salón where the sessions would be held. Still, their minds had been far from politics when they had taken a streetcar to the principal business section of Bogotá at the noon hour, when people were pouring out of their offices for lunch.

A singular commotion ahead had made both the men crane their necks out the window to see whatever excitement the city had to offer. The streetcar ground to a screeching stop as it penetrated the edges of the roaring turbulence. Then Roberto saw it.

"They're dragging a man by the neck—naked!" he yelled, and then he became giddy with horror as he saw that the man's head had been pounded to bloody pulp. The crowd now engulfed the streetcar, and through the enraged screams they gathered the cause of the vicious killing.

"He assassinated our leader."

"He murdered Gaitán."

Most of the occupants had deserted the streetcar against which the mob was beating angrily as though it represented the men who had instigated the assassination.

"Who is the man?"

No one seemed to know who the man, now unrecognizable, had been. As the two *campesinos* joined the throng moving along Seventh Street toward the Capitol they learned more of the details. The assassin had been waiting for Dr. Gaitán as he walked out of the lobby of his office building for lunch and had shot him four times in the back of the head and neck.

A lottery vender, who had been standing in the doorway, dropped his book, grabbed the assassin and shouted, "This is the man!"

From a nearby cafe a patron dashed toward the fallen Gaitán, then turned and smashed a chair over the gunman's head. A crowd, which had gathered almost at the first shout following the shots, tore at the assassin's clothes and beat at him with their fists. Someone snatched a shoeshine box from a bootblack and beat at the head in frenzied revenge. The crowd kicked at his face and body. Then they knotted a tie around his neck and dragged his naked body six blocks to the presidential palace, where they abandoned it. It had been raining, and the gutter in which the corpse lay was filled with water.

The throng hardly paused there, and Don Mauricio and his son were borne along toward the Capitol building. The mob was yelling, "Death to Laureano Gómez!" "Down with the government." "Down with the Conservatives! They killed our leader."

The mob broke into the Capitol where the Panamerican Conference was in session. For twenty minutes rioters swarmed through the building, breaking up furniture and smashing typewriters. Conference delegates huddled together in a third floor office.[1]

Returning to their streetcar, Mauricio Aguilar and Roberto saw that the palace had been set ablaze. It was still raining, and water dammed up in the gutter behind the stiffening corpse, making little whirlpools around his bare heels.

At two o'clock word swept through the anxious crowds waiting outside the hospital. Gaitán was dead. The mob's rage, quieted earlier by federal troops, now broke out in insensate madness.

As Gaitán's most vicious enemy, Laureano Gómez was blamed. The mob made its way to the building that housed Laureano's newspaper, *El Siglo,* and set it ablaze. Then the Gómez home. They overturned streetcars and set them on fire. They wrecked automobiles. They broke into hardware stores and demanded or helped themselves to knives and machetes. Then other government buildings began to burn, and a pyromania seized the mob. Fires they set were not to burn themselves out for three days. Thirty-five buildings in the heart of the city were in smoldering ruins.

By six that evening flames were roaring up into the skies, and rioters had begun to use guns against the police and the army that again had been called to quell the open anarchy. As evening fell, looters filled the streets now lighted by a shifting red glow that emanated from heavy clouds reflecting the holocaust below. Troops fired into the crowds, and thieves dashed through the streets littered with merchandise, to get away safely with their own accessions. In the indefinite light, they stumbled over corpses of looters who had not been so fortunate, or over dead policemen who had stood in the plunderers' way.

[1]*Newsweek, Time,* & *Semana,* all dated 4/19/48.

When Don Mauricio and Roberto left Bogotá early on Saturday morning, the government troops had restored some order. The morgue, they had been told, reported over three hundred dead. They had considered themselves well away from trouble when they left the bus and started along the trail toward home.

Marco and Antonio had helped bury Don Mauricio's body and before morning had managed to find a trucker from Conservative Boyaca who agreed to take the widow and what little they had been able to salvage after the collapsed roof had burned itself out.

"It was so senseless," Marco repeated. "Don Mauricio was a good man. He had no real enemies here."

"But he was a Conservative," said Antonio.

"He might even have voted for Gaitán. He probably would have. He was for peace," said Marco, voicing his own sentiments.

The violence that had begun in Bogotá swept like epidemic madness throughout the country. *Campesinos,* who knew little about politics and cared less, became bewildered, innocent victims of the boiling national frenzy, or took sides, impelled by terror or driven by a passion for personal retaliation. Marco's neutral stand as an evangelical meant little in a land whose populace had gone mad with fear and suspicion and revenge. Within a fortnight he had lost his job.

"We'll have to go back to Ocaña," said Marco, acknowledging defeat. "It'll take every *peso* we have, but it's a matter of survival."

7

"Better'n Angels"

AFTER THEIR BUS disgorged its occupants near the Parque Santander in Ocaña, Rosa lagged behind the others to pick up the odds and ends that the children had left behind in their eager scramble to get off. When she stepped down from the bus, she noted that Marco had mustered the family forces for a well-organized march. Even Chico had his share of the accumulation of bundles.

"Don Francisco isn't here?"

"We're on time," Marco replied, grinning. "Whoever would have expected that the bus would arrive on time?"

Still Rosa was disappointed. Knowing that the descent of the whole Franco tribe on a household could be considered a great inconvenience, she had asked Alicia to write a letter explaining the necessity for their return.

"I promise," she had told her to write, "that we will not impose on you many days. Perhaps even now you will know of a house we can rent, for we feel we must remain in Ocaña until these riots and political hatreds are over." Rosa wondered uneasily whether the letter might not have arrived.

Antonio, bent under the basket of rattling housewares, took the lead; the others straggled behind. Marco had waited for her. Halfway down the first block, they were hailed by a shrill voice behind them. A boy, younger than their Emalina, was vigorously waving both arms at them, shouting a stream of unintelligible information, which he repeated in a gush when he had caught up with them.

125

"Don José said to watch for you," he exclaimed, panting, "but I didn't get there quick enough."

By this time the whole procession had come to a halt, and the boy found himself surrounded by the still unenlightened family.

"Don José?"

"Doña Emma went away for when a baby is going to be born, and Don Francisco went, too."

"A baby?" asked Rosa, puzzled.

"Not for Doña Emma. It's somebody else's."

"Did Don José say where they went?"

The boy swung toward Marco, his dark face serious under a shock of black thatch. "Mamá says they didn't say, but that God will know where to go."

Marco chuckled. "That He will. Now the problem left is Where do we go? To Don José's house?"

"Yes, and Mamá says not to worry. They have room for you, and tomorrow you're to come over to our place for meals." He fell into step beside Carmelo. "I'm Pedro." Then, before Carmelo had found his tongue to reply, Pedro asked, "What's an *almajara?*"

Carmelo shrugged and looked at Antonio.

"An *almajara?* That's where they put coffee seedlings to make them grow fast. I guess they use them to start other things, too."

"Like trouble? Don Isaias says Tolima is an *almajara* for trouble. That would be worse than the *Carro Fantasma*, wouldn't it? To be right in the *almajara?* Is that why you came to Ocaña, because of the *almajara?*"

He seemed about to go on with a few more questions, but Antonio stopped him. "Well, what's a *Carro Fantasma?*"

"It's the one that goes past and shoots, and the people inside have the black things on so you can't know who they are. I saw it once, but they didn't shoot me." He turned to Marco now, for his own questions had not been answered. "Is that why you came to Ocaña, so that trouble wouldn't grow so fast?"

Rosa caught Marco's glance of amusement. "I guess you

could say that's why we came. But I hope *some* things grow fast here. What about the church meetings? When I was here—"

"Not after they shot through the door, Don Marco. Mamá won't let us go either, except in daytime for Sunday School."

"Oh, they shot in through the church door, did they? During a service?"

"No, Don Marco. It was when Papá and Don José and Don Isaias and Don Francisco—they went to talk to the missionary about something. We weren't there."

"So they've never shot into the door while the people were there for a meeting."

"Well, no, Don Marco. But it's sort of scary when they chop at the door with machetes, isn't it?"

"It could scare a person some."

"And small kids get scared even when they throw stones."

"That we can understand," said Rosa.

"It sounds something awful because the roof is tin, but *I'm* not scared." He looked up at Rosa with artless candor. "Anyway, all us *evangélico* kids—even babies—have guardian angels. They'll watch out for us—especially if it's in the daytime, and we're in Sunday school."

Rosa laughed. "Let me tell you something else, Pedro. Jesus Himself has promised never to leave anybody who trusts Him. Not even at night. And you don't have to be in church."

"Even us kids?"

"Even kids."

"Why, that's better'n angels, even."

"That's *besides* your guardian angel, Pedro."

"You don't say! Just wait till I tell the kids. That'll make them feel a lot better."

"Faith in Jesus always does," said Rosa. "Even big people."

Meanwhile they had approached the suburb area where the oiled streets branched out into phalanges intended for primitive traffic. Antonio turned to help the younger children who had difficulty clambering over a mound of abandoned building clay that had been dumped at the entrance to the constricted street. Pedro, feeling the authority of his important mission, knocked imperiously on one of the doors in a rambling line of house fronts.

"Who's there?" questioned a woman's voice.

"It's me," Pedro replied loftily, though with dubious enlightenment of the occupants. Then he added, "And your company."

The door swung open, and Rosa found herself in the arms of their hostess, hearing words of sympathy and comfort. Doña Cecilia's warm friendliness and concern, after the months of loneliness in Tolima, seemed like a haven amid the lashings of a storm. To her own amazement, Rosa burst into tears.

Suddenly she caught sight of Santo gaping at her in wide-eyed wonder. Chico, behind him, also was staring at her in awe. Even Emalina was silent and solemn. They could not understand why their mother should be sobbing. Rosa fumbled for a handkerchief.

"Don't look so—so doleful!" she exclaimed, laughing through her tears. She stooped to kiss the unmistakable beginnings of a sob from Chico's face. "I'm just so happy to be among people who understand—among *evangélicos!*"

Marco, too, had been observing her with some distress. He was surprised at her reaction, perhaps even hurt. She put a hand on his arm. "I didn't realize I felt like that, Marco, until I knew we were leaving Tolima."

"It's been hard for you down there in Tolima," said Don José."

"From what Pedro has been telling us," retorted Marco, "things haven't been exactly quiet around here. What's this about them shooting in through the doors?"

"Oh, that," Don José shrugged. "A few of us men had gathered at the mssionary's place after the police confiscated all his Bibles and all his other literature. He didn't know just what to do about it, and neither did we."

"From the North American they took it?"

"Sure. You see the law's all on one side. The police came to his door with a search warrant. They were looking for Communist propaganda, they said. So he felt he had to let them in. Well, that's where anything lawful stopped. They just grabbed his literature—said it was illegal to possess such printed material. The missionary kept telling them that the Colombian constitution guarantees religious liberty. They just told him to hold his tongue."

"So that's what they wanted right from the start!"

"Well, they're after us all, because we've become *evangélicos.* But the missionary called us over to ask what we thought about getting more Bibles. We were about to go home—standing in the meeting hall praying—when they tried to break the door in. When it didn't give, they began shooting at it."

"I see you've put in new doors here, too."

"They'll wear out a couple dozen machetes to get in through these. This house—I'm one of the elders—has been stoned a number of times. They don't miss any of us. But to tell you the truth, Marco, that kind of antagonism doesn't worry us nearly so much as what we should do when it's the police."

Don José moved toward the barred window and looked down the street in both directions. When he swung around, he lowered his voice cautiously. His face revealed his fear. "They say it's police in the *Carro Fantasma,* you know. At least some are police."

"Pedro tried to tell us about *Carro Fantasma.* What is it?"

"Masked men in black robes. The car seems to come from nowhere; it races by with machine guns at every window. Just let a few Liberals gather anywhere on the street, and from somewhere the information gets to the scoundrels. The car streaks by, and the whole crowd is mowed down before anyone has had time to give warning. No one knows where the car comes from nor where it goes."

"But you think it's police."

"Who else is always on hand—either to give the word or to climb into a car? Who else has the arms?"

"And we used to think police stood for the law."

"Right now the police are the law, but that has little to do with the Colombian Constitution."

"Can you men stop talking politics long enough to eat some supper?" inquired their hostess. She had drawn Rosa into the patio where she was working. Pedro took a large, red-cheeked mango from her with some reluctance. He suspected that the gift was not only offered as a reward for guiding the family there, but also as a gentle means of dismissal. Rosa realized that her large family probably stifled any inclination on Doña Cecilia's part to extend hospitality toward one more robust appetite.

Again and again, in the days to come, the strong bond that knits evangelicals into a loving family made itself felt. Not only did the Ocaña church people find a house with very reasonable rent, but from here and there pieces of necessary furniture were supplied. Rosa knew that her own response was not mere gratitude, but instant and instinctive recognition of a kindred commitment toward the same Lord she worshiped with all her soul. Men called each other brother, but the spiritual bond seemed stronger than human blood relationship. Rosa knew Marco felt this, too, for he often thanked God for the companionship of other evangelicals and for the privilege they now enjoyed of attending worship services on Sundays.

Since he was again working on farms at a peon's wage, Rosa found all her ingenuity taxed to keep her active children in clothes. Shoes, naturally, were worn only to church, and the smaller children could do without even these. In Tolima they had begun to grow some of their own food. Except for raising a few chickens, that was impossible in Ocaña. Marco often chafed at their continued penury in spite of his long grueling hours of hard labor and the necessity of living most of the time away from home.

"I've got to find some way of providing a better life for us!"

"You may feel frustrated," she comforted him. "But as long as you can come in for weekends, we are being enriched while we live here. We are hearing the Scriptures. We are learning what the Christian way of life can become if we're totally committed."

Secretly, however, Rosa also wished for better days. Especially for Marco's sake, for he had become lank and thin as a reed. They kept telling each other that, as soon as the political situation improved, they would be able to live normal lives again.

Contrary to their oft reiterated hope, the national unrest did not wear itself out but proliferated. Gaitán's death had sparked a wave of violence beyond wildest nightmares. Reports of rape and arson and looting and brutal murder came from all directions. Too often for comfort, tragedy struck very near. No one slept soundly during those days. Rosa, habitually a light sleeper, often trembled at the sounds of shots fired somewhere in the city's streets.

Everyone in Ocaña attended well to the security of his home. The bolt on the bar extending across their own double doors had worn a rather large hole into the wood, so Marco had made a second heavy wooden bar for the doors. Besides that, heavy poles were invariably propped against the doors, which opened inward. All city dwellings were walled, but Marco and Antonio had added three rows of adobe bricks all around for added height.

One night, Rosa wakened with a sense of impending danger. She was certain she had heard someone scream, "Police!"

One did not call for the police when in trouble. One was in trouble if the police arrived. Marco, too, had heard, and Rosa felt his hand urgent on her shoulder. He sat up in bed and shoved his feet into sandals. Coarse, drunken laughter and shouted obscenities sounded very near. They could even hear the purposeful grunts of men hacking with machetes at doors on their own street.

After Marco had checked their doors, he came back to the bed and knelt. Rosa slipped out of bed to kneel beside him. Hand in hand they waited, recognizing the sound of approaching death in raucous shouting, in heavy scrapings of military boots on cobblestones, in frightened whimperings somewhere in the stifling darkness. They prayed, for God was their only recourse.

They prayed, not so much for themselves but for the children who might be done to death by torture or who, surviving a raid, might suffer more as orphans. And they clung to the precious promises of God, who—they had discovered—meant every word He said.

Diminishing sounds indicated that the night's threat had taken another direction. They remained on their knees, now tearfully praising God for timely intervention.

"It seems so easy," Marco muttered in a cautious tone. "Maybe someday we'll think it just happened that they went off somewhere else. But God delivered us, as sure as if He let the enemy see His chariots of fire in the sky. And we must be just as thankful."

Just the same, terror had driven sleep from them for the night, and they wondered upon whom among their neighbors the clutching talons of death had closed in the darkness. In the morning they would hear, in hushed whispers, what horror had transpired and the real or fancied pretext for insensate crimes.

To be an outspoken witness for the evangelical faith became increasingly hazardous. Again and again, Marco and Rosa faced the choice of silence or added hardship and danger. So great an animosity against evangelicals had been aroused that their landlord came to them under cover of the night.

"As much as I hate to lose good tenants, I have to ask you to move. I've asked you to quit your preaching, but you don't listen. When they start cutting throats, they may not stop with my renters but come for me, too, because I'm renting to you."

"Give us a little time, will you, to find another place?"

"If you'd just stop telling people you're *evangélicos!* People have enough trouble without this talk of sin and hellfire."

"Repentance is only the door into reality and into such a good life a man can't shut his mouth about it. It has to be shared."

"Well, can't you be quiet about it until this blows over?"

Marco tried to console Rosa for the added work of moving and getting settled into another home. Rosa knew, as did Marco, that some evangelicals were very secretive about their faith, but Marco did not ask her whether she agreed with their landlord's insistence that he be silent until the trouble had passed.

"I'd feel like a traitor, if I stopped telling people of a salvation the Son of God died to bring people," muttered Marco.

"Jesus thought our salvation important enough to carry His cross in public. He is worthy our bearing a few inconveniences so that people find out about the salvation He died to provide."

"So you're still with me!" exclaimed Marco, with a sigh of relief.

"Whatever it costs," replied Rosa.

In the next home they remained only two months before they were forced to move again and for the same reason.

Each morning the whole family committed into God's care those who had to leave the security of the house to go to work or who were away for several days. Antonio had been going out regularly with Marco; recently even Carmelo had been employed. Rosa kept telling herself that the God who had done such marvelous things for them in the past could be trusted with the welfare of her loved ones, yet she found that fear of impending grief was never far from her thoughts.

Some of Marco's jobs lay in the direction of Aspasica. Rosa remembered the temper of that community too well. Otherwise they worked in the valley, and Aguachica also was a source of many reports of brutality. A few times, when rumors of violent acts came in from those areas, her faith broke down into panic.

Marco, who had to come and go on trucks loaded with passengers bound to and from the fanatically Conservative valley, heard much, Rosa was sure, that he did not tell her. Often, by the manner in which Marco prayed for someone he might not even have mentioned to her, she knew that he had been threatened or even mistreated. Rosa understood, with pride as well as misgivings, that no form of intimidation would keep him from sharing his great and wonderful discovery. The evangelical faith had brought reality of such a dimension that he could not endure the thought of others missing this kind of a relationship with God. So he witnessed constantly, enthusiastically, and without consideration of consequences to himself.

"What if they seem to resent me?" he argued. "Did *I* listen right from the start? Somebody has to tell them."

While Marco braved death for his faith, Rosa was facing a trial that she had begun to find very distressing. In the last place they had moved, their neighbors on either hand, it seemed to Rosa, had conspired to exhaust her inner spiritual resources. Though outwardly affable, they were demonstrating most effectively their disdain for their evangelical neighbors. Almost every morning Rosa found adult human feces that had been loosely wrapped in a fold of newspaper or a banana leaf and tossed over one of the adjoining walls into the Franco patio.

Rosa had never mentioned this offensive matter to Marco for fear that remonstrance of any kind from him might become a motive for attacking Marco with gun or machete.

At first she had disposed of the revolting contributions with the thought that she must never say anything, but always bear everything in love. Hadn't the crowd spat upon the Lord of glory? And He had never spoken a harsh word to anyone in the jeering crowd. She must suffer this indignity for Jesus' sake. But when the flying excrement spattered in the patio or drew flies before she found it, she began to burn with indignation in spite of her greatest efforts to maintain a humble attitude.

Once Rosa saw a folded newspaper sail over the wall and land with a heavy thud near her cooking area. She knew that the family on that side had guests at that very moment. She stood over the loathsome object, trembling with anger and a burning desire for retaliation.

This was too much. She had tried so hard to repay evil with good. She would wrap it up, as she often did her loving offerings of good things to eat, and take the parcel around to the door.

"I think this belongs to you," she would say.

They would not anticipate a return of their own filth and almost certainly would unwrap it before their guests. She savored her revenge, long overdue.

Though Rosa fought down her impulse, her anger remained. She felt her daily chore become an increasing temptation, and often she felt as guilty as if she had, indeed, followed her in-, clinations. During those trying days, she became increasingly aware that God was teaching her the difference between her studied acts of friendliness and the yearning love that Christ alone could impart. For such love she prayed fervently.

One day, after the long, uneasy year, Marco came home with a wide grin lighting his thin face. Rosa knew at once that he brought good news and that he was bursting to share it.

"I think I've found us a farm."

Marco's announcement that they would be moving was relief far beyond her prayers, even though she knew that she would miss the warm friendliness of her evangelical friends.

Santa Inés was a point along the only road from the Magdalena River valley to Ocaña where several mule trails converged. Just off the road sat one large dwelling—most of it a *tienda* of the kind Marco himself had had in Aspasica. Doña Juana Lazzco sold hard liquor as well as *gaseosas*.

"Just wait till you meet that woman," confided Marco, chuckling. "A heart as big and warm as the Magdalena Valley, but she'd be furious to find out someone had guessed it. If she's got any children of her own, they're married; but she's taken some orphans in, three of them. The boys are about Toño's age; the girl is younger than Tive."

"Is she a widow—this Doña Juana?"

Marco hesitated. Since he had broken off his own illicit affair, he seldom brought up the subject of a similar situation. Certainly he never attempted to justify his own past by arguing that concubinage was common in Colombia.

"The man is Germán Vanegas," he muttered.

To Marco, this farm meant far more than a better standard

of living for all of them. He would continue to work long, hard hours—as would they all—but now he would be master of his own time. The dissemination of this tremendous gospel of new life with purpose and peace would come first. He would have no master to hound him if he spent a few minutes or half a day speaking to someone on matters of eternal consequence.

The older girls helped Marco and the boys on the Saturdays he spent at Santa Inés erecting a temporarily adequate house of adobe bricks and thatch. Since they anticipated building a more permanent house later, the roof was low and the walls were left rough. By mid July, Marco announced that the roof was up, and the family could move into their new home.

It would be hot in Santa Inés, but they would have their very own home and their own land. Although Rosa realized that it would not be possible for the family to go often, it was only about two hours to Ocaña by bus. Marco would attend some Ocaña services, she was sure, but he had promised also, that, as soon as they could get anyone to listen to the gospel, they would try to begin regular services for the community right there in their home.

As the project had neared completion, Rosa had been sending such articles as were not a daily necessity to be stored in Santa Inés, so that moving was not a great undertaking. Santa Inés was located in the foothills just above the valley.

Doña Juana's unpainted house, the source of supplies for the Santa Inés community, lay parallel to the highway in a clearing. Their own house, not far away, was hidden by woods that spread into the surrounding hills. It seemed that their neighbor was expecting them.

"Come in here," she called brusquely. "I've got a business proposition."

"Well," said Marco aside to Rosa. "I haven't seen the old war horse lately. Wonder what she wants?"

"This is as good a time as any for me to get acquainted."

Doña Juana Lazzco walked heavily and with a slight limp across the earthen veranda as she led her new neighbors into the long, cement-floored room that did not even bear a pretense of being the family sala. It was a *tienda,* nothing else. Obviously, this woman was more interested in business than she was in social life. A scar cut across her bold, heavy features, slightly distorting the line of her determined mouth. She swung toward Marco.

"Ever run a store?" she demanded, her shrewd, grey eyes, slightly out of focus, fixed in his direction.

Marco stared at her for a moment, then shifted uneasily. "If I start one, *señora,*" he said, finally, "it won't be to run you out of business. I'll stock things you don't carry."

Juana Lazzco leaned over the battered wooden counter, her muscular arms supporting her bulky figure. She squinted at Marco as though sizing up a worthy opponent.

"Sit down," she ordered. "I'll get you some *gaseosas.*"

While she thumped around, opening the bottles, Marco murmured, "She makes me nervous. I can't figure out whether she's looking at me or trying to evade my eyes. What's she got up her sleeve?"

"Trouble?" Rosa conjectured. "You've been counting on setting up a store, haven't you?"

"Sure, but we don't have to fight over it. I'll let her tell me what she wants to handle. For the sake of the *evangelio,* it will be much better if we don't have trouble, even if she can't stop me from having anything I want to sell in my store."

Marco bowed his head briefly in impromptu prayer. Rosa knew that Marco was not dissembling. He was, indeed, more concerned that their neighbors should be among the first to visit their home for services than over the fact that this querulous woman might be the cause of real trouble for their family.

Doña Juana now thrust dripping bottles of pink soda at them. She tilted her own to her heavy lips and allowed half the liquid to gurgle down her throat. She wiped her mouth with the back of her fat, work-coarsened hand.

"I'll turn over my whole stock and let you sell it right out from here, if you give me costs and half the profits."

Marco sat down, staring at Doña Juana in shocked incredulity. She had seated herself on the edge of the counter. Noting Marco's reaction, she thumped the thigh under her voluminous skirt with a boisterous gust of amusement. "I told you to sit down."

"You're not leaving, Doña Juana," gasped Rosa in dismay, "just because we're coming?"

Her new neighbor swung bodily around toward her. "Now why would I do that? Because you're heretics? Hah! I myself am an *incredula*. It's not healthy to be in any kind of business these days. Me and my man, we're getting out of here."

"It's healthy to eat," said Marco. "If I run a store, it'll be so my family can eat—not to run my neighbor out of business."

Doña Juana swung back to Marco. "Well, you watch out for the police. Just watch out for the police." She shook a heavy finger at him.

Marco waited for her to go on.

"They came here, twenty-five of them, asking for drinks. Then they began to ask for this and that. You could tell they'd no thought of paying, by the way they put things right into their pockets or into a sack they had." She fixed Rosa with one hard gray eye. "You never know what those bandits will do, and my man in Barranca. That was the first of July." She swung back to eye Marco. "You never asked why I wasn't here since then. Did you know they beat me up?"

"Oh, no!" gasped Rosa.

"This is the first I hear of it. I saw your house was locked up, but I didn't know there'd been trouble."

"Well, so here they are, getting drunker by the minute, and on my own liquor. I'm alone in the *tienda* with this man we hired to help work on the farm, and I know he's not going to be much help. And he isn't. It's getting toward night, and I don't like it. So I say, 'All right, officers. It's time to pay up.'"

Doña Juana's muscular gesture at an area on one side of the counter recreated the scene—a detachment of rough men of vicious character, inebriated, temporarily cowed before this lone woman's determination. Perhaps they were also disconcerted by the shifting indirection of her baleful glare.

Marco glanced at Rosa, his eyes twinkling. He, too, was visualizing Doña Juana's stand against the ruffians. Juana's chin jutted out in renewed indignation. "They hit me," she rasped, "and say they'll kill me. They go through the place looking for money.

"I think, 'Let them look. I know where my money is.' " She tapped her ample bosom with a sly chuckle. "They're taking everything in sight, and still they yell, 'Where's the money?' That's where I draw the line. So I decide to get in there." She gestured with a flip of her thumb toward a door at the far end of the room. "And I'm getting the pole up in the bedroom, when one of them roughnecks opens the door so hard it knocks me over. Fact is, it nearly knocks me out. And him standing there yelling, 'Hand over your money,' and the others coming in hollering, 'Your money or your life!' And I'm sitting there on the floor, trying to see straight, things spinning around.

"That's when this hired man comes in. They've got him scared as a jack rabbit. *'Deles!'* he whispers, but you can hear him in the next room. 'Give it to them.'

"So now they know I have it; and, when I can get up, they come around yelling they want my money. One of them hits me again. I don't tell them I won't, but I'm not giving it to them yet. I go to a drawer of papers and shuffle around as if I'm looking, and here's this picture of Gaitán. I show it to the lieutenant. 'Ask this one,' I say. 'I have my rights. *He'll* tell you how police officers should act.' And they just laugh at me. You should hear them. 'He'll not help you any,' they say. 'Gaitán's dead.' "

"He is," Marco said. "He was assassinated last year while we were in Tolima."

"There's a man who stood up for people's rights. So they killed him, did they? Well, I let them yell, and they hit me again and put my neck out of joint. That's why I went to live with my son awhile. It still hurts."

Doña Juana moved her head about gingerly to demonstrate
her injury. "So I gave it to them." Her face reddened again
with anger. "Of my own free will, I gave it to them. Twenty-
five pesos!"

"She's hard to figure out," remarked Marco later. "She could
have been killed outright for holding onto her money. What's
twenty-five pesos? You can't buy a sack of beans for it. Yet she
turns around and hands me her business. It would have taken
me a long time to save enough money even to buy a small stock
of supplies."

"I've been repeating something in my mind that Toño read
us this morning," said Rosa thoughtfully. " 'This is the Lord's
doing; it is marvelous in our eyes.' "

Marco nodded. "It looks like God personally wants us to
get a good start here. Maybe He has something real special for
us to do out here. I get excited when I think God gets involved
in my affairs. This God we've found is real!"

A few minutes later, a chubby girl in her early teens knocked
at the door. Rosa was startled at her beauty. Her light-brown
hair—unusual in Latin America—would set this girl off from
the rest of the young people in the community, but the glint of
sharp wit and good humor in her grey eyes made her instantly
likeable.

"I'm Carmen," she announced. "My aunt said you might be
able to use these *bollos*."

"How very thoughtful!" Rosa exclaimed. *"Bollos* solve my
problem of getting a meal in this disorder. It's a good filling
meal, and we won't even need dishes. What could be more
perfect for a moving day?"

The leaf packets in which garbanzas and pork were enveloped
in corn mush had been tied into unusually neat squares. Doña
Juana, though affectedly masculine in her demeanor, was evidently a good cook. And by this warm gesture she was demonstrating the warmth of character that she, strangely, seemed
at pains to conceal under her harsh bluster.

Rosa saw Carmen's glance move toward the door through

which they could hear her own daughters' animated chatter. "Come," she said. "I want you to meet some girls about your own age."

She called to Alicia and Tive. "Tell me, is the name Carmen Lazzco? Aren't you a niece?"

Carmen laughed easily. "I call myself Carmen Vanegas."

"Then you're Don Germán's daughter?"

"No relation," retorted the girl. "But Don Germán brought me up—and Doña Juana. My mother died right after I was born. Her name was Díaz."

Later in the day, Carmen brought her brothers to meet their new neighbors. Both Arturo and José Quintero were lean and dark, and carried their machetes with the swaggering air of swashbuckling bandits. Rosa was not permitted to ponder the social complexities that had resulted in the diversity of surnames.

"Arturo plays the trombone," said Carmen proudly and then added, "for all the dances."

Even now, the bold manner in which José was staring at Alicia stirred in Rosa an apprehension that was not diminished when she learned further that Carmen and her brothers did not intend to accompany their foster parents to Barranca Bermeja but would remain here to do the farm work. Carmen, young as she was, would keep house for her brothers.

By Marco's contract to take over the management of the *tienda*, Rosa pondered, the Francos would be inextricably involved with whatever went on next door. Which household would have the stronger influence? Would they be able to win these two hard-shelled young men to faith in Christ? Or would *they* try to win her sons from the faith? And then Rosa was reminded that the older youth's interest might not lie in seducing her son from his faith. He was eyeing Alicia.

8

Calendar of Despair

GERMAN VANEGAS, a man of fewer words than his consort, came over a few days later in one of those increasingly rare moments when no other member of his family happened to be about. Now that Juana had made arrangements for someone to handle the store, they were leaving at once, Vanegas confided. It was high time to get to his farm in Barranca Bermeja. July soon would be past.

"Those young rapscallions of hers aren't bad youngsters, but even Juana knows better than to leave them in charge of the store. José's the oldest, but he likes his liquor a bit too well."

Marco looked thoughtful. "That's something I'll have to talk to her about," he said. "If I take over the store, it won't be to sell liquor. I don't even want it in the store."

"Why, hombre, that's what'll get you your real profit! You handle the rest of the stuff for your customers' convenience, but they come for the liquor."

Marco shook his head. "She made me a good deal, and I hate to give it up. But I'll have to, if it means selling liquor."

"What's the matter? Can't you hold liquor? Or what?"

"I used to drink as much as any," replied Marco, "but I've found something that's better."

Germán Vanegas' heavy brow puckered in perplexity. Then he eyed Marco in a sudden flash of suspicion. "You don't mean hemp?"

Marco chuckled. "No. I'll speak plainly. I've become an *evangélico,* and *evangélicos* don't drink."

Don Germán had demonstrated patent disapproval of the idea of smoking hemp; but Marco's announcement that he was an evangelical was, as far as Don Germán was concerned, a cause for far greater censure. When Marco began eagerly to tell his new neighbor what his faith meant to him, Don Germán remained for only a few seconds, stiff and outraged, and then interrupted Marco to say that he had some work to do.

Doña Juana stalked in only a few minutes later, out of breath and red of face. Without any preliminaries, she unleashed a stream of invective and violent vituperation, berating Marco for his lack of integrity. It was quite evident that Don Germán had told her that Marco was backing out on his deal, and she was furious that he should default just at the very time of her departure.

"Whoa, there!" exclaimed Marco, grinning, when she finally had to stop for breath. "Who said I was backing out of my deal?"

"Germán did."

"Well, Doña Juana, I think he may have misunderstood me. I still want to handle your stock. I think you made me the best deal I could get anywhere. I'm grateful to you."

"Then what was he grousing about?" sputtered Juana. "He says it sounds as if he's going to have to go to Barranca alone, and that makes him mad every time. He's acting balky like he always does when I let him go up there by himself."

"I mentioned one thing to him that I should have thought of sooner, Doña Juana. I don't sell liquor. But the rest—"

"And *that's* all?"

"Or tobacco. But that's all."

Doña Juana stared at Marco soberly for a fraction of a minute then burst into deep-throated mirth. "Well, the little liquor I have, I can lock up. I'd have to leave some, anyhow, for the boys. If that's all—" She stopped herself in the middle of a thought. "But *why* not? That's what makes the *tienda* pay."

"I gave up drinking when I committed my life to God. For

me, it had to be one or the other, and the trade-over was such a good one that I'd rather get one man to follow this way than to sell liquor to a hundred drunks."

"You don't get rich off it, though, I'll bet."

Marco chuckled. "The Bible tells us not to lay up riches down here where thieves can get it or where it can go wormy." He paused to let Juana digest this nugget of truth, since part of her scolding had centered around her stores of edibles going bad if they were not sold. " 'But lay up for yourselves treasure in heaven' " Marco quoted. "That's where I want my treasure, Doña Juana."

Unlike Don Germán, Juana did not bristle at Marco's declaration of faith. She grinned at him derisively and began needling him. She went off in a far better mood than when she'd come, but Rosa realized that Marco's eager testimony had made no more impression on her than it had on Don Germán. The pair left Santa Inés a day or two later, before the end of July.

Carmen, still very young to be left in charge of any household, spent far more time at the Franco home than she did keeping house. She was cheerful and friendly, but Rosa wondered what would be her influence, and her brothers', in her own children.

Rosa remembered, with a glow of pride, that Antonio had been the very first of them all to declare his break with the ways of this world. Still, her teenage children had suffered acutely through ridicule and scorn of young people. At a time in life when it is utterly important to conform to others of their own age, her children had had to stand alone in every neighborhood in which they had lived, except for a very few young people in Ocaña.

Like Carmen, Arturo and José were spending their free time at the Franco house, and Rosa was uneasy about José's intentions. He was definitely making advances to Alicia when Rosa was not around. Alicia was young. Would she lose her head—and her faith—over this young man who was openly contemptuous of the gospel?

The matter came to a head before many days had passed. With the house theirs to use as they wished, the young people next door lost little time planning a party. Perhaps their proximity to the Francos had even inspired the idea, for, like Marco, his tribe of ten were natural extroverts, continually sharpening their wits against one another. Their neighbors might be counting on the Francos to provide the spark that would make their party a success.

Rosa knew all too well the trend of such parties. When liquor was served—and it would be—the crowd became rowdy and often unmanageable. With no older adults to provide restraints, the party would be no place for young Christians. Marco would put his foot down, without doubt; but, since the party would be almost on their doorstep, it would offer a real temptation to their own children. She prayed much about it. She wanted the decision to come not from herself or Marco but from the children.

Rosa could have spared herself her concern. José soon revealed to Alicia that he expected her to be his date for the evening. Alicia firmly informed him not to expect her. He regarded her announcement as a personal affront.

"He's furious," said Alicia at table that night. "Says he'll never come back here again."

"Arturo understands," said Toño. "We've talked about things like parties and drinking before. He sort of expected we'd not go."

Marco put down his mug of *tinto* with a thump. "Well, I hope José keeps his word. I don't like anybody to hang around my girls like he's been doing. If he doesn't stop it, *I'll* have to talk to him. And I'll talk straighter than Alicia!"

"But Papá!" Alicia protested. "We can't have our neighbors hating us!"

"Well," barked Marco, "see that you keep that *bribón*[1] at arm's length or he'll feel the end of my boot!"

Alicia flushed with annoyance. Rosa regretted Marco's mak-

[1]Rascal.

ing an issue of it after Alicia had of her own accord taken a step in the right direction. In her rebellious teens, would Alicia assert her independence by flaunting the allure her father had been perceptive enough to note?

Rosa, remembering her own early disdain of parental wisdom and the grievous consequences in her own life, spent much time in secret prayer during the days that followed. Alicia, vivacious and desirable, would not have quelled José's interest in her with one rebuff. In a manner completely effective and highly satisfactory to Alicia as well as to herself, God answered Rosa's prayer.

In Latin America, social custom dictates that women must not live alone. Alicia was excited and enthusiastic when a woman missionary approached her about going to El Carmen as her companion. Marco gave his consent readily, considering it an honor for their daughter to have this opportunity. Señorita Carole had given them her assurance that Alicia would come home occasionally to visit her family.

The six-hour bus trip between them and El Carmen had sounded like a small matter of distance when Alicia left in August. It began to take on serious proportions as rumors of national violence reached a new pitch of sadism and brutality during the following weeks. Several small villages near Bucaramanga had been subjected to what appeared to be an organized advance. Rosa kept trying to ease her sense of impending calamity by telling herself that El Carmen was farther from Bucaramanga than was Santa Inés.

"That trouble near Bucaramanga?" retorted Alcario Mateus, a customer, in response to Rosa's anxious question about national news. "You know who's causing it? The new police."

" 'Military police,' they call them," added his brother, Margario. "The regular police force wasn't about to be ordered to burn houses and butcher Colombian citizens, so President Ospina's replacing them. A whole new police force."

"Yes, and you know where Ospina gets them? It says right here in this newspaper they've pulled out the most vicious criminals from the prisons. 'Blackguards inured to a life of crime and violence' it says. So now they've put police uniforms on them and turned them loose. That's who's setting fire to houses, raping and killing and looting. They're old hands at it."

"And Ospina pays them for it now."

"You don't think it's just the Liberal newspaper printing this kind of thing before election?"

"Doña Rosa," said Margario, "there's even fighting between those two police forces. It says here that these military police have vowed to kill the honest police to the last man."

"They'll have to fight the army as well, won't they?" Marco asked.

Margario nodded. "The army is in a queer position. They're bound by the constitution to support the President. And they're not fighting him, but they are protecting citizens against his military police. A citizen can still depend on the army."

The two brothers continued their summary of the current news. That President Ospina Pérez intended by fair means or foul to retain control of the country was becoming increasingly evident. Squads of military police turned machine gun fire on roomfuls of Liberals wherever they dared meet for political rallies. His network of power seemed to follow well laid plans of political victory through intimidation and liquidation. Military police attacked Liberal leaders on the streets; they looted and burned homes of those who had taken part in Liberal activities.

At the capital, President Ospina had manipulated his Cabinet so that he had a Conservative majority, though both houses of Congress were strongly Liberal. In the normal course of events, the next presidential election would not take place until the first Sunday in June, 1950; but, fearing further manipulating by the Conservatives, the Liberals introduced a measure to advance the date to the last Sunday of November, 1949, when congress would still be in session.

The course through the senate, according to the paper, had been violent. At one point senators threw ash trays, books and inkwells at each other. On September 7, in the Chamber of

Representatives, two rival legislators from Boyacá began to trade insults. Three men drew guns. Jiménez, a Liberal was killed.

"Think of it, Marco. A third of those lawmakers were carrying guns and used them to win their arguments. Three of them were hit, and I guess the place was shot up some."

"What you're saying, Margario, is that when the bedlam subsided and they pulled the bodies out, they passed the bill? It is now mid-September, so that means we vote in about ten weeks. We can sure look for trouble between now and then."

As the election date approached, riots were staged wherever Liberals attempted a political rally. Police armed with submachine guns would enter the rally and shoot into the crowd. In rural districts, Liberals, threatened by violent death, fled to the comparative safety of cities; but by doing so they forfeited their right to vote. Liberals now counted their dead in the thousands.

In October one of the members of the Ocaña church brought them news of trouble in Salazar. Someone had warned the missionaries at the teachers' training school there that he had overheard two police officers talking in low tones in a taxi. They were plotting to take all the rural communities near. Since such rumors were by no means rare, the missionaries carried on as usual.

"But one day the police drove a truck through the streets of Salazar and round and round the plaza. They had three dead bodies in some kind of a big box they'd set up so that everybody was supposed to see them. Well, that scared the teachers. They made arrangements to take the next bus out—on a Monday. The night before they left, they saw seven houses go up in flames on the surrounding mountains, but near town. They were lucky. That was the last bus that left Salazar."

"So they got out?"

"Yes, but in their minds, they were just getting the girls off to their homes. So they left everything in the house together with a lot of stuff other people had brought to be kept safe. They had a United States flag up over the house, but headquarters must have talked them out of going back. So they sent a man back to get their refrigerator a couple of days later. He had the thing loaded when the police ran into him. They wouldn't let him leave with it, and they had got into the house, too, and robbed them of about everything they could move out."

"How far is Salazar from El Carmen?" Rosa asked.

"Oh, it's nowhere near. It's in the opposite direction from us—close to Cúcuta.

"Well, he slept on the truck. When things were quiet he left town with it, but he wouldn't do it again for any money, he says."

A day or two later, Antonio spied a newspaper under the arm of a man who stepped off a truck on his way back into the foothills.

"Is that a paper from today?"

The man was willing to share his news. Rosa quickly put on a kettle for *tinto* while Carmelo dashed out to find his father.

"It looks to me like they're tightening up on news. There's enough question marks on this page to hang yourself on."

"How do you mean?"

"I mean you have to put two and two together to know what's happening. The paper is scared to put it into headlines. Or even into plain Spanish. Like here it says they've pulled out fifty army men that had been called to La Vega. The government ordered them out. And then over here you see that all the telephone wires along the route have been cut. The paper doesn't come right out and say what it means, but I hope those people get out of there. When the government goes after you, you don't have a chance."

The man sat rustling the paper, chewing his upper lip. Rosa hovered nearby, having asked Tive to bring in the *tinto*.

"Is there anything about trouble north of us—near El Carmen?" she ventured just as Marco strode in with Carmelo at his heels.

The man glanced at her momentarily. "La Vega is north.

And here it says something about a riot in Santa Marta, and some haciendas burned in Magdalena, and El Carmen in Norte de Santander—"

"What does it say about El Carmen?" said Marco, instantly alert.

"Oh, it's nothing much. Not a headline. Roadblocks—and the telephone line is down. There's trouble brewing there."

"You think they want to attack the town?"

"It doesn't say. But that's getting awfully close to us."

"I'll tell you how close it is to me. I have a daughter in El Carmen."

"Well, a person can't say. They just mention it once here, in fine print. Still—" The man left his thought unspoken.

"I wish a person could know what's going on!"

"I can't see a thing more," said the man, "but I'll tell you this. I'll read it line by line; and, if it seems that there's anything you ought to know, I'll send my boy up here with it marked." He hitched himself up in his chair suddenly and scowled at the paper. "How far is it to La Vega?"

"By road," replied Marco, "I'd say it's about a hundred kilometers from El Carmen. Almost straight north, I guess."

When Rosa saw that Marco was going into Ocaña directly, she insisted on going with him. "I know you'll tell me what they say," she argued stubbornly, "but this time I just can't bear the agony of waiting."

Knowing that Don Francisco always read the newspapers, they hurried to the Velásquez home right from the market where their truck had unloaded its passengers. Doña Emma led them out to the patio. Don Francisco looked up from his workbench with a mouthful of cobbler's tacks. Seeing the Francos, he quickly put down his tools and divested himself of a coarse canvas apron before he came to clasp Marco's hand and Rosa's with warm welcome.

"We haven't come to visit," said Marco. "We came to find out if you know about trouble in the direction of El Carmen."

"I haven't seen anything from there, but it's coming straight at us from near Bogotá. And from the west."

"Tell them what happened in Piedecuesta, Francisco," urged Doña Emma, serving them *tinto* sweetened with homemade cane syrup.

"That Piedecuesta business started the first of September. That's when I realized how involved the government is in this."

"Piedecuesta—the village just outside of Bucaramanga?"

"Yes, on the other side. But anything close to Bucaramanga is plenty close to us."

"What happened, Francisco?"

"Well, that Monday night the mayor, Ruiz, went to a canteen called La Roca, which is right north of the plaza. He took a couple of drinks. Then, without a word, Ruiz walked toward the table where Prada, the director of the local market, was talking to some other men. Ruiz pulled out his gun and shot Prada twice in the stomach. Prada tried to grab the mayor to defend himself, and then a bunch of police that the mayor had left outside pounced on Prada, who still tried to get away. They finished him off right at the edge of the street, which was as far as he had been able to get. Then the mayor ordered the police to take the body to the theater."

"Imagine it," said Doña Emma. "The people couldn't leave the theater. They just did it to scare them all."

"The mayor had given the police a black list of thirty Liberals. They were supposed to shoot them on sight. Piedecuesta citizens begged the governor for military help when they heard that many Liberals had been carted to jail and then shot to death. In Enciso, many were burned alive. There was hardly a day when we didn't read about houses burned or Liberals killed. Then it crept up to Matanza, and right after that they shot a young Liberal who had just driven to El Playón on Sunday morning. The army captured the man that did that."

"Thank God, the army is still in favor of the constitution."

"Yes, Marco, but the military police have an encampment

nearby at La Ceiba, and the news that a Conservative had been arrested must have traveled like fire along a bomb fuse."

"What makes you say that?"

"When they heard of the arrest, most of the police must have been drunk. They decided to show El Playón how Liberals should really be treated. When they started shooting up the town, the people decided to fight it out. They killed five of the police.

"So then the Conservative brass-hats in Bucaramanga heard that police had been killed. They didn't bother to find out who was to blame. They sent a hundred police to finish what the drunk policemen had begun on a whim. When the military police—sent by the government in Santander, mind you—when they got out of El Playón, the survivors were able to report their atrocities."

"One of the people from there said a tornado could not have done as much damage," said Doña Emma.

"When they finished with the stores," resumed Don Francisco, "they went down the line of homes and looted them. The owners took to the mountains for their lives. Fifty-seven homes in El Playón are in ashes, and the rest are practically in ruins. The police set the stores on fire after they had plundered them. And in La Ceiba there were twenty stores. They looted every one of them. And these bandits represent the law of Colombia. Besides stealing everything, they broke up windows, showcases and shelves. They destroyed the merchandise they couldn't carry away.

"When newspaper reporters came in on Saturday, they found bodies in the streets; they had been partly eaten by buzzards. Some had died on the way to their farms. Some were still agonizing in homes they ran to for help. Nobody dared come out on the trails to get a doctor or bring them medicine."

"That following Monday," interjected Doña Emma, "the women from Piedecuesta appealed to the governor to send the army to help them. He ignored them."

"Then the women went to the *comandante* of the Fifth Army

Brigade and begged him to come and rescue the people still left in their homes, but the *comandante* couldn't do a thing without an order from the governor."

"So what good is the army? Where can people finally turn?"

"Do you realize, Marco, that we're not up against a few packs of guerrillas now? We're up against the government. Still, Santander's police captain, Pontón—of the old order— and a lieutenant called Carvajal got wind of what had happened in El Playón, so they made a tour to find out just what had happened. And they reported the killings and destruction to the Chamber of Representatives. When the newspaper approached Governor Sórzano for information, he just said, '*Allí no ha pasado nada.*'[2]

"They're not going to allow the papers to print what they're doing, and they're not putting up with anyone who stands against this lawlessness. The Medellín paper, *El Colombiano,* is closed. And over the weekend of September 25, the governors of Caldas and Norte de Santandre were replaced. You can guess what that means."

"And in Piedecuesta, people telephoned to Bogotá," said Doña Emma, reverting to the terror in the homes, "saying they were locked up in their houses, but they could hear firing on the plaza. They were begging somebody to come and rescue them."

"You'd think the nation's capital would do something to protect its citizens, wouldn't you? But the next day's paper reported a night of terror in Piedecuesta. Who knows how many were killed? A lot of wounded people came to Bucaramanga, but they were not allowed into the hospital, and doctors were not allowed to go and see them."

"How terrible," cried Rosa. "God have mercy on them."

"And on us, Rosa," replied Emma. "It's coming here."

"They broke down the doors into the mission school at Piedecuesta and hacked the organ in pieces as well as the altar and the benches. But that's a small thing when you think of what's

[2]Nothing has happened there.

happened in Matanza. Two hundred families are sleeping in the streets and plaza of Bucaramanga—all exiles from Matanza. More than a thousand people driven out of their homes. It's the same in Pamplona."

On the way back to Santa Inés, Rosa said, "They've heard of all those other places; so, since they've heard nothing of El Carmen, I suppose we have nothing to worry about."

"In a week or two I'm going up there," Marco replied. "I'm getting our girl home. She may be safer there than she is here, but at least we'll know what's happening."

"Surely the señorita—"

"My mind's made up," Marco retorted shortly.

A week later, however, they received a letter from Alicia. She was fairly bubbling with enthusiasm over the prospect of what sounded like a protracted tour of villages and mountain communities.

"It will be my first chance at really making a project of telling somebody else about our faith. It sort of makes a missionary out of me, too, doesn't it? Señorita Carole has told me what is good to say, but I have a feeling I'll end up just telling people, naturally, what God has done for us—our family—since we heard. And believed."

While Antonio was reading the letter, Marco became increasingly agitated. He got up and began pacing the floor, clenching and unclenching his hands.

"What can she be thinking of—this missionary?" he ejaculated, when Toño refolded the letter and put it back into the envelope.

"Why, Papá!" exclaimed Carmelo, with the flippant thoughtlessness of his years. "She's making a preacher out of Alicia. Isn't that what you wanted?"

Marco scowled at his son. "This is no time to be cocky!" he growled. "I'd think there'd be plenty of preaching to be done right there in El Carmen." He shoved his clenched fists into his pockets. "Now we don't even know where they are." He glanced at Rosa helplessly. Rosa knew he was seriously concerned.

"We must be hearing exaggerations of conditions in that neighborhood," she said. "You know how it is with rumors."

Rosa found that it was far easier to talk reassuringly than to convince herself. During her visit to Ocaña, the accumulation of reports from about a month of news had given her a terrifying picture of conditions in the country. She kept telling herself that there were thousands of towns untouched by violence; and, in almost all towns where violence had raged, only a few people, comparatively, had lost their lives. She must keep her emotional balance, she told herself, but her mind kept fretting about Alicia's safety.

Later, just before they called the family together for the usual evening devotions, Marco spoke about the matter that had occupied both their thoughts most of the day. "I wonder if God isn't trying to teach us something."

Rosa waited for him to go on. She could see by the nervous way he clenched and unclenched his fists that his worry over Alicia had not lessened since Alicia's letter had arrived.

"Now that I have no idea how to reach Alicia and don't even know what direction they took—" Marco paused, beginning to pace back and forth. He glanced at Rosa with a rueful smile. "It looks as if God wants me to put the matter in His hands."

"They're good hands, Marco. Maybe we need to learn more about trusting God."

"*Maybe?*" Marco turned so that he could look intently into her own eyes. She tried to meet his searching gaze, but she found her eyes filling with the tears that had been near the surface. He nodded. "We both know it's the thing to do."

"Yet neither of us have really managed it," Rosa moaned. "So we're being crowded into a corner, where we have to learn it."

"God knows where Alicia is," Marco said, when the children had gathered. "I want every single one of you to ask God to put His own hand over her and protect her. No matter what happens in El Carmen."

"Couldn't somebody shoot through His hand, maybe?" Chico wanted to know and was immediately put in his place by his older brother Carmelo's superior wisdom.

"God can make the gun not go off. Remember, at Aspasica?"

When the little fellow took his turn to pray, el Chico's specific directions for God gave them all they could do to stifle a chuckle. Rosa found that a weight had been lifted as she rose from her knees.

Later, Marco remarked wryly, "If our own faith breaks down, we have el Chico to fall back on. He's got the whole thing organized, right now."

"All jokes aside," responded Rosa, "I wish I had his simple faith."

October came to an end; November advanced slowly. Rumors—widespread and varied—kept filtering in. The violence seemed to be moving closer. El Carmen, a Liberal town, could be right on the fringe of the wave of violence. Men of the Santa Inés area now usually stopped by their store on the way in toward the mountains. If they didn't, Marco would waylay them and prod them for news.

"They're still fighting about whether a man can vote from some place else than the address on his *cédula*,"[3] said one of the men who had stopped by. "If they get that law through, people who've had to leave their homes can vote anyway, just so they have their *cédula* to identify themselves. Echandia won't be any Gaitán, but he's no butcher. May the Holy Mother help us if Laureano gets in. Did you know that *El Espectador* has been put out of print? They put out their last paper on the ninth of November."

"*El Espectador?* Why, that's one of the biggest in the country! What's that one you have, then?"

"This?" said the man. "This is *Vanguardia Liberal*. They might as well close this one. All that seems to be going on is

[3]Cédula—identity card.

some pink teas in Bogotá, the foreign news and picture shows. Here's a bit in the paper that says it's always been very discreet in its reporting. Well, it sure is now, that's for sure. They've got it by the throat—if they haven't cut the owner's throat and started running it themselves."

"There's nothing about El Carmen?"

"There's nothing about nothing. I'm telling you. *This* is worse than reading the news, bad as it was. Now we don't know where we are."

"You haven't heard anything in town about El Carmen?" Marco persisted.

One of two men who had just come in spoke up. "What I heard isn't good. They say the police have the town under siege—the whole town."

"It's not just another rumor?"

"Police have roadblocks up, Don Marco. It doesn't look good for El Carmen. There's no way those people can run."

Marco got on the next truck that passed in the direction of Ocaña and went straight to the missionary's home. There he learned that the missionary's wife had had to leave the station with a seriously sick child. The missionary, however, seemed to be as anxious for news of El Carmen as Marco.

"The mission school at Salazar near the Venezuelan border has closed a week early, but all the girls from there got home safely. And I've sent a message to the señorita at El Carmen to come here to stay with us if she saw any sign of trouble. If she comes, she will not come without your daughter, Don Marco." He added somewhat ruefully, "I'd be glad if they came. I need somebody to cook for me."

"Do you think I should go after them? El Carmen is Liberal. It may be on the Conservatives' list for attack."

"Most of the towns that have been damaged were small villages, Don Marco. I'll let you know if I hear of anything really authentic. She'll come out if there is trouble; be sure of that!"

"What about the police roadblocks?"

The missionary shrugged. "Where don't they have road-blocks? She can always send me a wire."

Marco went back to Santa Inés, since it was not the day for the bus into El Carmen, but with a strange feeling of foreboding. Since the newspapers carried no local news, the people depended on rumors; and some of these conflicted or were plainly inventions of terror. No one could believe anything, and yet no one could afford to disbelieve anything. That the military police had blocked the road to El Carmen had been established by several eye witnesses.

One morning, during the second week of November, they heard another blood-chilling rumor that El Carmen had not only been sacked, but that the whole town had been set on fire. Again, without delay, Marco announced that he was going in to Ocaña. He sent Tive and Carmelo to watch the road and to halt the first vehicle that came by. Then he strode toward the store. Rosa saw him take extra cash and felt assured that Marco would do whatever he needed to do to find Alicia and bring her home. This time he would not rest until he had rescued her and Señorita Carole—if they were still alive.

To Rosa's amazement, Marco returned late that afternoon. One glance at his face, and she burst into tears. "Tell me," she cried, "you have to tell me what happened to my little girl!"

Marco took her gently into his arms without a word. When at last she had regained her composure, he told her in detail all that had happened.

He had hurried, first of all, to the home of the missionary. In his anxiety he had knocked on the door more loudly than was his habit; and, when he did not get an immediate response, he revealed his desperation by the way he pounded on it. A neighbor across the street came to her door.

"He's not there, señor."

"Do you know where he is?"

The woman shrugged. "The military came and got him out of here. He left, bag and baggage, the same day."

"When was that?"

"A couple of days ago."

Evidently the missionary had been forced to leave in such a hurry that he had had no way of sending him word. Deep in thought, Marco retraced his steps to the plaza. In an hour the bus was due to leave for El Carmen. He would go to get his daughter now and bring the missionary, too, if he could find them. He went to the Copetrán bus office facing the plaza.

"That bus isn't running, señor. It hasn't been running for a week."

"Well," said Marco, thinking aloud, mentally counting the money in his pocket, "then I'll have to take a taxi."

A queer look came into the face of the Copetrán agent. "You can always try," he said cryptically.

The man considered him a fool, Marco thought. To take a taxi to an unscheduled place like El Carmen, he knew, would cost a small fortune. He was glad that several of the taxis were lined up, apparently without fares. If he were shrewd, he might be able to dicker them down to half price. Even that would be very much money.

"How much to El Carmen?" he asked the driver of the first taxi he came to.

"I'm not going there."

"I am."

The man shrugged. "I'm *not*."

Marco went to the next taxi in line.

"That road's closed, señor," said the driver. "I wouldn't take you to El Carmen for any money."

"Is it true that they burned the town?" cried Marco, out of his mounting despair. He wiped the perspiration from his forehead with clammy, shaking hands as he waited for the noncommittal reply of the taxi driver.

"Who knows? Has anybody gotten out of there?" The man answered warily.

Approaching a few more taxis, Marco heard even more disheartening reports, though none of them was more than a repetition of rumor. Abandoning that approach, he wandered about the streets, watching the plaza for the small clusters of men who gathered to share bits of information. He ran into a wealthy sawmill owner from south of El Carmen. He questioned him anxiously for any news.

"Why, yes," said Miguel Hernandez. "I saw that missionary in La Vega—tall, blonde woman."

"La Vega?" cried Marco, recalling the news he had heard of broken communications and of a detachment of police moving in. Alicia had entered a town police might have been preparing to massacre.

"I bought a Bible from her. That's what I came to Ocaña for. I've found some things in here I'd like explained."

It was a rare day indeed that Marco would voluntarily permit another to have the thrill of sharing the wonderful good news of what the living, gracious Saviour had done for him, and what He would do for anyone who would believe Him for it. However, this day Marco directed Don Miguel to another evangelical home, after he had extracted from him all the information he could get.

Don Miguel actually had gone to the missionary to warn her to leave La Vega area, because of the gathering threat of Conservative activity there. "I wasn't sure they'd get a bus or truck, so I took them to Pailas myself early the next morning. From there they shouldn't have had trouble getting to El Carmen. Trucks are always passing on that main road."

The fact that Don Miguel had seen them out of an area where Marco had every reason to believe danger was great brought only small relief. He had ample evidence that El Carmen had been marked for similar disaster. In this dilemma of anxiety, he recalled the missionary's suggestion of sending a telegram. He had never sent a wire, but he decided that this was the time to find out how it is done.

"A wire to El Carmen?" said the man behind the metal grill. "Why, señor, we haven't had any communication with El Carmen since the eleventh—four days now!"

"You mean you can't send a wire across the roadblock?"

The man smiled. "Telegrams don't travel the roads, señor," he said, in amused condescension of the ignorance of illiterate mountaineers. "They just stopped the mails, the telegraph office and everything else when they took over the town."

"How can I get word into El Carmen?" insisted Marco tremulously. "I have a daughter in El Carmen."

The man's supercilious expression changed to one of compassion, and he crossed himself. "Don't worry too much, señor. Maybe they didn't burn the whole town to the ground as they say. May the Holy Virgin have mercy on your daughter's innocent soul."

9

Massacre

EL CARMEN, a quaint and prosperous little city, had snuggled itself into a narrow Andean gorge of lavish beauty. An enormous spring hidden high in the mountain gushed over rocky ledges to fall in one last glistening leap down a precipitous cliff. El Carmen's enterprising habitants had harnessed its churning power to produce electricity. Still swift and clear, the stream chuckled its way over a boulder-strewn bed that led it right through the length of the rustic, terraced town.

Before anyone had dreamed that this sequestered spot would ever be reached by anything that could not follow a burro trail, the people of El Carmen had paved their steep, narrow streets with cobblestones. They had not worked with a deliberate design toward picturesque charm; still El Carmen's serene enchantment provided a worthy background for fantasy or light romance.

A road weaving down like the folds of corner-store taffy reached El Carmen and ended there. In spite of the arduous and dangerously narrow road leading down to a cul-de-sac, in living conditions and progressiveness this thriving little city far surpassed the languid Aguachica, approachable by road and river and air.

Like chains of children's colored wooden beads, the lines of connected houses yielded to the contour of the mountain. Wide stone-paved stairs led steeply from one terrace of dwellings to the next level above. High above the gurgling stream, but not

162

out of earshot, the formal plaza marked the center of El Carmen.
Beds of bright flowers and well-kept plots of grass further demonstrated the progressive spirit and communal pride of the
townspeople.

In her letter, Alicia had mentioned that on October 15—just
before they were to leave town—in the plaza and just in front
of the ornate, ivory-towered church, the citizens had erected
a statue of the beloved Liberal hero, Jorge Gaitán, assassinated
the previous year. Marco knew that the colored bands at the
bases of the meandering house fronts revealed an unbroken red
line of Liberal sentiment. That El Carmen should be a prime
target for Conservative attack was not surprising. And the
news Marco brought from Ocaña left no doubt of the assault or
of its gravity.

"I'll have to go by horse, Rosa. I have no idea—"

"It will take days, won't it?"

"By horse, it's a long trip to El Carmen. But if I have to
dodge roadblocks in the mountains, I could be a day trying to
bypass one, only to run into another. I hate to leave you with
no idea when to expect me back, but that's the way it is."

"Don't worry about us, Marco. We have to do what we can."

What we can. Perhaps after all Marco's hardship and personal risk there would be nothing left to do but bring her news
of Alicia's fate. Rosa refused to follow that trend of thought.

"Haven't we been praying? God may have kept them from
going back to El Carmen. The man you met did not know what
happened to them after he left them."

Marco was distracted and weary with the weight of his problem. Rosa knew he was trying to visualize the route, to anticipate roadblock locations and plan his long ride accordingly. He
did not know the area well enough. He would have to find
people who would help.

Two horses clattered by the house. Rosa saw them stop at
the *tienda* and sent Antonio to wait on the men who had swung
from their saddles. Antonio came back, a moment later, looking for Marco. His young face, Rosa noticed, was serious and

pale. The reality of Alicia's possible danger must be as clear to him as it was to Marco and herself.

"Papá, there's a man wants to talk to you."

"Well, I don't want to talk to him."

"It's about—it's about Licha, Papá. And about El Carmen."

"Why didn't you say so?" barked Marco, unreasonable in his anxiety. He hurried across to the store. Rosa followed, her knees shaking so that they hardly carried her weight. When she arrived, Marco was questioning a man wearing spurs and heavy leather chaps. The latter appeared uneasy when he saw Rosa, and his request for a cup of *tinto* was far too obviously a ruse. He wanted to speak with Marco alone.

"It's true then." Marco did not wait for preliminaries. "El Carmen has been burned. You've come to tell us?"

The man, who had introduced himself as Pérez, evaded Marco's searching eyes. "They say it has," he said, hedging. "I heard you were asking about it, so I came to tell you."

"What do you know?"

"What I have to tell you is from before—before they burned the town." Pérez hesitated, glancing nervously at Rosa, who had not gone for *tinto* as he had hoped but had sent Antonio for it.

"Well, about a week ago, José Pérez—that's my cousin—and his brother-in-law, Ramón Nieto, were going to El Carmen. They've been having it pretty bad there in Guamalito for about eighteen months. It's getting so a family can't live there. They often have to sleep out in the mountains. So they were going to El Carmen to see if they could find a house to rent."

Antonio returned from the kitchen. A moment later, Tive appeared with the pot of black coffee, quite breathless in her haste and anxiety not to miss any news of Alicia. Rosa poured the *tinto*, but her hand trembled so that the cup rattled on the saucer as she set one before each of the men. Marco ignored his. His visitor cleared his throat nervously. He dropped his hat and picked it up again.

Tears sprang to Rosa's eyes. "Señor Pérez," she sobbed,

"don't keep anything from us. The truth won't hurt any more than this terrible suspense!"

Pérez glanced for confirmation at Marco. In his reluctance to break his news, he sipped his *tinto,* frowning meanwhile at his shoes. At last he set his cup down.

"Well, as I was saying, this Ramón Nieto and my cousin were getting pretty close to El Carmen when they began to see people in the woods, climbing up the mountain toward them. Some of them were wounded—gunshots. They told José and Ramón that as soon as the police got into town they went to the plaza and shot down the statue of Gaitán. Then they lined up the men—the Liberal leaders—and were shooting them down like dogs."

Pérez glanced at Rosa then at Marco's set face.

"Go on," Rosa whispered. "I have to know what happened."

"Well, there's something they are saying. It's the priest that furnished the list of names. He went to Cúcuta before the attack, and he came back on the truck with the military police. They were knocking down doors if people didn't let them right in. And, of course, they're looting. They always do."

"That's all you know?"

"That's as much as they knew—the people who got out of El Carmen. José and Ramón never could have got into the town, and by the time they'd heard what was going on they didn't want to. Even where they were, they made pretty good targets. The police were watching for people trying to get away, and you know how the mountain goes straight up from the edge of town. If it hadn't been for the trees, nobody'd have made it.

"They caught sight of Ramón and took a pot shot at him. They kept shooting at the tree Ramón got behind. After he'd crawled away, along the ground, they turned a machine gun on it. That's when the two of them got right down into a muddy dip and lay low. Then after a while they crawled out of there on chest and elbows, keeping to the brush. Ramón took his family to La Peña. He's an *evangélico,* isn't he?"

"Nieto? He's never been to meetings in Ocaña."

"Anyway, José said the police had taken Ramón's Bible away later on the road. He wants to move to Aguachica; but, if he's an *evangélico,* Aguachica won't be a healthy place for him, if you ask me."

"We don't become *evangélicos* to protect our skins," replied Marco. "Unto us 'it is *given* in the behalf of Christ, not only to believe on him, but also to suffer for his sake'!"

"That's far-fetched religious bunk."

"I was quoting from the Sacred Scriptures."

"Who wants to suffer?"

"Nobody wants it, Señor Pérez, but when it comes it also brings blessing. And it comes, no matter what a man's political party. I'm a Conservative. I live surrounded by Conservatives. But when the dogs bark at night I think, 'Well, here they come!' "

"And *that's* a blessing? Is it a blessing that your girl got caught in El Carmen? Don't lie to me. I can see what your wife's going through, and even your loud talk doesn't hide what you feel. Don't stand there and tell me you call that a blessing!"

Marco cringed as from a physical blow and for a moment evaded Pérez' scathing stare. Then he faced him squarely. "When you think of death, señor, what's your reaction?"

"I don't know what you're getting at, but I'm no liar—even if you are. When I think of dying, I'm scared. So are you."

"Of dying, yes," admitted Marco. "But I'm speaking of death itself."

"Well, isn't that exactly why we're afraid to die? Anyone can endure the pain. It's what comes afterwards that makes us scared of death. Not pain, but fear. I've seen it, señor, in the eyes of some of my best friends."

"I have, too," said Marco. "It was fear of death that made me an *evangélico.* And so, if I suffer for talking about the peace I got from the *evangelio,* I feel like I've had a chance to show God I'm really thankful to Him for letting me in on it. So, even the thought of dying for it brings a blessing."

Marco went on, in spite of the stranger's look of scornful incredulity. "By what you've said, Señor Pérez, there's not much hope of seeing my daughter again—on this earth. But if she died, I know that right now—this minute —she is safely in the presence of her Saviour, the Lord Jesus Christ.'

"If I could know that, Señor Franco, I'd become an *evangélico* right along with you!"

For the moment, Marco forgot his sorrow while he spoke with eager enthusiasm of the hope of the gospel and of faith in Jesus Christ. Rosa, however, withdrew to the patio where she broke down and wept unrestrainedly. The children stood about her in frozen wonderment. They sensed the awful truth that she had lost hope, but they did not understand all the implications of their mother's outburst of wild grief.

Many revolting stories of rape and torture had come to their ears. They had shocked and horrified Rosa though the victims had been unknown. That her daughter—beautiful, vivacious Alicia—had fallen into the hands of brutal, lust-driven sadists, was a thought too horrible to bear. Though she had committed Alicia to a loving Father's care, it was impossible not to envision the girl's fate.

Marco came back through the house, pale and shaken, but he was still determined to make the trip to El Carmen to gain some definite word of his daughter's fate.

Señor Pérez followed him into the patio. "I tell you," he argued, "the town is burned. Dozens of people saw the smoke."

"Fires burn themselves out. She might be in there somewhere, burned and needing help. I have to get to her."

"Don't think you can get in there with a mule," retorted Pérez. "It's not only along the highways that the police have road blocks, señor. They've got police along all the mountain trails. You couldn't get through. Stay with your family."

Other customers, not finding Marco at the *tienda*, wandered in. All advised Marco to abandon thought of his hopeless project.

"They'll get you, Marco."

"Your family needs a living man a whole lot more than it needs two dead corpses, Marco. Don't try to be a hero."

"A dead one. Don't go off and leave your family without a provider—and with nobody to fight off those beasts when they start on us up here. And they're coming, don't you forget it!"

"They turn machine guns on anything that moves on the mountains, both sides of El Carmen. How do you think you'll get down there while there's anybody left alive in there?" advised Pérez.

At last Rosa joined the others in persuading Marco to remain in Santa Inés.

True to their proclaimed beliefs, the Franco family broke accepted custom by refusing to go into deep mourning. Their Bible had told them that they did not need to sorrow as those who have no hope; they would not allow others to believe that they were doing so. They even kept the store open to those who came to buy or to exchange bits of news with others.

People spoke of little besides politics. During the week preceding Pérez's visit, the heat of the political campaign had developed, in Bogotá, into a "revolution carried out by the government in office,"[1] in which President Mariano Ospina Pérez proclaimed a state of siege. By doing so, he had a pretext to suspend the Liberal Congress and to impose complete censorship of press, radio and cables. He banned meetings and demonstrations and gave authority to dismiss all remaining Liberal government employees. He annulled the powers of the Liberal Supreme Court to prevent its halting any of his unconstitutional acts.

All hope that the government would take a stand against the atrocities committed by the police in its name was now lost. The Conservative government was openly committed to destroy the Liberal party. Identification *cédulas,* necessary for voting, were confiscated or destroyed. Political hatred and murder had invaded the most peaceful communities. The feelingless fingers of fear were crushing out rationalism and fairness; retributions

[1]*Time,* Nov. 21, 1949.

were set on foot as people, filled with suspicion and frenzy, joined guerrilla bands already roaming the hills.

Weeks of national and local unrest had stretched into months. Still life had to go on. On the surface, at least, it went on very much as it always had. So accustomed had Colombians become to rumors of savagery and crime that neither Señorita Carole nor Alicia had considered them a hindrance to a routine evangelistic tour which, in late October, had taken them a hundred kilometers from El Carmen.

Miguel Hernández, the sawmill owner who had bought a Bible from the missionary on November 8, had sensed something of imminent danger when he had urged them to leave the area of La Vega. As he told Marco later, he himself had taken them to Pailitas; but, had he been fully aware of the gravity of the situation, he would have taken them on to El Carmen or even to the oil industry's airfield.

At Pailitas he had fully expected them to catch a truck or other vehicle home, for, when off main highway routes, all travelers depended on occasional trucks or cars passing in the right direction. The two young women—as the Franco family learned some time later—had been forced to stand at the roadside in a cold drizzle until two o'clock that afternoon before they were able to get on a truck heading toward El Carmen.

Rains had raised a river on their route to a depth their truck could not pass. By wading across, they were able to transfer to another truck stranded on the other side. That truck took them only to nearby Simaña. By walking another hour and a half, they reached a junction of mountain roads where they could expect to find a vehicle bound for El Carmen. However, this hope was not realized. Darkness came upon them as they walked on, drenched to the skin and loaded down with their luggage.

In La Mata they spent the night with a family sympathetic with the evangelicals. Next morning they hired a burro for carrying their bags and walked to Ayacucho. Had they been alerted to the seriousness of the situation, they could have escaped from the airport there to Venezuela or one of Colombia's more secure areas.

However, they were intent on getting back to El Carmen; and, when they found a truck, they discovered that they were not the only refugees from La Vega vicinity. Twenty people, including two national police, were packed into the truck bound for El Carmen.

As their truck entered El Carmen, Señorita Carole's attention was attracted to people who were watching them from windows and doorways on the higher terraces of the town.

"I suppose it's the bayonets," said Alicia, chuckling, with a toss of her head at the policemen's arms. "They're scared of the men with bayonets and rifles."

She had guessed correctly, still unaware of the underlying terror that had sent news of their approach from one household to another. They wondered that people who met them at the plaza should appear tense and pale. When, however, the officers were recognized as from the national, law-enforcing body of police, the tension broke up into loud, hilarious relief.

Stopping at the post office, they picked up the letter inviting them to join the missionaries in Ocaña if they felt insecure in El Carmen. Both of the young women realized that people in El Carmen were near panic, but after their prolonged isolation from news, they could find no cause for the mounting fear.

"People are still coming into El Carmen for safety," said Alicia, "so I don't see why we should run away from here."

The political situation seemed to be chronic, so the missionary decided against deserting her work.

On Friday morning, November 11, a neighbor wakened them by knocking agitatedly at their shutters. "Armed men are on the road coming down at us. It's an invasion!"

Again the panic was a false alarm, for the armed men who had been observed belonged to a small army detachment. From them, they could expect protection rather than molestation. The townspeople, the girls learned, had sent the government a request for soldiers. Around El Carmen, as well as in most mountain districts, echoes of spasmodic shootings provided a valid cause to fear attack. Some people were so afraid that they hardly slept. Rumors of guerrilla invasion continued to filter into town.

"Everybody's got the jitters," remarked Alicia on Monday. "The soldiers were supposed to leave town today, but they're still here."

"If the soldiers are leaving, I think we'd better leave," said Señorita Carole. "There must be some reason for all this panic."

They went together to make arrangements with the man who routinely made trips to Ocaña. He promised to hold places for the two young women. Packed and ready to leave for what they thought would be a short absence, they waited for the promised word from the driver. When they discovered that he had driven off without them, they were chagrined but not alarmed.

"Should we have gone to Ocaña when the letter came?" wondered the missionary. "They may know something we haven't heard."

"Well, the army is still here, though people don't know what it means—their deciding to stay after all."

Tuesday's grapevine provided the news that the soldiers had left during the night. The information that followed, that very same day, should have electrified the townspeople with alarm, had they been informed on current political maneuverings. The promise that a military mayor would be coming to take over during the crisis—news accepted with general relief—should have alerted the city leaders. The unsuspecting president of El Carmen's city council repeated the news to Señorita Carole on Wednesday with unfeigned satisfaction.

"And we have word that the national police are sending another detachment from Cúcuta," he said. "Now we can all sleep in peace."

Two hours after this reassuring conversation, the girls had gone to the home of a woman who had agreed to sew a dress for Alicia. With such an encouraging prospect, life took on a more relaxed mood.

In the midst of Alicia's dress fitting, a sudden clatter of feet on the cobblestone street caused Doña Otilia to rush to the door. Doors and wooden shutters slammed all along the street. Their hostess gasped, and they saw her face blanch.

A group of heavily armed police—the feared military police —passed noisily just outside the door on their way toward the town plaza, about a half block higher and one block to the left. As the women stood breathlessly wondering what they should do, the police gained the plaza. Heavy shooting began immediately.

"They're shooting everybody—all our men!" screamed Doña Otilia.

"Was the judge in his office?"

The woman in whose home they found themselves was not Judge Reál's wife, but she was mother to most of his children and was expecting another before the week was out. She nodded. "He thinks he'll be safe. He has his office on the second floor and can lock himself in."

Because of deliberately deceptive messages of reassurance from the capital, the town had been caught completely off guard. Men had been standing about in the plaza and in the doorways of business houses. The moment the military police arrived, they had begun to shoot. After the crowds scattered, the police proceeded to search out the prominent Liberals and were working from a list. Within an hour, thirty of El Carmen's leading citizens had been shot in the plaza or on the street.

Totally demoralized and bereft of the key men who might have led a counterattack, the townspeople never attempted united resistance. Each man's utmost effort seemed that for self-preservation. A few managed to flee to the wooded mountain rising only three or four blocks from the plaza.

These details were unknown, at the moment, to the women who stood paralyzed with horror behind the barred wooden shutters. Shouts, gunfire and screams of agony or fear from the direction of the plaza gave them an inkling of how ruthless a massacre was being carried out. Señorita Carole fell on her knees to pray. Alicia and Doña Otilia joined her. Even the children crouched on their knees, mute with terror.

Darkness came. About seven o'clock, Doña Otilia responded to a knock at the door, opening it when she recognized Judge Reál's voice. Between them, Judge Reál and a police lieutenant brought in a wounded man and conducted him to bed. The judge stepped back quickly into the sala, before the lieutenant left his companion.

"What's *she* doing here?" Judge Reál was trembling visibly.

The judge had no time for social amenities. The foreign woman, tall and blonde, could become the cause of troublesome questions. Before Doña Otilia could reply, he brusquely ordered Señorita Carole to the rear of the house.

"She came with the Franco girl," stammered Doña Otilia. "I was making a dress for her."

"Well, keep her out of sight. These fellows are trigger-happy. If I hadn't offered my place for their wounded, they'd probably have killed me by now."

Señorita Carole went to the kitchen—the place farthest from the street door—but that still did not isolate her from the intruders. Soldiers soon began bringing plantains, yuca and other food, piling it in the patio as well as in the kitchen. When the officer came in too, Carole asked for permission for herself and Alicia to return to their home.

"Why, señorita," he snapped, "I think we'll need your help."

"We've got to cook for these assassins!" sobbed Doña Otilia. "The food they've looted from our own neighbors."

Before midnight, with Alicia and her own daughters helping, Doña Otilia had served meals to about two hundred policemen. Toward morning guerrillas began drifting in, and they had to start all over. They lost count of the meals they served to the men milling about in the house, detachments coming in for food, others being dispatched to their duties somewhere in the town.

"We're right in the enemy's headquarters!" whispered Alicia to the missionary, who still tried to remain inconspicuously in the background. Still, remarks had been made several times about the foreigner. Though she had been detained there through no fault of her own, the missionary was sensitive to the danger her presence might cause. She asked again, at daybreak, for permission to leave. The lieutenant mumbled something about the streets being an ugly sight, but later he detailed one of his men to accompany the señorita and Alicia to their own home.

"Put a towel or something white in the door," advised their escort. "That's to show you've been inspected."

The two young women put out their banner and barred their doors and shutters. Both of them were exhausted from the work and strain of the night and had mentioned going to bed, when a most terrifying barrage of gunshot occurred. Bullets whizzed directly over their patio. Not knowing the object of the shooting, they dropped to the floor. After awhile, they realized that the police were shooting up at Monte Sagrado, the mountain that sloped up steeply from right behind their house.

The day wore on. Police fired spasmodic volleys at the mountain slope as they caught a glimpse of fugitives who had slipped out of town by way of the woods.

"Nobody can get away from here," exclaimed Alicia. "They ferret them out from the bushes as if they were hunting animals."

An old woman opened her rooming house for all the women along their street to spend the nights together. Señorita Carole accepted her invitation gratefully, for the day had brought to light stories of lone women who had been subjected to heinous abuses. Police were breaking into houses by force if doors were not opened to them, and several had already eyed the attractive Alicia speculatively. No woman was safe.

Throughout the night the cobblestone streets resounded with

heavy footfalls. By this time, liquor from the looted taverns was flowing freely; and, with the town politically in hand, the police were a greater threat to the women than during the first night. As they strode by on their patrols, some paused to push against the doors, which had been braced with heavy poles. A few times they prodded the doors with bayonets, and on two occasions they even yelled that the door must be opened. Doña Nacha maintained a frightened silence.

Only small children slept. The women clutched at each other in the darkness, listening tensely to the spreading horror in their familiar streets. Occasional shots were exchanged throughout the hours of darkness, but they had begun to dread the periods of silence more. Almost invariably such lulls were followed by a volley of shooting.

"My God," whispered one of the women, "they've broken into another home."

Señorita Carole brought out her Bible and began reading aloud, more to distract the women's attention than to seize the opportunity of a captive audience. The women began to gather around her gratefully, welcoming the comfort of the Psalms and of the missionary's assurances that Jesus Christ had died that they could have peace of heart though death and eternity seemed imminent.

On Friday morning, Alicia stepped across the street to buy something for their breakfast. Billows of smoke were rising from the center of town only about two blocks away. Alicia rushed back into the house.

"Señorita," she screamed, "the town's on fire!"

A policeman happened by. "If you want to save your lives, señora, you'd better run. This town is going to burn!"

Snatching a small bag previously packed with their most necessary belongings, the young women dashed into the street, turning downward and away from the town's center. El Carmen's long streets followed terraces cut from the sides of the mountain. Though terraced, the steep sloping of the streets impeded their headlong flight; but their feet were spurred on by horror that spread itself, tangible and pungent, all around them.

Sprawled in their own blood lay bodies of people they knew (for everyone in El Carmen knew everyone else). They cringed at the sight of blood spattered against the whitewashed walls in patterns that depicted graphically the drama of ruthlessness and sheer desperation—a drama which would reenact itself in their minds with sickening vividness, haunting them for weeks to come. A sinister fascination drew their eyes even while it made them ill. In spots, the cobblestones were slippery with blood that was still bright red—a grim reminder that the horror was in progress, and they were caught in its meshes.

"Halt!"

The girls whirled in terror toward the source of the command. An armed policeman yelled to them again from a doorway.

"Where do you think you're going? You're not allowed on the street."

"A policeman just above here told us to run for our lives," quavered the missionary.

"You get into the first house you can get into."

So frightened were they and so benumbed by horror that they dashed into the first open door.

"Oh, no!" cried Alicia, in a strangled voice. "We're back at the judge's!"

In a moment, an even deeper comprehension of the situation dawned on them. In this four-room house, which swarmed with people, communicating doors led around from one room into another. Lieutenant Alba and several of his police were charging from room to room in a gruesome game of ring-around-the-rosy. As the lieutenant entered one room, yelling for someone to go and put out the fire, terrified men would slip into another. For them it was no game.

"They just set the fires," whispered one of the women, "so that the men would go out on the plaza. Then they can line them up and shoot them."

A man's feet could be seen sticking out from under a bed.

Some were trying to squeeze into and behind a wardrobe closet. Women threw their arms around the necks of the police to distract them or to implore them not to take their sons, their sweethearts or their husbands. Women were selling their bodies for the lives of their men, hoping against hope that the protection they were purchasing would be valid.

The cocky, pint-size lieutenant seemed to enjoy the sense of power his brutalities brought him. By clubbing and jabbing with bayonets, or by kicks and hard words, he got most of the men out of the house. The judge picked up a couple of pails and assured Doña Otilia he'd be back.

As the door closed after them, Doña Otilia threw herself down onto the floor, screaming in an hysteria of terror and despair. Alicia sat down beside her, knowing she had little comfort to offer.

"They'll just line them up and shoot them," cried the unhappy woman. "We'll never see them again."

A few old men had remained in the house, and perhaps a dozen women who also were wailing in grief and hopelessness. In their frenzy some of them cast themselves upon the missionary, clutching at her convulsively.

"Pray for us. Pray for us. It seems God hears your prayers."

Most of them were too distraught with fear and anxiety, however, to listen to any words of promise or comfort. Somehow, the need of the others brought new calm and strength to Señorita Carole and Alicia, who had entered the home on the verge of panic. Now that the frantic women turned to them for strength, they were able to speak with conviction of the faithfulness of the heavenly Father and of the peace of heart that He can provide.

Reminded of their own faith, some of the women began to repeat the prayers they had always known. Others commented bitterly that they had lost the ability to believe.

"It was our priest who started this."

The deceptive message of reassurance of military aid to the townspeople had, in fact, come from the priest. From him, too, had come the death list of prominent Liberals. The police were being quartered in the church, and an inquisition of blood was daily being perpetrated on the platform above the church steps.

A nurse, who could walk in and out of the houses without being questioned, urged the women to scatter and put a white flag in their doors.

"It will protect you."

She told how she had rescued a friend's husband through a window and then had taken him for safety to a house where a good number of women had congregated for mutual protection.

"They wouldn't open the door for me," she related, her voice rising with the recollection of her desperation. "But I screamed it was me and beat on the door. So they let us in, and we put a white cloth in the door."

The woman went on, her somewhat coarse, insensitive voice piercing into the hysterical crying and bringing about a semblance of calm. She seemed unaware that her stories only added to the crushing grief of the women. Perhaps her garrulousness was a release, a means of keeping her own pent-up horror from driving her mad. Because she had been called hither and yon to help policemen who were wounded, this woman had seen more than the ones who had barricaded themselves behind closed doors.

"All the men who are lying dead in the plaza," she said, "have been shot in the back."

After the first day's assassination of the town's leaders, she revealed, the police had been employing more brutal means of satisfying their sadistic lust for blood.

"They lined up the men they brought out the next day and made them walk barefoot on glass. That crippled Torres boy— the one that can hardly walk—told them, 'Kill me outright. I can't walk without my shoes.' So they let him go. They made the other men carry off the dead bodies. Germán Graciani— they killed him under a bed. And a boy of the Bonet family."

"A boy like that?"

"He's only one of the children they've killed. And Manuelito Carvajalino—he fed a lot of these people just like the judge has. That doesn't make any difference. They shoved him out on the street and killed him. From the back they shot him, like the others. He turned around, before he fell, and said, *'Asi no se matan los hombres!'*[2]

"The city treasurer and another man from his office had locked themselves up in their toilet. A whole day. They made them come out so that the treasurer could go and get the man who runs the light plant. He told us that a police sergeant they passed on the street hollered, 'Take him on ahead, so I can shoot him from the back.' The other said, 'No, don't. We're on an errand.' And on the way back to his house, he says, are two men, dead, and another near his own door, and one on his neighbors' doorstep. And a dead donkey. He couldn't find the man who runs the light plant, so the treasurer ran it. He was glad enough that they needed him."

The nurse talked on. She told of the looting.

"They've chopped up the doors or burned them out. Then you look in at the shelves, and they're all empty. There aren't any pigs or chickens left in town, either. It was Señor Cianci's store—the best store in town—they set fire to."

"Let's go back home," whispered Señorita Carole to Alicia. "I have a horrible premonition that this is a bad place to be."

Later that afternoon, word reached them that, just after they walked out of the judge's house, the police had made one more search and found Miguel Carvajalino, a leading Liberal, hidden under the rafters of the house. As though they were after a rat, they routed him out, shoved him out of the front door and killed him. Had the girls been there, they would have had to watch this barbarous murder.

From the back patio of Doña Nacha's pensione, to which they had returned at nightfall, they could see a house burning on the street above them. Again fear of a general conflagration kept them wakeful throughout the long hours of the night. More women had listened to the reading of the Scriptures that evening and had joined in the quiet prayer time that followed. God was

[2]*Men* don't kill like this!

the only reality that could be depended on during these frightful days.

The streets were comparatively quiet on that Saturday morning when the missionary and Alicia walked together toward the church at the end of the plaza. The señorita had decided on an open move toward safety. On the church steps they saw Lieutenant Alba—whom they wanted to see—and a line of local young men.

As they came within earshot, they understood that the young men were being forced to identify themselves and their party affiliation. All said they were Conservative. The Lieutenant knew they were lying, of course. Each one was given a green ribbon to wear around his sleeve to mark him as an active Conservative.

"How dreadful," whispered Señorita Carole. "They'll be fighting against their own people."

"The first chance they get," Alicia said, "they'll slip off and join the guerrillas."

After the girls had been made to wait a long time, Lieutenant Alba turned to the missionary. "What is it?" he asked shortly.

"Could I get a ride in one of the trucks we see leaving town? I have a Colombian girl with me. I'm responsible for her, and I want to get her home to her family."

"Trucks are coming with food. You won't starve here."

"I want to get this girl home to her own people."

"I'm not letting *anybody* leave this town," he snapped and turned on his heel.

"I suppose I should not even have made the attempt," said Señorita Carole drearily. She knew, of course, that communications had been cut off from the moment the military police had taken over the town. No help could be expected from outside.

An attempt to hold a Sunday service was defeated. People who had gathered took precipitate flight at someone's tense warning that police were approaching. On this unpropitious Sunday, and in that house filled with commotion and tragedy,

Doña Otilia bore the judge another son. That day, too, the owner of the house occupied by the missionary and her companion asked them to vacate.

"The rumors are now that they are going into all the houses of the heretics," said Don Enrique.

The Liberal leaders were dead or they had gotten away. The stores had been looted. So now the police were systematically going to the homes. It was not surprising that Don Enrique was anxious not to be considered a reactionary of any sort. The missionary recounted her unsuccessful attempt to get permission to leave town openly with a safe-conduct ordered by the lieutenant.

"So you see there's not much I can do," she said.

"I don't want you in my house." Don Enrique's stubborn insistence was not meanness, just fear.

"Where shall we go?"

"At least pack your stuff together in the back part of the house," he said, grudgingly. "I'm not sure that will do you any good, but it's a sign I asked you to move out."

Some people, he explained, had buried money or personal treasures in their patios. Now police were making everyone dig up any spot where the ground had been turned up or disturbed.

Don Enrique contacted them again on Monday morning. "You have to leave. They're going into the houses looking for Bibles. They say they'll throw any Protestants they find into jail. They've already got the Adventists there," he said. "But I'll tell you what they made them do first. They made them dig a big trench in the cemetery. Then they had to go and pick up all those corpses and throw them in. Some were rotting by this time."

"Yes," piped up a boy who had come in with Don Enrique. "And a donkey. They put the donkey right on top of the people."

"That's as much respect as they have for human life," said their landlord. "And those who had no part in that had heavy crosses tied to their backs. They kicked them and beat them, too. For my sake—for your own—I'm asking you to leave town."

Even before Don Enrique had come, the girls had decided they must find some way to leave El Carmen. Both of them had watched groups of policemen disappearing into the woods with some of the town's prettiest girls. They were still finding girls who would sell themselves to protect someone they loved. When girls lost their cause for further bargaining, the police would probably take them by force. One or another of the police agents had leered at Alicia again and again. No matter what the risk, they had to leave El Carmen.

They decided, right after Don Enrique left, to make an attempt to reach Brotaré. Since no road passed the small mountain village, its isolation made it the most likely route to safety. The trail up toward Brotaré was difficult, they knew, and crossed streams thirty times.

They waited until after lunch, when most of the police would be taking a siesta. Sadi, Doña Nacha's grandson, took a string bag in which they had packed their essentials and wandered down the street with it. Señorita Carole took papers and valuables she could not carry with her to Doña Nacha for safekeeping. Just as they stepped from her house, a messenger ran up with a telegram.

"Does this mean that they're opening up communications again?" Alicia asked the boy, while Señorita Carole tore open the envelope with shaking fingers.

"*Quien sabe?*" retorted the boy, shrugging. "This came through."

Señorita Carole showed Alicia the telegram. It came from Cúcuta—a judiciously worded message from the Ocaña missionary who had invited them to his home for refuge.

ALL WELL HERE. HOW ARE YOU?

Those six innocent words conveyed a great deal. They meant that the Ocaña mission station had been vacated. It warned that grave trouble had reached the very neighborhood they planned to enter. Much prayer would be going up for their safety; they knew that from the cautious inquiry into their welfare.

"You've reproached yourself so often for not getting me out of here sooner. If we'd been in Ocaña, it might have been worse," comforted Alicia. She spoke out of her own relief. Her first thought had been for Santa Inés, but surely the missionary would have mentioned it obliquely if there had been trouble there.

The telegram was a blow, but it caused only momentary hesitation. Whatever menace lay ahead, remaining in El Carmen invited disaster.

Walking along the street with nothing in their hands, the girls spoke casually to the townspeople, who were forced to keep their doors open all day long. They sauntered on as though they were merely going to visit someone in town. A policeman stood guard on the terrace *gradas*—the wide stone stairway that led to the level below. He let them go by without question. They strolled leisurely by another policeman who leaned against a wall, drowsing in the sun. At last they came to where Sadi stood at the end of the street, where they planned to slip into the woods.

Forewarned by the first days' gunfire, the girls had dressed inconspicuously and crept cautiously from bush to bush. Not a shot was fired at them in their long, difficult climb.

Darkness overtook them before they had climbed to Brotaré, a cluster of houses on a single street that ran along a mountain ridge. They trudged on to a home where they previously had spent a night. To their bewilderment, Don Juan told them that his wife and most of the Brotaré women had left town several days before. Rumors had reached them that their town would be the next to be sacked. The men were polishing up all their guns. Brotaré—though very small—was going to make a stand against the enemy. A corporal with a command of ten national soldiers had come to join their meager forces.

"We're famished," said Alicia. "Can you give us something to eat?"

"What little I have," replied the man. He explained that people were not even going to their farms. Very little food was available. He gave them some dry bread and one egg each before he directed them to a house where the remaining women were spending their nights together. Their men would not be at home to protect them.

Their arrival had caused no small stir in town, for they were the first refugees out of El Carmen to appear in Brotaré since the first day, and the villagers were eager to find out what had really happened. The corporal, who also spoke to them, was aghast when he discovered that they intended to go on to Río de Oro the next day.

"Just you two women—on that trail?"

"We thought that trail, so far from the road, would be safe."

"Just yesterday there were killings on that trail. With all these guerrillas roaming around, there's no safe trail."

"Brotaré's not safe either, is it? Why have the women gone?"

"Next Monday we're going to Cúcuta. Stay, and I'll take you."

Cúcuta, near the Venezuelan border, would be safe. But Monday was a week away, and almost anything could happen in that time.

"We've just escaped from the police in El Carmen," was the firm decision. "We're not going to wait and let them catch us here."

The corporal accompanied them to the lodging and knocked at the door. When it was opened, he left them. Inside, a candle's flickering light revealed that something was decidedly wrong. Women were rushing back and forth. In another room they could hear crying, moaning and a frantic reciting of prayers.

"A woman's had an attack," explained someone. "We think she's dying."

The woman was lying on a bed—twitching, pale. Señorita Carole knew little about medicine, but she did know the power of prayer. While she rubbed the cold, clammy arms and legs, she prayed. Before long the woman—possibly a victim of hysteria—quieted down and went to sleep.

Outside, all night long, the men paced back and forth along the one street, talking to each other in low tones. They were guarding against surprise attack. The night was cold, for Brotaré lay high in the mountains. Very little bedding was available in the overcrowded house.

"Don't let them catch up with us here!" prayed the girls, shivering in the uneasy darkness. Again and again, details of El Carmen's horror, etched indelibly in their minds, clutched at their vitals with sickening remembrance. They could not hope to escape the same vicious police the second time.

In the pre-dawn darkness, they recognized the answer to their prayers, for it began to rain hard. Skirmishes on the trail that day were improbable. Their hike would be cold and miserable, and dangerous because of slippery trails, but they would not be molested.

Because of the food shortage, they were forced to start out, soon after dawn, with very empty stomachs. But they were given *tinto* and *arepas* at another village in exchange for the news that they brought from El Carmen. As the day advanced, they began repeating the ninety-first Psalm, which they had memorized together.

> He that dwelleth in the secret place of the most High shall abide under the shadow of the Almighty. . . . Thou shalt not be afraid for the terror by night; nor for the arrow that flieth by day . . . . there shall no evil befall thee . . . . he shall give his angels charge over thee, to keep thee in all thy ways. . . .

They needed the strengthening of these assurances, for the corporal had warned them of a road block set up near Río de Oro in a spot so strategic that no one could evade it by detouring in the woods or in the mountains.

"You have to show your *cédulas,* and give a reason for traveling."

Neither of the girls would be able to comply with this de-

mand. Alicia, under legal age, had no *cédula,* and Señorita
Carole had recently sent hers away for renewal. They were both
without identifying documents. God who had sent rain to make
the trails safe—could He provide them with papers? or a diversion of the police?

After added hours of plodding along slippery trails, always
watchful, they sat down to rest. A young man, following the
same trail, added his own warning about the blockade ahead.

"I can say Papá is a Conservative," Alicia suggested.

"You can, but they may think you're lying. You need *cédulas.*"

As they talked with the young man, they spoke of peace in
the face of possible death through their evangelical faith. Not
only did the young man appear interested, he asked for directions
to Alicia's home and the time he might attend a service there.
He accompanied them for an hour, escorting them down the
steep, treacherously slick descent.

"I'd go with you to the barricade," he said, "but my being
with you might even arouse more suspicion. I haven't my *cédula* either. It's better the two of you go on alone."

As they neared the road block, it was obvious they would
have no chance of slipping through unobserved while a car
was being inspected as they had hoped. There were two men—
a young policeman and a stern-faced officer. With a last hurried prayer for God's help, they started toward the older man,
but the younger man halted them.

"Where are you going?"

"Just to Santa Inés," said Alicia, casually. "I live there. We're
just waiting for a truck."

"Well, you're in luck. I think I hear one coming now."

An old, dilapidated truck careened around the curve and
stopped. The girls were not sure what they should or could do.

"What are you waiting for? Get in! The truck goes to Aguachica."

At three-thirty that afternoon, on the twenty-third day of
November, the two girls arrived at Santa Inés and started to-

ward the Franco home. Señorita Carole walked slowly, partly because of painfully blistered feet, but mostly because she did not want to detract from Alicia's welcome home.

El Chico caught sight of Alicia and ran into the house shrieking. "Mamá! Papá! Licha's come home. Licha's coming!"

Rosa, who had sorrowed for her daughter, sure that she was dead, felt herself grow weak. It was Marco who ran out, his arms wide, his face aglow.

"Oh," he exclaimed, crying unashamedly as he held Alicia in a hearty embrace. "I had you girls in heaven two weeks ago."

Tears and shrieks of joy were a part of the family reunion as Rosa and the children hurried out to the trail. Marco did not forget to include the Lord in his rejoicing.

"We'll thank Him right here where I first had you back in my arms," said Marco. "He was faithful, even if we didn't trust Him as we should have."

"And Papá—"

"Well?"

"We should pray for—" Alicia stopped, somewhat disconcerted by her own eagerness to introduce the subject. "Well, at one place where we were resting, we met a wonderful young man from right near Santa Inés. The señorita and I talked to him about the *evangelio*. We have to pray for Manuel. He's going to come here."

"Manuel? Manuel *who?*"

"Manuel Gómez. Papá, he's wonder—"

Marco eyed his daughter sharply. She crimsoned under his stare.

"Manuel Gómez, huh?" Then Marco doubled with hearty laughter. "What is this generation coming to? They run for their lives, but they pick out a husband on the run!"

"Oh, Papá!" gasped Alicia chidingly, but she could not bring herself to deny the attractiveness of his shrewd prophecy.

All the rest of the evening Marco appeared unusually preoccupied. Occasionally he glanced at Alicia with an enigmatic expression, partly amusement, partly serious contemplation.

Then Rosa was surprised to find his eyes on herself with the same expression. Later, on retiring, Marco cleared his throat ceremoniously.

"Rosa, we can't let our children get ahead of us."

"That sounds logical, Marco; but, by the look of you, I'm afraid you're about to spring something on me."

"You shouldn't always get ahead of me, Rosa."

"I assure you, I'm not even catching up."

"Do you realize that Alicia may soon be thinking of marriage?   And here we are—"

"Go on, Marco. *Where* are we?"

"As I said, we can't let our children get ahead of us. Rosa, *querida,* will you marry me?"

Rosa gasped, then began to laugh. "But of course, Marco! I'd rather marry you than anyone I know!"

10

On Whose Shoulders

TWO MEN AND A WOMAN left the air taxi into which Marco helped Señorita Carole. Almost immediately the small plane scuttled off like a pompous cricket along the single lane runway that was almost obscured by tall grass. The station agent was packing mailbags and two bales of newspapers into the baggage compartment of the only taxi. His office was little more than an adobe stall that offered shelter from the almost insufferable heat. His business completed in less than fifteen minutes, the agent locked up the station and joined the group waiting near the taxi.

Marco had remained on the grassy runway watching as the plane hopped off and then faded into a tiny dot that gradually became invisible. Up beyond the blue of the sky, Marco thought, was the God who had brought his daughter and Señorita Carole out of the very jaws of death. In his heart he had relinquished Alicia to God, though he had cringed at the thought of how her life had been wrested from her. Now he stood there on the open field praising God, once again, for His marvelous deliverance.

At home, Rosa was recalling her own earnest prayers for her daughter's deliverance as she listened to Alicia, who was repeating the whole story of the sack of El Carmen to Carmen Vanegas. Silently, while the girls chattered on, Rosa thanked God again and again, as she followed the story. How gracious had been His providence for their timely escape from La Vega and

189

their protection at that time from roving guerrillas, who must have infested most of the trails in the area even then.

Alicia recounted the details of the horror that had stalked them through all the intervening days, yet had never touched or harmed them. Rosa knew that God had answered her prayers beyond her expectations. She brought out the Bible that she herself could not read but in which she had marked a verse upon which to anchor her faith.

"Here," she said, as Alicia finished her tale, "read this to Carmen, so that she'll know what a great God we worship." She opened the Bible to where she had turned the page down.

Carmen listened intently while Alicia read the verse, Jeremiah 33:3, "Call unto me, and I will answer thee, and show thee great and mighty things, which thou knowest not."

"You see, Carmen," said Rosa, "I didn't know what was happening, so I didn't know how to pray. But you know that even when I had given up hope, God was still working. And now He is showing me the great and mighty things that I didn't even know about."

Carmen turned a serious face toward Rosa. "Think of all those beasts—hundreds of them—seeing Alicia that first night, and Alicia as pretty as she is! They all knew where she was and that there wasn't even a man there to protect her. I believe it was God. I really do."

Though their own immediate crisis had ended happily, Marco brought back news that boded ill for the whole land. Many Colombians had hoped that the election, only three days away, would wrest power from the Conservatives and, specifically, from Laureano Gómez, and thus halt the mass slaughter of Liberals. Not even the most optimistic doubted, of course, that the Liberal candidate, Darío Echandia, would still have his hands full putting a stop to the vengeance slayings and the sadistic atrocities of marauding bands of guerrillas, but the election scheduled for the following Sunday had been a bright ray of hope on the political horizon.

Echandia made the mistake of walking openly in the capital

—a thing that the much-hated Laureano would never have done. A group of Liberal leaders, including the presidential candidate and two of his brothers, had been crossing Plaza San Martín when military police fired on them. Darío Echandia's brother, Vicente, and two others were killed.

"From what I make out," said Marco, "the Liberals are withdrawing their candidate and boycotting the election. With military police shooting Liberals at the polls, and shooting at the candidate himself, they say they can't hope for a fair election."

"Then Laureano gets in again!" exclaimed Antonio in dismay.

"You could say he *is* in," said Alicia. "With no opposing candidate, he's got the election in the bag."

"Well," said Marco, "Laureano didn't seem so sure about it. You see, they set this election up so congress would still be in session when people voted. Laureano got wind that congress was all set to impeach him for not keeping democratic order, so he had Ospina proclaim the government in a 'state of siege'— that's what he called it. He used that as an excuse to close the congress. Ospina says now that the Supreme Court's got no power to interfere with anything he decides to do. He banned all meetings and demonstrations—and that means no Liberals can get together. And now he's given orders for all Liberal employees to be fired. He's already kicked out two governors, and they put what they call 'military mayors' into the places they're taking over."

"That's what they did in El Carmen," cried Alicia. "But nobody knew what he had in mind, until they took over."

"Pamplona and a lot of other towns have military mayors now. One of the men I talked to said they just stick one of their military police into command. And one other thing. He's closed down on news like you turn off a faucet—radio, newspapers, everything. Even cables to other countries. Now we know why we couldn't get any news of El Carmen."

"So what will happen?"

"Everybody's saying it will mean a fight to the death of the

Liberal party. After they burned Laureano's *El Siglo,* he's sworn to exterminate the Liberals."

"Well, he's already well on the way. Arturo says he heard that in September alone, 392 deaths had been reported. And now we know why the papers didn't report anything after that. Nobody will know exactly what's happening."

"Except that things are getting worse. How glad I am to be back here at home," cried Alicia.

News of the nation's politics seemed of much less consequence now that Alicia had come home. Its gloomy foreboding was almost forgotten when, later that afternoon, a man brought a note from Francisco Velásquez. The children could hardly wait for Marco to return from the field, for the news they had might mean a trip to Ocaña for the family. Emalina had been poking her father's damp shirt for a few minutes before he finished washing, but it was Antonio who finally got his attention.

"Don Francisco sent us a note, Papá. It's important."

"Well, then read it, Toño. Read it."

Antonio drew the carefully folded missive from his pocket; but the younger children shrilly proclaimed its contents, each one shrieking his bit of information with excited anticipation of Marco's decision.

"A preacher's coming."

"Can we go—all of us? Don Francisco says to."

"For all day? They'll have two services. And Doña Emma—"

"Stop hollering!" Antonio, waving the letter, outshouted the others. Marco turned to Emalina, who was still poking at him for his attention to her own shrill eagerness, allowing his eyes to twinkle in Rosa's direction. Then he put up his hand authoritatively.

"How in the world am I going to hear anything if you all yell at once? Now, Toño, let's hear this exciting letter."

"Well, I guess you've heard everything," said Antonio, sulking a bit because he, the most literate of the family until Alicia's return from El Carmen, had been cheated out of reading this important piece of news. "Anyway, they're sending a preacher from Cúcuta to take the missionary's place. He's going to be there on Sunday, and Don Francisco says for all of us—"

Antonio's voice was again quite drowned out by the shrill importunities of the younger children who feared Marco would go alone to hear the new preacher. Far too often—as far as they were concerned—their father went on important missions and left them at home. The specific invitation in the letter for the whole family had given them hope that this time they would be included.

"Do you want to go?" Marco had turned to Rosa and spoke to her under the familiar din.

"Can we afford it?" Rosa knew how much it would cost for all of them to go to Ocaña, but she herself had been yearning for fellowship with the evangelicals in the city. Marco seemed to read her wish in her eyes.

"All right," he proclaimed into the hulabaloo, "we go. All of us."

The momentary lull, during which Marco made his announcement, exploded immediately into a roar of hilarious anticipation.

"Who are they sending us?" Marco inquired, when the storm had settled to some extent.

"Don Vicente Gómez, it says here," Antonio replied. "He's from Bogotá, but he's been to the seminary at San Cristóbal."

"A city-bred dandy?"

Rosa understood the disappointment in Marco's face. They had seen plantation-reared young men return from a short university experience to their own communities and act so overbearing that these pseudo intellectuals were rejected by the very people whom they regarded with withering condescension.

When the letter had come, she had thought only of God's prompt provision of another spiritual leader for the community. But now that Marco had voiced his first thoughts, she herself began to visualize the type of person that probably had been sent to fill the missionary's place. If his attitude were not superior and pompous, his polish and educational advantages would still set him high on a pedestal and make him unapproachable.

"But he will teach us what is right," she stammered, then added a hint of her treasured, secret anticipation. "It takes a preacher for weddings and such."

"You promised, Papá," protested Antonio, who had missed Marco's quick flashing grin. Antonio had seen only the prospect of the family outing dwindle with Marco's lack of enthusiasm.

"That's right. I promised. That means we'll have to work harder than ever until Sunday. You've been on the farm this morning?"

"Yes, Papá, from early morning," returned Antonio. "Ask Mamá!"

Rosa was busy during the two days that remained of the week. Alicia and Tive helped her mend the children's best clothing, now truly shabby because the repeated financial reverses had made it impossible to buy new clothes for the active youngsters. They painstakingly polished the scuffed leather of shoes that still held together.

In Ocaña, when Rosa marshalled her brood into the large sala that was being used for church services with homemade benches placed on either side of a center aisle, she felt proud. Who cared whether the patches showed a very little and the smaller ones were bare of foot? Who had a beautiful daughter like her Alicia, whom she had had returned to her as from the grave—from the appalling fate that her contemplations had filled with anguish and horror. And Tive! Natividad, at fifteen, was blooming into a young woman no less charming. Rosa looked from one to another of them as they slipped into one of the long backless benches. She wouldn't trade one of them for all the rest of the children in the building. Her glance lay long on Santander, who now walked normally, without a trace of his former disability. Somehow he would always be dearest. Through Santander's deformity they had learned to know the reality and reliability of God, and they had learned what it really means to be Christian. Her eyes wandered to Marco.

There, she thought, *is the man who should be a leader for God. Marco would give his life to share with others the wonder of what God had done for them. But for the fact that he was illiterate*—

Marco sat abruptly upright, his face toward the door leading from the living quarters of the building. Don Francisco was entering, followed by a small man with an intense, serious face under a shock of unruly black hair that bore the unmistakable notches of unskilled barbering. His blue serge suit, shiny and purple from much ironing, had probably not been pressed since his arrival. Don Vicente Gómez wore it with casual poise, and Rosa saw that this man was not concerned with his own appearance. His dark eyes were moving about in the audience as though the man were praying for each one there.

Like a shepherd, Rosa thought, *taking stock of his flock.* Her eyes met Marco's, and she caught in them a reflection of her own thoughts. He smiled and his almost imperceptible nod showed that he approved of this new pastor—this man from the city.

Don Vicente had not come directly from a seminary, they were to learn as Don Francisco introduced him. She watched the young pastor's swarthy face redden as Don Francisco read a glowing recommendation from the elders of the church in San Cristóbal where Don Vicente had pastored to pay his way through seminary.

"Then they sent him to El Páramo de la Paz," said Don Francisco. "And we all know he went there to take the place of the elder, José de la Cruz Bolívar, and it took courage to take the same trail that their other leader was shot on. They built a church during that year and dedicated it on the very date José was killed the year before. And the assassin came for the dedication. They've got thirty members in that church now, and that's more than we have here."

Don Francisco's long introduction had made Don Vicente self-conscious, and he stumbled awkwardly as he took his place to face his congregation. Rosa was startled to note that he had a strange impediment in his speech that made it difficult to catch what he was saying. Besides, his whole lower jaw seemed to be set at a queer angle—perhaps that was the reason he garbled his words queerly. The slant of his teeth strangely disfigured his face.

Others were having trouble, too, she saw, for a few people were sitting forward as if to hear better. She felt embarrassed for the young man who, she could see, was painfully aware that he was not leaving a very favorable impression in a pulpit ordinarily occupied by a polished European missionary.

The text of scripture that Don Vicente announced after the preliminaries were over was the Old Testament story of David who killed the giant Goliath. Certainly he had not chosen this tale to impress anyone with his erudition, Rosa thought. The children would understand this story, and she herself would not be left at sea, uneducated and ignorant as she felt herself to be.

Rosa settled back to enjoy the narrative, noting with real pleasure that the children—who had sometimes squirmed restlessly in the meetings—were gazing at Don Vicente with rapt attention. But so were the older members of the congregation, who had soon accustomed themselves to his peculiarity of speech.

Afterwards Rosa could not recall anything new about the story that had been sketched briefly, but she had come away inspired to greater faith in God. She remembered vividly Don Vicente's account of David refusing Saul's armor when it seemed, in everybody's opinion, his only logical means of security.

"He was being foolish—or so Saul and others of God's own people thought. And so did the giant. But David said, 'I haven't proved it.' So he went in the Lord's strength. *Him* he had proved!

"Remember how scared everybody was of the giant? But after David set the pace, it didn't even make headlines in the papers to kill giants. Why, in the twenty-first chapter of Second Samuel, everybody, you might say, was killing giants."

Rosa saw that Marco was elated when Don Francisco said that they had invited the preacher to join them for the noon meal. The children flocked around their new pastor without the slightest hesitancy; and Don Vicente, having lost completely that stiffness of a humble man who has been put out on parade, was entirely in his element. In fact, he was checking to see if the small fry had followed his message.

"He didn't know how to put on the king's long iron underwear," chirped Chico, giving his version of the story, "but he knew God would help him throw the stones straight."

"*One* stone," corrected Carmelo. "That had to be God doing it. To kill a giant!"

Don Vicente nodded, and Antonio added his own comment. "All those people up there were letting that one big-mouth tell them how he wanted them to fight. And they were fighting on *his* terms."

"No, they weren't! They weren't doing a thing—just hunkered up behind rocks, shivering. And scared stiff."

Antonio ignored Emalina's interruption. "Then David came along and said, 'Now we're going to fight on God's terms.' And that did it."

"You have an excellent idea there, Antonio." Don Vicente looked with new interest at the lanky youth. "Do you have any idea how that would work in your own way of life—say, in witnessing?"

Antonio studied his worn shoe for a moment. "I guess it's like people keep saying, 'Do your preaching in church. If anybody wants your way, they'll go there.' They're making the rules; and, if we let them get away with it, we'd end up, like Emalina said, not doing anything."

"And so?"

"So I've got to believe that if I say something, God will make it hit home. But I've got to stick my neck out and face the guy and let him have it, straight from the shoulder." Antonio fidgeted on his chair uneasily, then he met the new pastor's steady inquiring eyes. "Do you suppose David was a little bit—" Antonio hesitated, then plunged on—"well, *scared?*"

"I think so," replied Don Vicente. "I'd say he was scared when he tackled the lion barehanded, too. That was the way he had proved God—or tested Him, you know. But he had to make the decision of tackling the lion or letting him get a sheep. And if he got one—"

"And *that* had to be God, too, didn't it? Like the stone, when he threw it. He must have been praying, this David."

"But do you see, Antonio? The first time was probably the hardest. And the oftener he saw God take over, the easier it was to tackle something else—even the giant everybody else was afraid of."

"So by that time, he wasn't even bluffing when he talked."

"Exactly. He had proved God." Don Vicente, watching Antonio, remarked shrewdly, "You've got your own giant on your mind, haven't you? But so far, he's been making the terms?"

Antonio nodded. "And he's even been ridiculing what I believe, just like that Goliath, and I let him get by with it."

"Well, Antonio, remember that you have to have a true aim, but it's God who makes the impact. And David took five smooth stones."

"His first did it."

"But he still had four left. He wouldn't have given up right away, would he?"

"Or he had four left to take on anybody else."

After Doña Emma's sumptuous meal, served in the cool patio, the conversation gravitated toward the trouble that had left the Ocaña church without a pastor.

"The missionaries from Salazar and Señorita Carole of El Carmen will be in Venezuela for awhile," said Don Vicente. "They're still praying for one of the elders from Salazar that somehow he did escape, but nobody has heard of him for a long time."

"There may be hope for him," Rosa said. "We didn't hear of Alicia for a long time."

"Señorita Carole's air taxi came in while I was waiting for mine, so she told me something of what she and your daughter went through."

"Today is the election," said Marco, "but there's only one candidate, and we know what he's like."

"Yes, and today is also the funeral day for Echandia. I hope they don't have the kind of rioting again in Bogotá that they had last year. One person I talked to said they have tanks in the plazas and military police stationed all over the city. People are panicky, he said, but so far they haven't done anything violent. After the tanks came into town, people stampeded. One woman, asked why she was running, answered, 'Because everyone else is.' "

Don Francisco shoved his chair away from the table. He came back into the room a few minutes later wearing steel-rimmed glasses. He shuffled through a sheaf of papers stuffed into a wire wall rack.

"Wait, Francisco," said Doña Emma. "Let me wipe off the table first."

Don Francisco put a stack of papers on the flowery oilcloth after the dampness had dried sufficiently. "Look at this," he said, pointing to an article with his leather-stained finger. "Somebody from Pamplona brought this in to Bucaramanga."

Don Vicente's wide brow furrowed as he read the article his host had pointed out to him. Marco was leaning toward the other men as if to read from their faces what he could not read from the paper. It was hard for him, Rosa knew, to admit to this educated man that he could not even read.

"Would you read it for us?" she said timidly.

"Certainly!" said Don Vicente. "It's a sort of ultimatum from the diocese of New Pamplona. They start it out with 'I' and then have a blank for someone to put in his name. 'I'—and then this blank—'a Catholic, member of the parish of Matanza, united in heart with the infallible Roman Pontiff by whose mouth speaks Jesus Christ, my God and Redeemer, with him and like him, and without any reservation whatever, I con-

demn Liberalism—religious and political—in all its shadings.
I condemn it with all my heart for all its false liberties which
damage the Catholic faith, as this leads to the separation from
God and from Jesus Christ, legislator and King of nations and
individuals—' "

"They had to sign that," said Marco, interrupting, "the people of Matanza?"

"So they'd be scared to vote Liberal, Papá," suggested Antonio.

"Yes," said Don Francisco. "Apparently, those who were
unwilling to sign their names were marked for death or driven
from the community. We know about two hundred came to
Bucaramanga. Other Liberals may have gone east—to Venezuela."

Their new pastor was running his slim dark fingers through
his curly hair with a distracted air of troubled concentration.
He glanced at his host meditatively, then at Marco.

Liberalism—a political system which conceded to every man
his constitutional right of choosing his own religious faith—had
become an enemy of the "Conservative faith." Thus, in the
violence that was creeping up toward Magdalena and Norte de
Santander provinces, the political and the religious issue had
become synonymous. If the Conservative leadership could im-
plant the concept of Conservatism as being the "faith" of the
people, the revolution could take on a far more sinister aspect
for evangelicals.

"You wouldn't have shown me this notice, I'm sure, if you
did not already know what it is saying."

Don Francisco nodded as he met Don Vicente's eyes unfal-
teringly. "This notice makes evangelicals political opponents
of the state, even if we don't vote or take any part in political
activities."

"So now even the fair-minded people who have openly op-
posed persecution of *evangélicos* as religious bigotry will be
quiet," said Antonio, almost incredulously. "It puts them all
against us."

"For all practical purposes, it looks like it. But this notice is false representation of the pope's opinion of Liberalism. He would not endorse this ultimatum at all. Look here, on page one of this newspaper, under the photograph of the pope."[1]

Under heavy headlines announcing that "Colombian Liberalism is not incompatible with *La Religión*," was quoted a circular that had been issued to the national clergy by Pope Pius XII, whose picture appeared with the directive. Liberalism, specifically Liberalism in Colombia, it stated, was not incompatible with the Church, and any Catholic might be Liberal without denying the standards or doctrines of the Catholic Church.

"What paper is that?" asked Marco.

"Vanguardia Liberal."

"So this, from the pope, may not get into Conservative papers. Most people will still think they are serving God when they kill Liberals."

"And evangelicals."

"The priests will have received this, if it's from the pope," suggested Rosa, hopefully.

"By the look of Otálora's ultimatum from Pamplona, it looks as if the curates of those rural areas, at least, prefer to ignore the pope's decree, though he be 'infallible,' and though he be the very 'mouth-piece of God.'" Don Francisco quoted bitterly from the notice, anger shaking his voice. "We may all have to take to the mountains—like a bunch of guerrillas."

"We have to remember, Don Francisco," said his pastor, rumpling his hair abstractedly, "that it has been the ignorant priests from rural areas who have been venting their hatred on the evangelicals. Most of them cannot read much. Fanaticism is a symptom of ignorance."

"Don't tell me you don't know—"

Don Vicente held up a restraining hand against Francisco's obvious anger. "The sheep are not responsible if the shepherd leads them astray. If we ever begin to hate the deluded people,

[1]These articles appeared in *Vanguardia Liberal*, Sept. 27, 1949.

Don Francisco, we will have lost our chance to win them to Christ."

While Don Vicente talked, Don Francisco's face had become distorted with an inner conflict. Emma came softly from the kitchen area to sit down at the table, a deeply serious look on her face. She folded her hands on the bright oilcloth and looked intently at the new pastor's earnest face.

Tears appeared and slowly rolled down Don Francisco's leathery cheeks. "God forgive me," he admitted. "I've already allowed myself to hate, Don Vicente. I wonder if that isn't why we aren't getting anywhere in this church? After all these years, there aren't more than about half a dozen of us who are sold out to Jesus Christ. I'm wondering, right this minute, how deep my own commitment really is."

"And I," said Marco, "have been striking up arguments with people. Maybe I wanted to prove I was right more than to prove that I love these others or that God loves them. I keep talking of hell and judgment for people who break God's commandments."

"Jesus said the most important commandment is to love."

"Maybe that's why I haven't been getting them to believe."

Rosa had often argued with Marco that his approach was too harsh, but he had never agreed. Now, she thought somewhat triumphantly, though he wouldn't listen to her, finally he was seeing his negative angle as wrong. With a few words this new pastor had led Marco to see his weakness.

Don Vicente sat for a moment, quietly tapping a finger on the table as though lost in thought. Or was he praying? Rosa began to tremble, aware of a presence within the patio and a power that penetrated her thoughts and shook her to her very soul.

Perhaps she had argued with Marco about the power of love, but her very thoughts about the argument now had been critical and self-righteous. She remembered her resentment and hatred of the offensive neighbors here in Ocaña. Hot tears filled her eyes, and even as she blinked them away it seemed to her that a strange inner glow emanated from Don Vicente.

She had thought him disappointingly homely, this frail-bodied mestizo. No visible radiance surrounded him, but Rosa would always know that she had seen a man whose prayers could call down the presence of God.

"In times like these," said Don Vicente at last, "it is going to take total commitment. Christ and His cause will have to be more important than life itself. But if we make Him the center of our lives, I believe He will preserve us alive—some of us, at least—because He will be using us for His own purposes. God knows, better than you or I, how great is the need of a fearless witness in Colombia."

"Then we'll have to pray that we'll become so important to Jesus and His work here that He'll feel obligated to protect us," said Alicia, who with Tive had finished the dishes and had just rejoined them.

Don Vicente's eyes twinkled, and his whole face lighted with that rare humor that was to endear him to all who knew him.

"Let's watch our motives, Alicia. If we do it because we want to save our own skins, our lives aren't going to draw many to Christ."

"It's ourselves we'll be loving," remarked Antonio, then added a moment later, "It's like David. We have to tackle the lion because we're thinking about the sheep, not about *us*."

Don Francisco spoke abruptly. "We usually kneel to pray. I feel as if I have something to clear up right now, Don Vicente."

They knelt on the uneven cement floor and placed before God the gravity of their predicament and that of the evangelicals in Colombia. But even more earnest were the petitions for a deeper understanding of what it meant to be absolutely committed to Christ and the gospel. Only God, and each individual, knew how great were the personal battles fought out that day.

Entregarse al evangelio was to become a phrase oft repeated in their witnessing. People were never to be invited to an easy believism or shallow acceptance of a magic formula that promised to erase all problems and make life smooth. To be committed to the gospel, as the phrase indicated, meant that Christ and His message had become the focus and main incentive for everything a Christian did.

As they rose from their knees, Marco looked about the room as though he had been so completely withdrawn that he had forgotten, for the moment, where he was. Rosa knew that she, too, had been nearer God's throne than ever before. Don Vicente was leafing through the worn Bible that he had drawn from a pocket.

"I thank the good Lord," said Don Francisco, "that they sent you here. It would have fallen to me, as senior elder, to preach and guide the people of the church." He grinned somewhat wryly. "It's a relief to shrug the responsibility of the church onto the shoulders of someone who is more worthy to bear it."

"And I thank God that those shoulders won't be mine," retorted Don Vicente, the twinkle reappearing in his eyes.

"What do you mean?" cried Don Francisco. "You're staying to be our pastor in Ocaña, aren't you?"

"If the congregation will have me," replied Don Vicente, "after having had a foreign preacher for all this time."

"Then?"

"Then the burden will fall upon the Lord, on whose shoulders even the troubles of these days do not weigh too heavily to be borne."

11

The Death's-Head

ONLY A FEW DAYS after the visit to Ocaña, Emalina and Chico
came boiling into the patio where Rosa was preparing bananas
for drying. Santander, too chubby to keep up with the other
youngsters, churned in on their foaming wake. All of them
were shrilly excited.

"Don Francisco!" Emalina proclaimed. "He's come to visit,
Mamá! He's come to visit us!"

"Don Francisco?"

"He's getting off a truck right in front of Doña Juana's."

Francisco Velásquez coming to see them on a weekday morning? Surely he knew that Marco and the boys would have gone
to work on the farm as soon as the sun was up. Had Marco
ordered something that Don Francisco needed to deliver personally? Wouldn't Marco have mentioned it to her? Perhaps
he was just coming by Santa Inés on his way to visit someone
in the foothills? But wouldn't he have arranged for Marco to
accompany him? No man voluntarily headed into the mountains alone these days.

Rosa hurried out to meet Don Francisco, a chill of premonition forming an icy constriction around her pounding heart.

"I'll send the children to the farm at once, if you can stay,"
Rosa offered as soon as they had exchanged greetings. "Or are
you on your way into the foothills?"

Don Francisco strode along beside Rosa to the house, wearing a strained, preoccupied air. "Is Marco home?" he asked, revealing that he had not heard anything Rosa had said.

Without further question, she sent Tive to summon Marco. Whatever Don Francisco's errand, he had not come just to pass the time of day.

"They left him a *pasquín*," said Rosa's guest when she brought him a cup of *tinto*. He saw that she did not comprehend. "Don Vicente, the pastor," he explained, "they left him a paper with a death's-head drawn on it. They give him one week to leave town."

At the thought of the new pastor leaving, Rosa felt her heart sink with a sense of bereavement. So deeply had their one day with Don Vicente affected Marco as well as herself that he had agreed that the entire family would go once a month to the Ocaña meetings.

"We haven't the money for it," he had told her, "but we can't afford not to hear that man preach. He doesn't use high-sounding language like some, but that man's been with God. He's got something I want. And," he added with a chuckle, as he acknowledged his defeat in their previous disagreements about legalism, "it doesn't seem to be a new list of rules. It's a deeper relationship. When that man prays, you can feel him making contact."

As soon as Marco and Antonio hurried in from the farm, Don Francisco repeated his devastating news.

"What does Don Vicente plan to do?" Marco asked guardedly.

"The question is Can we let him stay? If he's marked for assassination—"

"What does *he* say?" Marco insisted.

Knowing Marco so well, Rosa divined his thoughts. She knew Marco's own rash fearlessness in the face of threats where his testimony for Christ was concerned. In his mind the "city preacher" was facing a test of the sincerity of the commitment to Christ to which he had challenged Don Francisco and his guests a few days past.

"Marco," she cried, "a man doesn't have to be foolhardy just to prove a point. Would he really be doing God's will—as scarce as pastors are—to be killed here in Ocaña?"

Marco ignored her protest. "What does the preacher say?"

"Wel," replied Don Francisco, "he's not treating the thing as a joke. He locks his doors, sure. Don't we all? But as far as I can see, with him it's 'business as usual.' "

Marco's eyes lighted as though he had just achieved a personal triumph. He pounded on the table so hard that Don Francisco's cup skipped on its saucer.

"I knew it! I knew it!" Marco exulted. "Don't let that pastor get away from here. We'll never get another like him."

That Don Vicente Gómez recognized in Marco a kindred spirit was obvious. Whenever the pastor could spare a day or an afternoon in visitation in their neighborhood, Marco eagerly joined him, though it meant that Marco—together with every member of the family—began to work even harder on the farm, rising long before dawn and working until darkness forced them to yield to the demands of their weary bodies.

Because Marco was working such long hours, he had moved Doña Juana's store supplies into their own sala. The arrangement crowded their front room, but it also made it more convenient for Rosa to take care of daytime customers. Before long, of course, Marco had tacked up the poster of the two ways and their eternal destinations. As in Aspasica, the picture drew attention and provided openings for discussion. Marco would report to Don Vicente the reaction of his customers to his own eager witnessing as a basis to the direction their next visit would take.

"Alcario Mateus and his brother Margario, they often stop in here on their way back from Aguachica. I've got Alcario to the place now where he'll read to me from the Bible."

"So he's interested in the gospel?"

"Well, I'm not sure if you could say that, but he often reads to me from the newspaper, because he knows I can't read. So then it wasn't too hard just to ask him to read something short I'd marked."

"Some of these days," chuckled Antonio, "you'll give yourself away on that trick!"

"You *do* read then?"

Antonio replied for his father. "No, he doesn't read; but, if we've marked a place in the Bible, he's already heard it."

"And if he hears something once, Don Vicente," said Alicia, who was standing by, "he knows what it says."

"That's why I say he'll give himself away." Antonio spoke out of his own experience. "Let Alcario make a mistake, and Papá'll correct him. Then Alcario will know he's being roped in."

"Don't worry yourself about that too much, Toño," said Marco. "The Book says for us to be sly as a snake. It's paying off."

Rosa nodded agreement. "The next time Margario comes in, he seems to know about that portion of scripture and has the page turned down. Margario likes to argue, so before long they haven't only reread that bit but have found something else to discuss."

"Reread?" said Don Vicente. "Then they have a Bible?"

"I sold them each one."

"So, there are a couple of people in this community who are coming to see this isn't just a place to buy their salt and matches."

"A couple?" exclaimed Antonio. "Don't forget Alicia's boyfriend. *He's* not after salt and matches."

"Now Toño," chided his sister, blushing furiously.

"Not only that, he's underfoot most of the week—evenings."

"Well, he's learning to read the Bible," Alicia retorted defensively. "We promised him—Señorita Carole did herself—right there on the trail where we met him."

"You see, Don Vicente," explained Marco proudly, "while those two girls were running for their lives, they never stopped showing themselves real *evangélicos*. They even sold a Bible on the run."

"Señor Miguel Hernández. Señorita Carole sold him her own Bible. But that was before we got back to El Carmen."

"So they find this *muchacho* on the trail," injected Antonio, "tell him he's on the trail to hell, and ask him to follow them— *they'll* put him on the right track. So he follows. And he's been following Alicia."

"Make him stop, Mamá!" Alicia appealed to Rosa, since Marco was studying her with open amusement. Rosa, following his glance, glowed with pride in this comely daughter, prettier, if anything, flushed as she was with embarrassment or indignation.

"She likes it, Toño," commented Marco. "Just give it to her bit by bit so she can savor it more."

"Oh, Papá!"

"And Toño," Marco added drily, throwing one last faggot upon Alicia's vehement dismay of her family, "keep it for when there are no fine, bachelor parsons in the house."

Don Vicente flushed crimson in his turn, and Marco voiced the thought that had leaped into Rosa's mind. "Now *there's* the man to set your cap for, Alicia."

Suddenly Marco changed the subject, exposing to Don Vicente the emptiness and restlessness he had known in Aspasica, his unfaithfulness to Rosa, whom he had never granted the security of a proper marriage, and his family of five children by Efigenia Castilla.

"I've not told the family until this hour," confessed Marco, "but Efigenia died of a lung infection and fever not long after we came back from Tolima province. God permitted me to accompany her home after she saw a doctor in Ocaña, and she was very weak then. I spoke to her again of the Lord and of the *evangelio,* but she died without receiving salvation."

"And the chlidren?"

"With Efi's parents. They are all satisfied with the arrangement except Jorge, who wants to come to live with us. He loves Rosa."

"And I love him!" exclaimed Rosa, to whom the news of

Efi's death was a shock, though she had suspected that Marco must have been seeing his family in Aspasica. She would have wanted him to see that they were provided for. "By all means, let Jorge come here to live with us!"

"Why have you told me all this?" probed Don Vicente.

"Rosa agrees that we should be properly married. Would you be willing to perform the belated ceremony? We love each other."

Francisco and Luis Velásquez and Pablo Peñaranda accompanied Rosa and Marco to the judge's office for the required civil ceremony. Then they met their friends in the home of José and Josefa Herrara, who had once given them refuge while they were looking for a home amid the many evictions they had experienced in Ocaña. There, before their children and their friends, Rosa and Marco repeated their marriage vows. Rosa wore a dark dress, while her three daughters each had a new white frock. The people of the church had prepared a wedding supper of *sancocho de gallina,* a delicious chicken dish reserved for greatest occasions. Later, that same month, Jorge joined them in Santa Inés.

The young pastor continued to come often. His compelling motive continued to be the sharing of his own vital relationship with God. Rosa was not too sure about Manuel Gómez, who came regularly, apparently to be tutored in learning to read.

Whether or not a romance was involved, the young man's visits produced some very desirable effects. Rosa had often urged Antonio and Alicia that they teach the younger children to read, for they were not near a school. Marco had endorsed her desire; but, since he had set no specific schedule, the children's education had continued to be neglected.

Now, as the family gathered around the one lamp set on the board table in the patio, the children clustered around watching the painful progress of young Gómez as he learned to recognize the symbols that represented spoken sounds. Because the Bible and hymn book were the texts used, the letters were small, and Manuel despaired of ever learning them all.

"There must be thousands," he muttered one day.

"Gobs of thousands," commented Emalina, breathing down Manuel's neck to see into the book with him. "But look!" She used her usual method of getting attention. "Some are more than once."

"Stop leaning on Manuel," Alicia ordered, "and for pity's sake, stop poking." She appealed to higher authority. "Mamá!"

Rosa came to stand behind the education process that had been disturbed. "You're growing up," Rosa said, putting her arm around the lithe, squirming young body with its sharp index finger. "You're too big to be poking at people for attention."

"Why?"

"Poking and shrieking at people is for little ones, like Jonas, before they know how to talk. Now that you're learning to read, you'll keep your finger to point out the letters you know."

"Am I learning to read, Mamá?"

Rosa whispered a challenge into the child's ear. "Let's see who reads first, you or Manuel!" She put a finger on her lips.

Emalina's eyes grew wide with the idea of a conspiracy. She nodded almost imperceptibly and returned demurely to the table, her inquisitive mind sharpened with the challenge of competition with an adult.

Though he considered himself too old to learn to read, Marco superintended the reading classes, encouraging both the tutors and the despairing pupils. When a rancher dropped in for a purchase or to pass the time, Marco often brought him out to the patio, too. At first Rosa found this hospitality of Marco's trying, since he did not seem to realize that the conversation of these casual visitors and his own incisive comments often distracted attention. Still, Marco seemed to have a deliberate motive for such interruptions. He would snatch at a sentence as Manuel or one of the children was laboriously sounding it out from the Book.

"Now there's something to pay attention to!" he would ejaculate. "Read that again."

As often as not, he would plunge them all into a discussion, and the reading lesson would be terminated for that night. However, the visitor, who would have resented anyone reading anything from the Bible to him specifically, went away with knowledge of the evangelical faith that would erode his prejudices against it.

Carmen Vanegas and her brother Arturo still spent much time at the Franco home, though José avoided them. Alicia's apparent snub of his attentions had aroused his animosity. They joined the Franco family for Sunday worship, as did Manuel Gómez.

The two men from La Vega del Gusto began to come quite regularly to these meetings in the open patio. Occasionally they brought a friend. A cousin, Cristóbal Mateus, who lived as near Santa Inés as they, but in another direction, also began dropping in for the services. When that spring brought the worst rainy season in remembered Colombian history and the meetings had to be held indoors, the sala was quite crowded out. The crowding did not deter Marco from advertising next Sunday's meeting strenuously throughout the week or drumming up impromptu *cultos* when what looked like a promising audience drifted in.

Not all the men Marco invited reacted graciously. Rosa became more and more concerned at some of the brusque refusals and open threats that she heard even though she was busy in another part of the house.

"We'll give the *evangelio* a reception, all right," she heard a man shout one day. "With guns and bullets."

On another occasion she heard men shout threats of personal violence to Marco, and she knew that once again Marco had been too persistent in his invitation.

"Sure, we'll come back for the meeting," promised a man acridly.

"That'd be a good time to burn this house down," barked another.

"I'm afraid," Rosa confessed to Marco, "if they talk like that when there are several others around. Later they may dare each other to follow through on their threats, especially if they've been drinking." She could not forget the dreadful days in Aspasica.

"Well, Rosa," Marco replied, "I keep thinking that one of them may not come back again. So I just go ahead and talk to them all."

Rosa knew Marco too well to persist in her protests. A threat of danger challenged Marco to prove the sincerity of his commitment to Christ. Under that bravado, Marco might even be afraid. So he had to keep proving to himself that he was willing to die for Christ. Rosa knew in her heart that she was not, nor was she willing to spare Marco to a bullet fired in a flare of resentment or temper.

When Don Vicente visited again, Rosa approached him. "Can't you talk to Marco? Does he have to ask for trouble?"

"Have they been threatening you again, Marco?"

"More than ever, lately," said Rosa. "This week the police from Totumal came to the store and ended up threatening Marco, but he won't pay attention."

"Papá doesn't let any one escape him," said Carmelo. "If they come to the store, he talks to them. And if they don't come in, he goes outside."

"Sure they threaten me," snapped Marco. "They've always done that." Then he used an argument he felt would effectively squelch any remonstrance from Don Vicente. "But I've never had a *pasquín!*"

"I didn't ask for that *pasquín,* Marco," said his friend. "Be sure you don't go out looking for trouble."

"Well, then," retorted Marco, his eyes twinkling, "I guess we'd better not go to follow up some of the leads I got during the week."

Don Vicente swung on him. "But that's what I came for, and you know it."

"Well, we might be asking for trouble. One of the men

that's been studying our picture here was Juan Machado. I think he's ready to listen now."

"He's the one," put in Jorge, "that lives near the Mateus plantation. But he's dangerous when he's had a few too many."

"That's the way he is, Don Vicente," said Rosa, hoping that Marco's friend would influence him toward a course of greater discretion. "And if he's shot on someone else's premises, they can make excuses, even accusations."

She stopped talking. Don Vicente was not listening to her at all. His eyes were alight, and he exclaimed, "You don't say! You think he'll listen, this time?"

To increase Rosa's sense of helplessness before such brash zeal, Jorge was clamoring for permission to go along. She knew that, if Antonio had not been on the farm, he would have done the same. She had no alternative but to commit them to God and follow them with her earnest prayers.

Later that summer, Don Vicente spoke of Francisco Liévano, a young evangelist who had been touring Colombian churches. "He's written me that he'd like to come to Ocaña to hold a revival."

Marco was immediately enthusiastic. "If it's not right during our harvest, we'll all come to town for the whole series of meetings," he promised.

Don Vicente shook his head. "I guess he won't be coming. Don Francisco Velásquez wants him, but the others voted against having him come right now."

"But young Liévano, I've heard say, has a ringing testimony. Every place he's preached has grown. If anyone can reach Ocaña's people—"

"That's just it. He makes a stipulation in his letter. If the congregation will invite outsiders to services, he'll come. If they don't want to risk that, he'll go where others will."

"You mean *that's* keeping them—they don't want to run the risk of publicizing the meetings?"

Don Vicente nodded gravely. "If he'd come and preach to them, they want him. But they know the danger of getting outsiders in there. Anything could happen, they say. And they're right, of course."

"Would this young preacher come to a place where there's no church built? Like here—to Santa Inés?"

"Why not?" responded Don Vicente. "He wants to preach to *people*—that he's made clear. And you've got more people coming here, right now, than we have in Ocaña."

"I'll get him people," promised Marco.

Rosa felt her heart swell with pride of her husband, even while she faced the fact that Marco was taking on single-handedly what the whole congregation of Ocaña had rejected as too dangerous a project. As she pondered, more seriously, that Marco would keep his promise to provide an audience no matter what such a promise involved, a chill crept along Rosa's spine, and she could feel the tiny hairs on her neck and arms prickle to erectness.

By previous arrangement, the men culminated their visits that day at the home of Cristóbal Mateus. Though the man had made no open profession of the evangelical faith, Marco reported to Rosa that Mateus had been in the saddle since morning, inviting his neighbors to the meeting.

"He had a houseful, too. Kids sprawled all over the patio and people sitting on chairs, benches, and a few set their saddles on the edge of the veranda. I'd say he had thirty-five."

"And I presume you invited them to the evangelistic meetings you hope we'll have here."

"Why sure!" Marco glanced up to find out why Rosa was questioning him about so obvious a matter. "A lot of them never come this way. They go to Aguachica to sell their produce, not to Ocaña. And they'll come, too. Don Vicente preached, and we dismissed the meeting. Then some fellow asked a question after half of them had started for their horses. They all came back and sat down. That's when the meeting really got good."

"Don Cristóbal says the La Playa justice of the peace lives up in that direction," said Antonio, who had accompanied Marco and Don Vicente. "He wants the preacher to visit him some time."

Again Rosa felt a prickling at the nape of her neck as hairs stood on end. "I hope you two don't stir up too much of a hornets' nest for these evangelistic meetings. You invite a judge, and all of Totumal's police may turn up—with machine guns."

"Cristóbal says the man is a sound thinker, not hot headed. He's got a fantastic plantation. If we could get him!"

As soon as harvest for grain crops was past, Doña Juana and Germán Vanegas returned from Barranca Bermeja. By that time, both Carmen and Arturo were openly acknowledging their faith in the gospel. Doña Juana strode over in high dudgeon before she had fully unpacked.

"What have you been doing to my children?" she demanded stormily. Rosa immediately perceived the cause of the large woman's outburst and wished fleetingly that Marco were there to ward off her fury. She met the situation in the manner that had soothed other explosive tempers.

"Sit down, Doña Juana. I'll bring you a cup of *tinto*."

"Don't try to soft-pedal me! I asked you a question."

"Well, then," said Rosa with some vigor on her own part. "One thing we've been doing—at least for Carmen and Arturo —is to feed them pretty regularly! Carmen was rather young to leave in charge of your house, Doña Juana. So she's been here with our youngsters more than half of the time."

"I can see," grumbled Doña Juana. "She's done precious little housekeeping over there. But this about the *evangelio*—"

By this time it was quite easy to tell Doña Juana that Carmen had been learning to read and that as the text had been God's own Word she had begun to believe it. Was there something wrong with believing the truths God Himself had inspired?

"The Bible?" retorted Doña Juana, becoming somewhat agitated again. "I'm scared of that book! A man had one of those down near Totumal. You know what happened? He went crazy—that's what happened. I'm scared of the Bible."

"The Bible," said Rosa gently, "will bring you peace of heart if you don't resist what it tries to tell you."

"Well, I'm scared of it. And I don't have any use for religion. It's never done me any good. I'll tell you what it did me—down there in Barranca. I had an altar right there in Barranca, and I prayed much for safety to it and burned candles for the Virgin of Chichinquirá. You know what happened? While I was away to market, the house burned right down to the ground. And the Virgin—she burned down just like everything else!"

Rosa could understand the older woman's disappointment and indignation. To her, the statue of El Cristo Rey had not been a likeness of the Christ who had become her living sovereign. She had believed that the statue itself would wield some sort of evil power over her if she desisted in the fulfillment of all she had promised before its stony ears. That Doña Juana's figure of the Virgin should burn rather than miraculously prevent catastrophe probably had robbed her of a faith that already had been wavering.

"Me? I'm an *incredula!*" Juana had said before she had left Santa Inés, when Rosa had spoken to her about her own faith.

That evening, when the children began singing a chorus that Don Vicente had taught them recently, Doña Juana, who had stepped out of the house to enjoy the coolness of the autumn evening, followed Carmen and Arturo to the Franco patio. Don Germán strolled in also.

"I had to come and hunt up my family," he said, somewhat self-consciously. He straddled a chair and tilted it against the wall, sighing comfortably. "You don't know how good it is to be back in Santa Inés. Trouble! We thought we were getting out of it when we went to Barranca Bermeja. That river draws the violence. Sometimes it fairly stinks of blood and corpses rotting."

Rosa shuddered. She could visualize the mutilated bodies borne along in the sluggish current, bloating in the valley heat.

"We kept thinking that after the election things would quiet down."

"Down there that's when things started getting worse, right around the time of the election."

"That's when they took over El Carmen," said Marco. "Just a couple of weeks before they voted Laureano into office. Alicia—"

"And that Laureano knows the only way he'll stay in office is to exterminate the Liberals. Then all the elections will go like the last one did—one candidate."

"I don't understand much about politics," ventured Rosa, "but do peace-loving Conservatives want him? We're not Liberals."

"Well," interrupted Germán, "but who's going to put up another candidate?" Then he explained further. "You see, the President and Congress are elected by us, but the state governors are not. Nor are the mayors, the police chiefs in the towns, or the heads of schools—they're appointed. Laureano kicked out three governors before the election—they didn't cooperate good enough. If the papers print anything against him—"

"And the congress," inserted Marco, "Laureano got around the Liberal congress by some sort of legal hocus-pocus about a siege."

"Legal?" snorted Germán. "North American newsmen[1] called it 'a revolution by the government in office'—they tell me."

"So there's no way to get him out."

"He's a dictator—that's what he is."

"And no place to go in Colombia where a person's safe. If it's not Laureano's police, it's guerrillas from both sides."

"I know what they're like," said Alicia. "I fed them. One night in El Carmen, the first night, we fed about four hundred men."

"Carmen was telling me," said Doña Juana. "Lascivious beasts, that's what they are. It's not enough to burn Cianci's store—I knew Cianci—and kill the grown-up Liberals. Kids

[1] *Time,* Nov. 21, 1949; *Scholastic,* Nov. 1949.

they kill and make them walk on glass and shoot them from the back. Cowards!"

"What do you expect?" growled Germán. "You know where Laureano gets these military police, don't you, Marco? Criminals. He took them out of jails and penitentiaries to do his dirty work."

"And that's how you get more guerrillas," said Juana. "We knew a boy down there at Barranca, from the Galindo family. The old man was Conservative, but his three sons started to go to Liberal rallies. They wanted Gaitán in.

"They were still living in San Vicente then, and they're Conservative down there. So, because of the boys, they couldn't so much as buy the salt they needed. And police were on the trails, grabbing anyone they found that was for the Liberals."

"Yes," growled Germán, "the mayor had got a commission of seventy police, and for fifteen days anyone they caught they beat at the end of a lash, from the plantations all the way into town."

"And put them in jail—not that they were thieves or evil."

"Well, they rounded them up in jail, but then they took them to a place called Boquerón. That's where they killed them."

Juana clenched her muscular fists. "There was no peace there, either for children or women, so they sold that place and moved near Puente Murcia to find a farm near sixty-six Liberal families. That would be safer, they thought."

"Those Liberals got together before the election, and the police attacked. But they expected it, and that time they drove those cowards back into their barracks. But on election day they had enough police to give them a real battle. All day they shot it out, and blood flowed, I'll tell you, all along that street." Germán passed his horny hand over his face as though he wanted to erase a very vivid memory. "After that, everybody had to stay right in their houses. There was no escape.

"But the Galindos, and other Liberals that had moved to Puente Murcia from here and there, had to go and settle some documents—contracts for land. So this Erasmo that we knew—"

"Erasmo Galindo Rueda. He was only about eighteen years old."

"That was in the middle of December," continued Germán. "They'd only found a place and lived there two weeks. It was a good farm, but the police had a road block near there. Right close. So Erasmo left—he'd got a card they called a safe conduct. He hadn't been accused of anything that had happened, so they gave him this card."

"Three days he was away."

"During those three days, they assassinated Erasmo's parents and one brother. And they burned the house, and them in it."

"The man was Conservative." Juana's voice shook with righteous indignation. "The only thing they had against him was his sons had turned Liberal."

"Well, he had forty thousand pesos in the house for selling his other farm. And somebody he had trusted and held for a friend was among the ones that came to attack. Erasmo thinks it could have been for the money.

"So what was the boy to do? No father. No mother. No place to go to. He got himself arms and joined the guerrillas and swore he'd get revenge. A few times—when he could—he came to us, and we gave him something to eat and to take along. Eleven months. Mostly they were in the mountains, hiding, sleeping in the open, wandering around hungry, and their clothes worn out.

"For five days, once, they had nothing to eat. That's when he came to us, knocking at the door, but with a gun ready. And they moved around mostly only at night—like wild animals. And that's the way they ate—what they could find in the woods."

"Expecting, like he said, an *almuerzo de plomo*,"[2] Juana put in. "That's what they were expecting. And boys no older than twelve years with them."

"So then one time their leader—the Vulture, they called

[2]Lunch of lead.

him—asked for volunteers to go into town. Erasmo volunteered, because he had an aunt there and thought he could get something to eat. So six of them went, and Erasmo thought nobody had recognized him.

"But the police came, and Erasmo saw them. His aunt wasn't going to tell them that he was there, locked up in a bedroom. But they forced her to tell them. They thought they'd get him; but, when they opened the door, Erasmo had them covered. He had eighteen bullets, he said, before he would have given up. He knew if the police got him, he'd not live out the night."

"Guerillas—the police killed every one of them they captured. Erasmo knew that much." Juana shrugged to hide a shudder. "They usually tortured them first."

"The captain reached for his gun, but Erasmo meant business with his. So he hollered, 'You're coming with us.' 'Maybe so,' says Erasmo, 'but not alive. And any one of you who puts his hand on his gun is going to be dead, too.' "

"But the boy saw he was trapped. Pretty soon some more police would come with their guns ready. He might shoot one, but then his number was up, too. So he says, 'I'll surrender, if you go to the commander of the garrison and get him to come with soldiers. I'll go with him.' " Germán hitched his chair to face Marco. "The army he wasn't afraid of. The army doesn't have any part in these lootings and massacres of innocent people. Mostly they don't rape. So he says, 'Come with soldiers. I'll surrender to them.' "

"So now he's in prison without anybody to bring him his food. His family's dead, and they aren't feeding these prisoners. Eight hundred they had in there—political prisoners. We brought him something and gave him some money, but he said it was worse in prison than living like animals in the mountains. For eighteen years he's in."

"Now there's someone that needs converting—that boy." Juana suggested pointedly. "He's near like a skeleton, but every living shred of what's left of him is full of hate and revenge. Well, what's he got left? By the time he gets out, he'll be middle-aged. No home. No family. That's what this violence is dishing out to people."

"We'll have to pray harder that God will put an end to this dreadful hate and these murders," said Rosa softly. "So far, our families have escaped. Juana—you've been hurt bad, but they might have killed you. And Alicia—"

Rosa stopped. Germán's casual remark about rape had caused her flesh to crawl. The abrupt recollection of her fears concerning Alicia had brought on a slight nausea.

"Don't leave everything to God," muttered Germán. "We've just got back a few hours, but already we hear things. One is that they threaten to burn your house down."

"Oh, that!" retorted Marco. "Somebody must have heard that they did it to us in Aspasica, so they try to scare me."

"Look, Marco. When the military police say they'll burn somebody's house down, I get chills. When they get a few too many drinks, they've already got you in mind. For them, burning a house is like making whoopee. And what's this I hear about some kind of a hellfire and brimstone preacher coming here to your place? Anything to it?"

"Say, who told you that?" exclaimed Arturo. "Carmen, did you?"

"No," replied Germán. "The same man as told about burning the house told me. He said maybe I could talk sense into Marco. What he hears isn't good. He says everybody knows about this Liévano."

"Well, good!" cried Marco. "Here I've been wondering how to get the word around."

"It's got around, Marco. And they're talking of ambush. Any blasted fool that starts out for your meetings—"

"One ambush won't stop us," blustered Marco. "We've got people coming from all directions right now. Last Sunday when Don Vicente was here, he had over sixty."

"They've had as high as eighty, counting the kids," interjected Arturo. "That's way above that church in Ocaña!"

"If they're not as big as Chico," shrilled Emalina, "we don't count them. Or if they don't listen!"

Marco frowned. "Nina," he said sternly, "why aren't you in bed?"

The child must have been hovering in the shadows of the patio for some time. Rosa had seen her padding out to get a drink.

"Kids like that oughtn't to hear these things," said Germán.

"Run along now," said Rosa. She turned to Germán. "I doubt if a few more stories of violence will affect the children. People never seem to come together these days without something being said. I've given up trying to protect them."

"What's talk?" commented Antonio. "Why, the kids were at home when the town tried to chop our doors down with machetes. And then, once they burned down the barn, and the roof fell in—"

"There's another thing I hear," interrupted Germán, pursuing his previous line of warnings. "This Vicente Gómez—they say he's starting to come here on Sundays for morning services. Three people have told me that, just since we came home."

"Do you hear that, Rosa?" cried Marco. "Why, the busybodies in these foothills are getting the advertising done for us."

"So it's true!"

"Sure. A missionary's going to be preaching alternate Sundays in Ocaña. That sets Vicente free to come here those days."

"Well, stop him coming," growled Germán. "What I hear, I don't like, and you've even got our kids mixed up in this— this *evangelio!*"

In spite of his bravado, Marco was more concerned about Germán's warnings than he had allowed him to see. To Rosa he admitted that evening that the threat of ambush made him uneasy.

"Machetes and shotguns won't hold a real man back," he said, "but these police, they've got machine guns. The people they mow down might not even be coming here. When they start killing—"

Rosa followed his unfinished thought. Her flesh crawled again with horror. After the ambush, with their blood lust stirred, they would come to the house. Were they inviting the kind of attention that could end in massacre?

A day or two later, another of Marco's customers warned him that trouble was brewing. "Stop talking to people about God, if you know what's healthy. They don't want their lives changed. Leave them be."

"I didn't think I wanted mine changed," said Marco. "Just wait till it happens to you," Marco retorted, "and you won't stop talking about it either. Why, when I lived back in Aspasica—"

"Now, don't start on me," snapped the man. "I hear they've got it in for anybody that listens to you. If you want trouble, that's up to you. Me—I want to keep on living!"

12

Gospel of Meekness

SOME OF THE WARNINGS that Marco received during those days were not given by well-meaning friends. On the evening that Marco came home with a blackened eye, he did not need much prodding to extract his story. In fact, he seemed to be particularly elated about having had a chance to suffer for the sake of the gospel.

"Or is it the eye you're proud of?" teased Rosa, noting his exultant attitude toward getting into trouble.

"Well, not exactly," said Marco. "But didn't God tell the children of Israel to have a memorial when they'd passed through something that showed how God was working?"

"I'd just as soon you didn't keep this one for posterity," said Rosa. "Now tell me what you got into a fight about."

Marco, it appeared, had been walking past a spot on the road toward Ocaña commonly referred to as La Cuesta, when he was accosted by a former acquaintance who offered him a drink.

"I've found something a lot better than your liquor, Alfonso," said Marco, after thanking him for his friendly gesture.

"This—it's good whiskey," Alfonso replied thickly. "What's better?"

"Remember what a soak I was?" said Marco. "What's better is not *having* to drink. And no more hangovers." Marco had followed Alfonso into the shade near a private *tienda* where

225

several other men were passing the time of day. "I'll take a drink of water, though."

"If you're thirsty," retorted his would-be host, "take a drink. One little drink won't hurt you."

"Now listen, Rosa," said Marco, his face lighting up. "You know I've always stayed far away from the stuff, thinking it might be too much for me to resist if I really got a whiff of it. Well, Alfonso filled a glass right up full. Too full, at least for him to hand it to me, as unsteady as he was. He sloshed part of it on me, and it sure smelled like good whiskey. But that's all. I didn't need to take it. I'm delivered from it. So that's what I said to him.

" 'Friend,' I said, 'you're only proving the power of the *evangelio*. God's taken away my desire for liquor. Like I told you, I don't have to drink now.'

"So then, you know what they did? They were going to pour it into me!"

Rosa could not restrain her laughter, in spite of Marco's patent indignation and the black eye that suggested a rather rough situation. She could easily imagine Marco's reaction to such forceful temptation and the inevitable scuffle.

"So you took a drink!" she prompted, roguishly.

"I should say *not!*" retorted Marco, as heatedly as she had anticipated. "But they were making a lot of racket trying to make me. And who would come around, right then, but one of these military police. So then he asked, 'What's going on here?' And they all started hollering worse than ever. I don't think he heard a word they were saying, and he wouldn't listen to me, either. All he knew was that I was in the middle of it. He decided I'd been making trouble, so he arrested me for causing a disturbance."

"He took you in to Ocaña?"

"No, to Río de Oro. And I had to tell them everything from start to finish about three times before they believed me."

"Did they apologize for arresting you then?"

"Apologize? Those rascals? They acted like being an *evan-*

gélico is the worst crime in the book. When I told about God changing my habits—I had to tell them all I'd said—one of them said, 'So, you're *that* one where people go for preaching."

"So people know about our meetings clear up in Río de Oro!"

"They warned me to stop having meetings here. 'Any more complaints about *evangélico* meetings,' they said, 'and you'll know what police are for.' So I said, 'I've never forced anybody to come to the house, so why should they complain? Besides, come up and see for yourself if *evangélico* meetings are evil.' So I told them to come over to hear Francisco Liévano preach here."

"The police? You told them that he's coming in October?"

"Look, Rosa, we're not going to hide these meetings. That's what they're for—to draw in the ones who haven't come yet. The more blood those assassins have on their hands, the more their conscience tells them they've got to clear things with God."

"Even if it's your blood?"

Marco stared at Rosa a moment, then barked, almost as though he were defying his own inner fears, "He gave His blood for me, didn't He?"

When Don Vicente came for the service on the following Sunday, Rosa told him about Marco's arrest.

"They threatened you?"

"Well, sure," retorted Marco. "They've always done that."

"And more lately?"

"Why, sure. We've been getting more people to come to our meetings, haven't we? So if more threats bring more people to listen—let them threaten!"

"There does seem to be a relationship," said Rosa. "We've got people here today, new ones, from that direction."

Don Vicente turned toward her, a thoughtful frown on his intense face. "They know, down deep in their hearts, that what they have isn't worth suffering for. So when they hear of Marco talking up to the military police like that, they have to admit he's got something real. So they come to find out what it is, and it's up to me to show them that what they're looking for isn't 'something'—it's *Someone.*"

Besides the visitors from the direction of Río de Oro, Doña Juana edged into the patio where scores of people had gathered before the time of the service. The large woman's curiosity finally had gotten the better of her boasted skepticism.

Carmen, who was helping the girls clear up breakfast dishes, giggled when she saw her foster mother. "She's been bursting to come. I wonder what she's going to give out as an excuse."

Juana had brought a bowl. "I'm out of flour," she explained in a stage whisper to Rosa, hoping that her excuse would carry. "Can you give me some before they get to preaching?"

Rosa saw Juana's face fall when she came back, at once, with the bowl well filled. She realized ruefully that she had robbed Juana of her apparently valid excuse for lingering.

"Why don't you sit a minute?" she invited. "You know everybody."

Juana nodded eagerly. "Till the singing starts," she said. She seemed clearly amazed—and relieved—at the number of people she recognized. Looking at them through Juana's eyes, Rosa noticed the timidity and cautious reserve of first-time visitors as they drew near the happily buzzing crowd. They were happy to see acquaintances and somewhat perturbed to be recognized at this evangelical gathering. Some relaxed as they spoke to personal friends; others sat stiffly self-conscious throughout the entire service.

Since the house had long since been crowded out, the meeting had an air of informality that helped break the ice. Horses and mules tethered nearby snorted contentedly as they grazed in the surrounding woods. The approach of other mounts occasionally initiated a rash of neighings and some crashing about in the underbrush. Hens walked sedately through the meeting, looking sharply on all sides for handouts, scratching for a fleeing bug and exchanging raucous fowl language in a singsong contralto. When disturbed at the peaceful pursuit of their livelihood, they rose into the air in a cloud of feathers and a furious barnyard uproar of sympathetic cackling. The unexpected bray of one of the donkeys usually interrupted the sermon until the strident vocal sawing had ceased.

The children still provided most of the volume when it came to singing, since the hymns were still unfamiliar to most of the visitors; but by now some adults were joining in the short choruses. Rosa met Carmen's sparkling eyes and followed her glance. Standing with muscular arms akimbo and a streak of flour across her customary scowl, Juana had given up all pretense of having come to borrow a bowl of flour. Rosa gestured Tive to take Juana a box to sit on.

Naturally, there were not chairs for all the guests, but Toño had drawn some fairly large logs under the trees around the patio. Children sprawled in the grass. At the outer fringe of this gathering, as usual, a few dissidents stood by to heckle the preacher and ridicule the listeners. Usually it was young hooligans or inebriates who appeared to achieve some sort of distorted satisfaction out of distracting acquaintances who were trying to listen. A few times the antagonism had been bitter and the threats real.

Now that Don Vicente was free to hold services on alternate Sundays and the audience had grown, Marco insisted on more reverence in the meetings than he had deemed necessary for the admittedly unconventional audiences he had previously scraped together at any chance visit Don Vicente made.

Rosa recollected how Marco's temper had flared during the first of these more formal services when a couple of drunken youths had persisted in making ribald comments during the reading of the Sacred Scriptures. He had gestured to Antonio and moved purposefully toward his unwelcome guests.

Don Vicente, who had continued to preach in spite of the loud and unsavory jibes, interrupted his sermon to ask everyone to bow their hearts and unite in the Lord's prayer. Marco, naturally, remained where he was and bowed his head in reverence. When he opened his eyes after the short, well-known prayer, the offenders had slipped away.

Afterwards, at the table, Marco confessed that he had lost his temper. "But can we let them get by with it in a Sunday service?"

"We never know, Marco," said Don Vicente, "whether they may not sincerely want to come and listen quietly, but they can't do so without losing face before their friends. So, whether they come to disrupt the service or to find something to bring peace to their souls, they have come; and the Holy Spirit can use just a phrase or a verse of Scripture to begin a work that He will also finish."

"Even when they're lit up like that?" Antonio asked.

"Is anything impossible with God?" returned Don Vicente.

Antonio nodded, reddening. He had heard Don Vicente pray, and he knew this man was not just voicing a pious idea. When Don Vicente prayed, he expected his heavenly Father to take over.

"Well, then," chirped Emalina. "From now on I'm going to start saying the Lord's prayer, in quiet, whenever those loud ones start up their racket. God'll put a stop to it."

Don Vicente's eyes had twinkled as he studied her serious, upturned face. Then he nodded. "I daresay Emalina's prayers might have more effect than mine. Children have a way of grasping the simplicity of faith when we become involved in processes and motives. A child seldom prays just to sound off. I've heard far too many prayers—"

"You mean," interrupted Alicia, "a snide way of finding fault with somebody—when they can't talk back at you?"

"How do you think God feels about that kind of praying?"

"Well, for one thing, He'll see through it quicker than the person that's getting told off. Will God pay attention to that kind of prayer at all?"

"Would Jesus pray spitefully?"

"He'd pray out of compassion—from love," replied Natividad.

"Yes, Tive," said Don Vicente, "but far more often, there's another weakness in people's prayers. Almost all so-called intercession is merely a way, loving and compassionate though it may be, of expressing sympathy with the troubles of another. There's no expectation—no assurance—of God's intervention."

"You make prayer sound exciting, Don Vicente," exclaimed Jorge.

"It is. What do you think it means to pray 'in Jesus' name'? Or let me ask it like this: is there any good tacking that phrase onto a prayer when it's completely out of character with Jesus? Doesn't something 'in His name' represent something God, knowing His Son, would expect of Him?"

"So *that's* what it means!" cried Antonio.

Rosa let her eyes fall to her hands, clasped without conscious thought. She thanked God with all her soul that the meetings were here in their home. Perhaps they were all learning as much at the table after the service as they did in the course of the morning's preaching.

She had seen Antonio—who did all the Bible reading in their family worship—grow into stalwart, spiritual maturity during this past year. He had outgrown the teenagers' natural pull toward conformity with other young men, who often belittled and ridiculed him in a particularly cruel manner. She had seen him witness earnestly and often to Arturo and others of the younger set. Alicia and Natividad talked to Carmen, of course, but they lacked the commitment to the gospel that Rosa sensed in her oldest son.

Antonio was joining Marco in a systematic visitation of all the plantations within several hours' riding distance of Santa Inés as the date of the Liévano meetings drew near. Though Marco had recognized the grapevine's effectiveness in publicizing the event, he was not laying the responsibility of getting the news out onto the shoulders of the opposition.

And opposition there was. Rosa heard echoes of various threats from a good many sources. As the day rapidly approached, menaces had become more direct and ominous. Police from Totumal seemed to be watching them closely. They had been in the store several times. Marco admitted that their threats frightened him more than all the loud talking of the mountaineers.

"Threatening makes those men feel like *machos*,"[1] he commented, shrugging his shoulders after a barrage of particularly vituperative abuse. He was more serious after a well-meaning acquaintance pleaded with him to call the meetings off, and more solemn still after a rather large detachment of military police rode in on horses.

Rosa expected Marco to come back into the house after they left, with his usual defiant chuckle, but he actually seemed to be puttering aimlessly in the sala. Was he evading any questions she might ask? She called to Antonio, who had also been in the store with his father.

"What did they want this time—the police?"

"Oh, just threats," said Antonio, trying to imitate his father's casual attitude. "Said they'd get Papá and me, and they threatened to burn the house down. And—"

"Go on, Toño. What else?"

Antonio hesitated and reddened under Rosa's scrutiny. Finally, while she waited, he swung around and painstakingly straightened a wire rack that held the enamelware plates they used every day. He pretended that he had forgotten that Rosa had addressed a question to him.

"Antonio," she said sternly. "I asked you something."

"Well, what he said was—the captain of the police—he said it." Antonio hesitated again and then turned suddenly to face her. "I think we ought to call this off, Mamá. Maybe we will. I think maybe we will."

Rosa did not urge him any farther, and when Marco came back into the house she saw that he was deeply agitated. Still, he did not mention to her anything more than that the police had been back. Though she invited his confidence, Marco changed the subject abruptly. As head of the house, Marco felt that he had to make his own decisions. Rosa understood this,

[1]Males.

but she could pray that God would guide him to do what was right.

Next day, when policemen had dropped in again, Marco spoke sharply to Rosa. "I won't have these wretches ogling you," he rasped, in a burst of anger. "And keep our girls out of sight!"

Later he apologized. "It was because of their threats yesterday. The captain went through his usual routine and then said, 'And the women will be herded to Totumal and Aguachica for the pleasure of the police.'" Then he confessed that this incentive—his two beautiful daughters and his still attractive wife—could inspire almost any form of violence. "They've got the pretext that they want in the meetings," he admitted.

As long as Marco could do his own suffering for the cause of Christ, he remained undaunted. Now he feared for Rosa and for his family. With the involvement of the military police, his apprehension of mob action and ambushes had also increased greatly, for he recognized the brutal effectiveness of machine gunning into a crowd—a tactic the police had demonstrated many times.

Later he instructed his family. "When any of you see the police, you go for the woods," he ordered. When no one spoke up, he barked, "You hear?"

"Aren't you going to have me write Señor Liévano?" Antonio asked after the evening devotions. Watching Marco closely, Rosa saw him battle the temptation to submit to this overwhelming situation, but he drew himself up and bit back the words that could release them all from this commitment.

"The men in Ocaña decided against it," said Rosa gently. "Nobody will blame you if you postpone it for a year or so."

"Antonio!"

"Yes, Papá," replied his son with a start at Marco's sharp tone of command.

"Can you find the place in the Bible where you read this morning?"

"Sure, Papá. I've got one of Don Vicente's tracts in the

place." He went to the cupboard where the Bible was kept and turned the pages somewhat nervously. "I can't remember."

"Just read it," snapped Marco. "That's the trouble with people that read. They know they can look it up again, so they don't remember. Read it," he commanded, when he saw that Antonio had found the marked place.

" 'Cast thy bread upon the waters,' read Antonio, 'for thou shalt find it after many days. Give a portion to seven, and also to eight; for thou knowest not what evil shall be upon the earth. If the clouds be full of rain, they empty themselves upon the earth: and if the tree fall toward the south, or toward the north, in the place where the tree falleth, there it shall be. He that observeth the wind shall not sow; and he that regardeth the clouds shall not reap.' "[2]

"That's it!" cried Marco, all his tension erased. "Now we've got God's opinion on it, and that's what we'll do. We have to dish it out before the violence gets worse. There's an evil on the earth right now. Who knows if some of these same people will even be alive by next year? 'He that observeth the wind shall not sow,' and if he doesn't sow he's not going to reap anything, that's for sure."

When Juana came next day to remonstrate with Marco over the trouble that seemed to be brewing, he laughed easily. "Do you think everybody knows about the threats, Juana?" he asked.

"There's not a soul that doesn't know you're a stubborn mule and that you're asking for trouble!" she retorted heatedly.

"Well, that's all I wanted to be sure of. I don't want to lure anybody else into danger they don't know about. And you just watch! The smell of some excitement will draw twice as many people. They'll come, for fear they'd be missing something!"

During that week Don Vicente was able to spend a day on the trails. He agreed with Marco, as Antonio saddled their horses, that they would not deny that there had been threats. In fact he felt that they must openly confirm the fact. "Still, we'll tell them what a wonderful work Don Francisco has been

[2]Ecclesiastes 11:1-4.

doing in many places, and how people bless God that he brought them the word of hope and peace through Jesus."

Just as Antonio led the horses to the edge of the veranda, a group of rowdies stumped into the store. Before Marco had time to hurry to the front of the house in response to their insolent shouts for service, they burst through the private part of the home and into the patio.

"A bunch of drunks," commented Carmelo disdainfully.

Vulgarity and rudeness on the part of some of their customers was nothing uncommon. One could anticipate some coarse blustering and shouting, and then the inebriates would subside or go off to stir up excitement elsewhere. Still, Rosa agreed with Alicia when she exclaimed, somewhat apprehensively, "I'm glad they came before Papá got away." Then she added, "They remind me of the guerrillas in El Carmen."

"See? I told you," shouted one of the ruffians, thick of speech. "It's the *evangélico* from Ocaña."

"It's him, all right." The speaker, a man whom Rosa recognized as one who had repeatedly disturbed their evening meetings, elbowed his way past the fellow still posed in the doorway. His unbuttoned plaid shirt was soiled and hung open to expose a hairy chest narrowed by rachitic deformity.

Three other men pushed their way into the patio. "What does he say?" asked one of them.

"You!" the heckler rasped. "You're bringing this hellfire-and-brimstone preacher here, no?"

"We've invited a preacher," replied Don Vicente, "but he'll probably speak more of the love of God than about eternal judgment."

"Well, we won't have him spouting about hell at us—you hear?"

"Nobody's forcing you to come and listen," Marco snapped. "But of course, you're invited to come like any other guest."

"You stop him from coming—that's what we're saying."

"Have I ever tried to tell you who can come to your house or who can't?" retorted Marco. "Since when are you—"

"What are you guys waiting for?" challenged a particularly uncouth ruffian wearing leather chaps and spurs which dug into the patio ground as he strode heavily toward the horses. He ripped the bridle from the one nearest the veranda. As Antonio started away with the other horse, another man lunged at him, thrust him roughly aside and grabbed for the leather straps. With two vicious strokes of the machete he'd yanked from his belt he severed them from the bridle.

Meanwhile, the man with the plaid shirt had snatched Don Vicente's Bible from his hands and struck him a savage blow across the face with it.

"Not in *my* house, you don't strike a minister of the gospel!" barked Marco sharply, even as the fellow struck at their guest again. Don Vicente staggered with the force of the blow and caught at the edge of the table to steady himself.

"Grab the *palo*," Marco yelled at him, motioning toward the heavy pole he used every night to prop against the doors. Marco gripped the offender's shoulders and spun him off to one side, then glanced about hurriedly for something he himself could lay hands on and use as a weapon. In former days, Marco would have been wearing a gun and would not have needed to match muscles with a scoundrel far heavier than he.

As the man in the plaid shirt regained his balance, the disreputable leader of the attack sprang forward and began belaboring Don Vicente with the bridle, shouting hoarse and abusive obscenities.

"So that's what you wanted the bridle for!" yelled Antonio. He flung himself upon the man who held the leather straps, attempting to wrest them from his grasp. He fell back with a sharp exclamation of pain when the stronger man ripped the rough leather through his fingers and swung them across his face and shoulders.

Don Vicente could have reached the pole without stepping from where he stood, but he made no move toward it. Had the blow on his head made him giddy? Marco leaped across the patio to seize it for himself, for his shout had prompted another man to go for it. As Marco whirled with the pole, he slashed at the man who was flailing at Don Vicente with the bridle, then raised it above his head, ready to fell the first man who approached.

As he stood there, poised to take the offensive in this fracas, Rosa saw the grim determination on his face change to a look of baffled uncertainty. In that instant, his shock struck Rosa as well. According to the poster on the wall of their sala, a Christian does not take up any weapon against another man.

As a family, they had often discussed that they must flee rather than fight. But now—when the men were out-numbered and flight was cut off—could it mean that they were not to defend themselves? Was that why Don Vicente had not made one move to retaliate? To turn the other cheek—had Jesus meant that to apply to literal blows on the face, such as Don Vicente had just suffered? All this sped through Rosa's mind before the end of the pole in Marco's hand had come to rest on the patio floor.

Seeing Marco's indecision, one of the belligerents snatched the pole and swung it at him. Marco dodged, only to cringe under the lash from one of the straps. Don Vicente plunged through an opening in the encircling assailants, and Marco was thrust out after him.

"Look out!" screamed Carmelo. "There's others out there."

So quickly had the scuffle developed that only now the children had begun to shriek with fright. Wild with anxiety and with a feeling of helplessness, Rosa hardly heard their screams. Marco and Don Vicente were being driven along, surrounded by the churning assailants whose angry shouts had altered into snarls of bestial sadism. Rosa followed, cringing with sickening horror, as she heard the swish of those leather straps, the cracking reports as they struck flesh, and the grunting of the men straining to flay Marco and Vicente with each savage lash.

Antonio rushed by her toward the tight circle about the two men. "They're killing them," he screamed. "My God, they're killing them!" He was sobbing unashamedly.

From near the main highway, another group of men dashed up with coarse shouts and brutal laughter, eager to join the fray. A dizzying nausea gripped Rosa as the dreadful certainty that this mob was beating her husband to death overwhelmed her. She followed, aghast, propelled along by the agony of her dying hope.

Suddenly she became conscious of Emalina's small hand gripping hers. In her concern over her husband, the anguish over his fate, and her wild longing to stand by, she was imperiling her children! Chico had followed her and was whimpering at her skirts. Marco had warned her repeatedly that, one act of violence consummated, a mob usually lusted for more blood.

"Get back to the patio," she screamed. "To the woods, Tive, Alicia!" Alas, all the children were out here on the trail. She rushed forward to pull Antonio back from the circle into which he had no hope of penetrating.

"Come back, Toño," she cried, "or they will massacre us all!"

"Not me, Mamá," he shouted, shrugging her from him. "Maybe I can do something."

What could Toño do? Even if he used a machete or a gun, he now had no hope of stopping what was happening before their eyes. It was too late to save the men now; they were too badly outnumbered.

Antonio turned upon Rosa urgently. "Go back now," he barked peremptorily. "Get those kids to safety!" In that moment he had grown up. He had become the man of the house. If she let him stay, she would lose him in the hour of his splendid maturing.

"I need you, Toño," she sobbed, but he pushed her gently toward the children, who stood unmoving along the path.

Emalina was praying shrilly. "Do something, God, or they'll get Papá! Do something!"

Chico had stopped whimpering and stood with folded hands, his eyes—large, frightened—fastened on Emalina, who sobbed even while she prayed.

"Yes, God," exclaimed Rosa, wondering that the tiny girl

should have thought of God when her own mind had been paralyzed with horror. She grasped Chico's hand and Emalina's, and prayed as she started running with them toward the house.

At that very moment, Marco broke away from his tormentors. He dodged a pursuer and saw that the tight knot of men had scattered to head him off. Doubling back unexpectedly, he pulled Don Vicente from the unsteady grasp of the drunken man who was concentrating his efforts in flailing at the pastor's face and shoulders.

Rosa whirled as she heard Marco cry, "Run for the house, Vicente!" His shout was almost drowned out by yells of rage from the mob. Conflicting orders, with no one carrying them out, brought the pursuit to confusion, though threats followed the running men.

"We're not through with you!" shouted someone. "Just you wait!"

"It'll go worse for you than ever," yelled another.

The children burst through the back door at the same instant that Marco stumbled into the front of the house, drawing Don Vicente in after him. The slamming of the front door cut off the bellowed promise of another visit.

"Call off those meetings, or else!"

"God be thanked," cried Marco hoarsely. "This time I thought we were done for."

"We all thought so," sobbed Tive, throwing her arms around him.

"Easy now, Tive," said Marco sharply. "My back's pretty raw."

"We asked God to let you get away," shrilled Chico.

"It was God that did it, Chico." Don Vicente spoke through distorted and swollen lips. "Without a miracle, how could two men get away from such a mob?"

Red bands of swelling on face and arms marked the severity of the lashings the men had received. Marco's face was covered with discolorations and swelling bruises. He fingered a particularly dark welt over his left eye and glanced toward Rosa.

Now that the danger was over, she found that she was trembling so violently she could hardly stand, and she could not control her sobbing.

"Whatever are you crying for now, Rosa? We're here—and safe."

"I guess I'm hysterical," replied Rosa, still sobbing. "I was so afraid you'd be killed." She swung toward Don Vicente. "Can this be God's will—just to stand by when someone is killing your husband? Can't we do anything but stand around wringing our hands? What if they'd killed you both?"

"You were praying," replied Don Vicente gently.

"I don't remember that I was," stammered Rosa. "I kept thinking of things I should be doing, and everything I thought of—" She burst into tears again. With great effort she gained control of herself and said briskly, with forced cheerfulness, "Look at your new shirt, Marco! You're bleeding all over it, too."

"That maniac hit him with the halter, rings and all," said Antonio. "Look at those black and blue spots on him!"

"Toño, is somebody watching the door? If they come back—"

"I'm here," called Carmelo. "So's Jorge. They're still standing out there, hollering and arguing and waving their arms around."

Rosa had unbuttoned Marco's tattered shirt, one sleeve of which was entirely gone. Blood was oozing through the cloth in several spots. She gasped as she laid bare his back. Antonio peeled back Don Vicente's shirt as well. Both their backs and shoulders were covered with welts and bruises, bleeding where the full force of violent blows had broken the skin.

"My back may look bad," remarked Don Vicente at the general exclamations of dismay, "but it doesn't hurt as much as my legs. I kept thinking that if they'd break a bone, then there'd be no chance to get away. Or if they'd knocked us down—"

"We'd have been clubbed to death."

While she was cleansing the broken bruises on Don Vicente's

back, Rosa reverted to the question that still burned in her mind.

"Before this, we've always been able to escape—we've never been cornered like this." She fumbled for the right words. "Prayer—is that all we can do, if it should ever happen again? If they had killed Marco, wouldn't I lie awake all my nights thinking of what I should have done?" Rose was crying again.

Don Vicente did not answer flippantly. "What is prayer, Doña Rosa?"

"Well, it's asking God to do something. Is that what you mean?"

Don Vicente nodded thoughtfully. He seemed to be feeling his way toward his next response. "Do you think you would be able to intervene more effectively than Almighty God?"

"Does God want us just to stand by, wringing our hands?"

"Doesn't God use people?" put in Antonio. The boy had shared her own agony, Rosa thought.

"I know you've read of Moses in the Bible. He saw the whole nation of his own people in serious trouble. He knew he was the only person who could do something about it, and he wanted to help them. So he acted—remember? What happened?"

"He had to get out himself," said Antonio, "and the people were no better off. Worse off, I guess."

"But after forty years, Moses had learned to know God a bit better. God sent Moses back, but this time Moses trusted God to handle the situation. When God took things in hand, He delivered all that nation at one time and destroyed the oppressors' army as well."

"But why did God wait forty years? What I mean is—why did God let you get beat up today? What if you'd have been killed?"

"They could not have killed us unless God allowed it. If we have been beaten, it was for God's glory, or for the building of His church."

"Well," blurted Antonio, "I wish He'd build it some other way."

"How do you know, Toño," said Don Vicente, "if God doesn't have a great burden for a few people who might never hear about Francisco Liévano coming here to preach. But now they may come—from curiosity or some other reason. And they will hear the gospel. How do we know?"

"And if my being knocked about a bit will keep just one person out of everlasting separation from such a loving God," ejaculated Marco, "it's well worth the pain."

Germán Vanegas came over later in the afternoon, after Don Vicente had gone back to Ocaña. The mob had not dissipated, it was clear, until they had proclaimed to all and sundry that they were going to stop the announced meetings by one means or another.

"You're not going to go on with the meetings after the beating they gave you?" he queried.

"They just came to help us advertise the revival," Marco retorted with his accustomed bravado.

Germán's jaw sagged in astonishment. "Hombre," he exclaimed, shaking his head as though he were trying to clear away a fog. "You're either a fool—or you've got something I want!"

13

To Set a Trap

JUAN MACHADO, a hard drinking, hard fighting man from the neighborhood of La Vega del Gusto, was sipping *tinto* in the patio with Don Vicente and Marco.

"Sure, I'll stay for a *culto*," he replied promptly. "Too bad Alcario Mateus and his brother don't know about it. They'd have ridden in, those two. They seem to dote on this Bible you keep reading."

"I didn't expect to be out during the week," explained Don Vicente. "I had to come out to discuss a few things that have come up about the meetings."

"The Liévano meetings," put in Marco. "I told you about the evangelist that's coming out."

"At least ten times," retorted Juan Machado chuckling. "I guess you've told us all often enough so nobody could forget."

"It's next week now, that they start. Don't let anything—"

Machado set down the enamel cup on the flowered oilcloth that flapped in the breeze. He grinned at Marco. "I'll do you one better, Marco. I'll see if I can get my brother, Sixto, from San José to come. It's four hours hard riding down as far as La Brisa, but I think I've got him curious. I warn you, Sixto's a gay one, but you keep saying God can take us off the bottle. Well, He'll have His work cut out for Him, if He wants to change Sixto." He added, after a moment, "Or me. We've both tried plenty often to cut down on liquor."

"Good!" said Marco heartily. "We haven't had anyone come here from up there on the east ridge. And I'm not worried about God taking both of you on. The worse soak you are, the more

243

you'll know it was God that set you free of the bottle."

It struck Rosa suddenly that most of the men who had been coming regularly to Don Vicente's Sunday meetings were men who had a drinking problem. Several of them had tried to fight the habit, deploring its effect on their health or their family relationships. Marco's repeated testimony of his own release was drawing them to listen to the gospel that had freed him.

Carmen had gone home to tell her foster parents of the impromptu meeting, and Antonio had ridden off to notify a few of the nearer neighbors. Heavy footfalls announced the arrival of several customers in the front part of the house.

"Good," said Marco. "I've got some customers to wait on, but maybe I can bring them back for the meeting."

Germán Vanegas, who had strolled over from his own house, took Marco by the sleeve just as he was going in toward the store. He tilted his head in the direction of the front room. "You know who you've got in there?"

"No, I was just going in to look," replied Marco.

"It's military police—from Totumal. Five of them."

Juan Machado knocked the empty cup to the floor as he shoved the homemade plank bench abruptly away from the heavy table.

"Those brigands from Totumal—what's with them?"

"Do you think they're here about the meetings again, Marco?" growled Germán, keeping his voice low. He knew that Marco had received several threats from that law enforcement body.

"What's the matter, Marco?" Juan demanded jocularly. "Are they so anxious not to miss the meetings that they're dropping in to ask when it is?"

Marco chuckled. "The police? Well, yes, they're taking a lot of interest in the meetings, at that. This is the fourth time in the past ten days they've come here. And I'd better get in there and wait on them. Sometimes they're short on patience."

"Threats?" Machado's tone was level, but as he turned toward Don Germán he was fingering the machete that swung from his belt. It was common knowledge that the military police stationed at Totumal had had an active part in several gruesome tragedies in the vicinity.

Rosa caught sight of Juana scurrying heavily across the clearing in their direction. She arrived breathless and with her customary scowl. She returned Rosa's greeting absently, then stood with arms akimbo, head cocked toward the area where gruff conversation seemed to be growing more animated.

"They must be looking at the picture of the ways," she commented. She held up her fleshy forefinger for silence, moving stealthily toward the front of the house. She returned precipitately, exploding in a harsh stage whisper. "Marco, the imbecile, is telling them to come to the meetings—so they'll know where they're heading. Hasn't he got any—"

She gasped as a roar of anger from the other part of the house was followed almost at once by a metallic click. Terror froze the blood in Rosa's veins. One of the policemen, she knew, had taken offense at Marco's characteristic direct approach to evangelizing and had drawn a gun. Even as she whispered a frantic prayer, she heard Marco's voice raised in an apparently nonchalant request.

"Hold it for a few minutes, friend. Now that you've figured it for yourself where you'll go, you'd better give me time enough to tell you how you can be saved from the curse of your sin. Then if you still feel like finishing me off, you'll never be able to say I didn't tell you the way to peace of heart."

Rosa dashed to the kitchen. Perhaps if she brought them *tinto* she could interrupt this explosive situation. Fortunately, she had just made a pot for Juan and Don Vicente. She clutched at a few cups and rushed into the store. A few of the men in uniform still stood around the poster depicting the heavenly pilgrimage. One of them held a gun on Marco. It wavered when Rosa entered.

"Tinto," she quavered. "I brought you all some *tinto.*" She began pouring the sweetened coffee into cups.

Raucous laughter and coarse comment rewarded her gesture

of hospitality, which had been recognized as a distracting maneuver. The gunman, his finger still on the trigger, flourished his weapon in Rosa's direction to emphasize his own advice.

"Better tell this old rooster to crow less, señora," he said, "unless you like the idea of being a widow."

"What of this Liévano?" The question came from another of the officers. "Will he leave a widow? Or will we get her and the kids when we shoot up the meeting?"

"Or do you think you can talk your man into calling him off?"

"Your *tinto* is growing cold, señor," murmured Rosa, her eyes following the erratic movements of the gun that was still pointed in her general direction. At this moment she would have liked nothing better than to be able to assure the man that Marco would, indeed, postpone the series of meetings. She was glad when he dropped the gun into his holster and took the proffered cup. Her eyes now free from the deadly peril of an unsteady finger on the trigger, she noted that Marco was glowering at her. His annoyance reminded her of his often repeated command not even to remain in the house when these men appeared.

"I'll take over your hospitality, Rosa," he growled.

Glancing quickly around the room, Rosa caught the sensuous leer on the faces of a couple of men, and her face flamed with the memory of their lewd remarks. Still, she was not about to leave Marco in here alone at the mercy of a brute who appeared to achieve a sense of power through pointing a cocked pistol at a defenseless man.

"I have cheese and *arepa*," she said, and her voice sounded strangely shrill in her own ears. "It's nearly lunchtime."

"Sure, bring them in," chortled one of the men, apparently the highest ranking officer. He followed Rosa's glance toward the gun, which his subaltern was again fingering dangerously.

"Put it up," he growled. "Today's not the day for fireworks, anyway."

"Is Toño home?" Marco's message was clear. She was not to

invite them into the patio. She reassured Marco with a nod. "I'll send the *arepa* in," she replied. Though Antonio had not returned, it would be well for these rowdies to know that Marco was not the only man at the house. She was about to send Don Vicente in with her hurriedy prepared sandwiches, but Juana caught him by an arm and pulled him back.

"Not you," she protested. "If they knew you were here, they could start something worse than happened the other time. You'd better make yourself scarce, for the good of us all. I'm taking the *arepa* in."

"No," barked Juan Machado decisively. He walked over and loosened Juana's firm grasp on the plate. "This isn't for women. Germán and I'll go in together."

A few minutes later, when the police had ridden away, Juan Machado swung toward Marco. "What did the lieutenant mean by what he hollered back at you?"

"You mean about them being a welcoming committee?" replied Germán. "They mean they'll be waiting with guns. They keep warning Marco to call off these Liévano meetings next week."

Machado eyed Marco sharply. Marco's tone was casual when he replied. "They talk some about ambush. Drop the word around, will you? They can't do much harm if people aren't caught off guard."

"Shotguns or machetes, I'm not afraid of," said Machado, voicing what Rosa knew was Marco's own fear, "but an ambush set up by those assassins from Totumal is something else again. What was that you said, Doña Juana, about 'last time'?"

"Oh, that wasn't the police, that time. It was a crowd of bullies that nearly knocked the living daylights out of Marco here, and Don Vicente." Juana gave Machado a succinct but colorful account of what had transpired. The children's interpolations of detail provided a clear picture of the gravity of the attack.

"Look here, Marco," counseled Machado. "If a bunch of rowdies can beat you up like that, you're not going to be able to handle a detail of policemen. At least six or eight of us will have to be ready with loaded guns, if they come up at us sudden like."

"I can see *you've* not learned the *evangelio* yet," retorted Juana, laughing hoarsely. "They just stand up and let you beat them. They don't even grab a *palo* and fight back."

Juan Machado glanced at Don Vicente incredulously.

"We come with a message of love, Señor Machado," replied the pastor of Ocaña. "Jesus never struck anyone back."

"He got killed, too," said Machado. He shook his head as though to clear it of an unbelievable idea or of a statement he could not possibly have heard correctly. "Then," he said, "you've got to cancel these meetings."

Rosa nodded. "I wish you'd talk Marco out of having the meetings. They intend to shoot up the meeting. They said, 'Will Liévano leave a widow? Or will we get her and the kids when we shoot up the meeting?' That's what they said. It means—"

"Liévano isn't married," said Marco, trying to be jocose. "So his widow and kids don't have much to worry about."

Rosa looked imploringly at Don Vicente. "The people who come to hear the *evangelio*—the other people—is it right, Don Vicente?"

Don Vicente was thoughtfully running his fingernail around the edge of his worn Bible. "If you say so," he said, turning to Marco, "I can still get a telegram to Francisco in time to stop his coming. Maybe it would be better."

"Later, Marco," pleaded Rosa. "Just a little later, maybe, we can have the meetings."

"Yes," said Germán. "It'll be safer for the whole neighborhood if you drop this idea now."

"Do you think I like the idea of being shot at?" barked Marco, almost angrily. He got up to pace the veranda, seemingly oblivious to their presence. Suddenly he swung toward them.

"All right," he snapped, looking at Juan. "Set me a date when things in Colombia will be better. Set me a date."

Juan Machado looked indignant and his face reddened. *"Quién sabe?* The violence grows worse rather than better. That's why we're trying to talk you out of these fool meetings."

"And the closer the violence comes, the more are killed?"

Juan shrugged. "That's to be expected."

"And if they die without being saved, where will they be? You know that much, Juan. You've looked at our picture."

"You're a brave man, Marco. You make this *evangelio* sound awfully important."

Marco resumed his agitated pacing back and forth on the veranda, but Rosa knew what his decision would be. In a moment he whirled again. "I don't see why I'm quibbling," he said brusquely, though his voice trembled. "God has already given us the answer to this. Will He change His mind? If you keep watching the clouds, the Bible says, you won't get around to sowing. And then you can't expect any harvest afterwards, of course."

Don Vicente nodded approval, though he certainly knew the gravity of threat that hung over his own head as a responsible agent for bringing about the meetings.

"Then we'll pray, right now, that the Lord of the Harvest will protect His laborers. He is more interested in these souls than we are. Nobody can touch one person who wants to come to these meetings unless He permits it."

"You think you'll still get people to come, if you let them know they'll be shot at?" said Germán, after Juan Machado had gone.

"I don't want anybody to be caught without I warned them," said Marco. "The smell of a good fight may bring some of the tough ones out. They're the kind that need the preaching worse than the ones that would stay at home, maybe."

"You get a few too many troublemakers here into your patio, Marco, and you may end with a brawl—not a revival."

"There's always some that come to make a nuisance of themselves. Sometimes they forget about their tomfoolery and start to listen before the meeting's out."

Rosa knew Marco anticipated real trouble during the meetings. His casual mention of ambush to people he was inviting demonstrated his anxiety that they should be alert to this danger. Marco was spending hours in prayer these days, and in their family services he prayed ever more earnestly that God would betray whatever ambush would be formed, that He would protect those who fell into ambush.

"Let their wrath fall on me," he had prayed more than once.

In spite of his bluster of indifference to personal danger, Marco was worried. Each time any military policeman approached, Marco ordered Rosa sharply to leave the house and make a dash for the woods. "And get the girls out of sight!"

Once, in her early girlhood, Rosa had been caught on a barren rocky pass when a storm broke in the mountains. She had never forgotten the terror of that experience. Static electricity had built up along the ridge to such a degree that at each flash of lightning she could hear a crackling of electricity leaping skyward from every prominence in every direction. She had crouched, trembling violently, knowing enough to avoid what appeared sheltering boulders and that if she got up to flee in her panic her body would almost surely close a circuit for the leaping deadly current. Each horrifying flash was followed by the ominous buildup toward the one that might be the fatal discharge. Only after the storm had abated had she dared to move.

The same kind of suspense and terror of death clung to her now each waking hour and startled her to trembling wakefulness during the nights. As on the mountain, she must remain right where she was, doing the ordinary work of caring for her large family. She could expect no lessening of danger until after the Liévano meetings were over.

Though Rosa concurred that Marco's resolution stemmed from his earnest desire to be a witness here in Santa Inés, she admitted sorrowfully that she did not share his courage. Men, she thought, are used to violence. They do not consider the grief and tragedy after the moment of crisis is past. Rosa felt trapped by the danger that Marco also obviously could foresee.

Many of the people who had promised to come to the meetings were coming from mountain areas far removed from Santa Inés. Rosa and the girls were as busy as they could be during those last few days before Don Francisco Liévano arrived. As Marco had boasted, the hint of danger connected with his invitations had provided sufficient challenge to bring some who otherwise would not have shown interest. Others seemed to have determined, because of the threats, to find out what was important enough to arouse such animosity. Some came because their sense of need had already been aroused by the house-to-house meetings in which Marco had joined Don Vicente, no matter how busy he was, and which he had carried on together with Antonio when Don Vicente could not come.

Young Francisco Liévano had a ringing message that struck home. A Colombian himself, he knew their background, their prejudices and their emptiness. He also knew the One who could bring fulfillment into their lives. As in Don Vicente's meetings, several visitors took pains to explain that they had come only to heckle and scoff.

"If they didn't say it so loudly and so often, I'd believe them," remarked Don Francisco. "But have you noticed? They don't miss a meeting, and each time they come they're getting a bit more understanding."

Strangers came to these meetings who heard the gospel for the first time in their lives. Several made open commitments to Christ. Carmen and Arturo, already believers, were first to take a public stand as evangelicals. Alcario and Margario Mateus and their cousin Cristóbal made public their avowal of faith. Juan Machado told the whole gathering of the day they had all tried to discourage Marco from having these meetings.

"But he risks his life and his family that we should hear. 'If the violence gets them and they die without being saved,' he asked me that night, 'where will they go?' And I knew where we'd go, and I knew where I'd go myself. So I gave myself to God on the trail home that day, even before these meetings took up."

14

"My Shoes, Rosa!"

"WELL, YOU CALLED THEIR BLUFF," remarked Doña Juana a few days after the Liévano meetings had been chalked up triumphantly as a huge success. "Just the same, I'm glad I wasn't the one to face it!"

"Now that it's past, I suppose it's all right to say I'm glad it's all over," admitted Rosa. "It was a strain."

"You mean the work? You had all those outside people to feed, besides your houseful. I didn't mean the work. I'd have been scared to death."

"Maybe we all were, so we prayed a lot. For all their threats, Juana, the police never came here once. We can't explain it any way but that God didn't let them come."

"I'd call it luck, and I sure wouldn't have the nerve to try it a second time. You know this crazy foolishness the boys talk about—Russian roulette they call it. Well, you can be lucky once, but after that your chances get less."

"You mean like Christmas?"

"Well, Christmas has to come on the calendar, but Carmen tells me that you invited all those that were at the Liévano meetings to come back to this program at Christmas. I warn you, don't stretch your luck too far."

"Was it luck—or providence?"

Juana snorted. "I'd like to see God stop a bullet. I'll tell you why they didn't come. Too many people were curious. They wanted to find out what the *evangelio* was all about, so maybe they told those bandits at Totumal not to shoot up a meeting when too many of their friends would get hurt."

"So then we'll have to make the Christmas program sound so interesting that they'll all want to come again. That way they may see to it that the police don't trouble us then."

"Don't keep God too busy holding back trouble is my advice!"

"Talk Marco into that. He's the one that makes the decisions."

Juana snorted and walked off growling about not being able to lead a hog or drive it. "Or a man."

The Liévano meetings had established Santa Inés as an evangelical center recognized even by mission representatives as more effective than Ocaña, not only for the number of people who continued to attend meetings but for the outreach far beyond its own immediate neighborhood. Perhaps because of the numbers of people now favorable to the gospel, the Totumal police had stopped dropping in with threats. Rosa was convinced that their hardest trials were over.

Toward the end of November, Marco went into Ocaña to buy holiday supplies for the store and to bring out more program materials for childen who were beginning to come regularly on Sundays. That Marco had remained in town overnight did not surprise them. He had not left too early, and few trucks came by toward Aguachica late in the day. One had to adapt oneself to the traffic.

After lunch Rosa settled down to catch up on her mending. Chico was in charge of a serious little *culto* with Jonas and Santo sitting on the veranda edge, and Emalina, who considered herself a bit too old for such childish affairs, giving stern direction as to the order of the service. The older children had gone to work in the yuca patch.

"And you don't read the Bible with it upside down." Emalina reached over the evangelist's shoulder and tried to grab the book he held tightly with both hands, his teeth set against Emalina's interference. Rosa put down her needle for a moment. It looked very much as though she would have to put an end to this *culto* herself. Emalina was the stronger, but Rosa was sure Chico was getting set to bite. He had previously been punished for it. Just as Rosa was getting up to prevent bloodshed, Santo remarked, "The truck's come. It's in front of Doña Juana's."

The meeting broke up precipitately, and the children dashed down the path shrieking, "Papá! Papá!" Rosa hurried to the kitchen to blow at the coals under the pot of *tinto*. She was still occupied with the fire when Don José Herrera from Ocaña strode into the patio followed by the children.

"How nice to see you!" cried Rosa. "Did you come with—"

Rosa's welcome disintegrated when she glimpsed Don José's solemn face. "Where's Marco?" she gasped. "What's happened to Marco?"

"Can you come into town with me?" said Don José. "Marco's very low."

Low? That was a phrase employed only for the gravely ill or mortally wounded. "Tell me quickly," she demanded. "Did they shoot him? Is he sick?"

"He's sick," the Ocaña elder said evasively. "While you get ready, I'll go hold up whatever car comes by."

He seemed ill at ease with her, perhaps wanting to break his bad news gently on the way in. Rosa sent Emalina to the field for the girls to take charge of the children. Her own packing took her only a few minutes even though, in the preoccupation of her anxiety, she found herself searching frantically through the dish cupboard for something she needed, then remembered that she was looking for her best shoes.

Even on the drive toward Ocaña, which took more than an hour, Don José was disappointingly uncommunicative.

"They attacked him," he said. Then he added, "But it's something inside him that's not right."

"Where is he?"

"Francisco Velásquez has him over there. He was the one that took him from the jail."

After that, Don José sank into an abstracted silence, and

Rosa's mind worried at the fragments of information with increasing desperation. Nor did the sight of Marco bring relief.

He was lying in the Velásquezes' own large wooden bed when she was bustled into the room. Marco pulled aside the cool cloth from his feverish forehead and uttered her name in a strange hoarse whisper. She had never seen him when he had not tried to make light of his circumstances. He seemed entirely too weak to make the effort. His eyes appeared sunken in the queer yellowish pallor of his face, which was broken by livid bruises.

"They beat you again," she murmured. "Who was it?"

"The police," he whispered through dry lips, stifling a moan with each breath. "It's inside me—things aren't right."

Rosa slipped the cool cloth back onto his brow. "Later," she murmured. "You can tell me later. Have you had a doctor?"

"The doctor says it's internal injuries," said Emma, who was right at Rosa's shoulder. "He's been vomiting blood, and we're not to feed him anything, the doctor says. He's given him something for pain, so he's not moaning so much."

Slowly, as Marco regained some strength, they pieced together the details of the atrocious attack. Marco had been walking down the narrow, crowded street on his way to the market to make his purchases, when he had been hailed by a policeman. He'd stopped to wait for the officer and his companion.

"You're Marco Franco, aren't you?"

"Yes, señor."

"I told you," said one of the policemen. "It's the *evangélico* from Santa Inés. Bring them out."

Before Marco had known what was happening, the man thus addressed had produced a pair of handcuffs and had clamped them on Marco's wrists. Then, with Marco safely shackled, the bully struck him a brutal blow across the face, announcing that he was being taken to jail.

"To jail! What for?"

"You think we don't hear what goes on? You were warned half a dozen times not to hold meetings. So what do you do?

You have the whole country mesmerized to hear this—this *evangelio.*"

The connotation of the last word was that of a pronouncement of witchcraft or some other very great evil. He emphasized his hatred of it by aiming another blow at Marco's face. When Marco dodged, the policeman, livid with rage, began beating Marco savagely with his club, while his companion jerked Marco here and there by the handcuffs. Two other policemen sauntered up, and at the whispered *"Evangélico!"* they joined the unequal conflict, brutally swinging their clubs at Marco from all sides.

"What are you beating that man for?" demanded a woman who had just joined the quickly amassed crowd of spectators.

"Because he's a cursed *evangélico!*"

"So that's it. Then let him have it!"

The crowd cheered her pronouncement, yelling, "Give it to him. Let him have it!"

Thus, receiving more acclaim for their sadistic actions than usual, the policemen proceeded to make Marco an object of public derision. Pulling Marco up to a raised sidewalk, so that their spectators could get a good view of their performance, one of the officers grabbed Marco by the nape of the neck and shoved him viciously to his knees. Completely at their mercy in his manacles, Marco could not even rise without their help. Instead of letting him get back onto his feet, the other officers of law beat him to the pavement with their clubs. Finding this amused the gathered rabble, they repeated the sadistic act. Then, tiring of that, they forced Marco to climb a telephone pole, clubbing him throughout the performance.

The hooting, jeering crowd formed a procession in the direction of the jail.

"They'd let me go a few steps on that raised sidewalk," said Marco, "then they'd beat me down to the gutter. They made me climb back up—and they wouldn't let me use my hands—and then they'd beat me down into the ditch again. And everybody thought it was funny. I don't know how many times they beat me down and then jerked me up again and told me to keep moving."

When they reached the jail, the mob fell back. Inside, with no pretense of questioning or of a fair hearing, they tore Marco's clothes from his already bruised body, and clubbed him to unconsciousness.

"And they never told you anything definite as a reason for this brutality?"

"Well, that we have meetings. And that we didn't listen to the military police in Totumal."

"So, because you have too many people standing up for you near Santa Inés, those cowards at Totumal set these hounds against you!" Rosa began to sob with anger at the bestial sadism and their helplessness to do anything about it. To go to court would only be placing themselves voluntarily into the same hands another time.

The doctor gave Rosa permission to move Marco home even though Marco continued to vomit blood and was able to take little nourishment other than small sips of broth. Gradually his strength began to return and his peculiar pallor receded, but Rosa noted a restlessness about Marco, and a depression that seemed unlike him. His natural optimism and resilience had often caused Marco to ignore physical pain or disease to an almost foolhardy degree. But this time he lay apathetic and indifferent to his surroundings. Often he seemed to avoid praying—pleading his physical weakness.

Since the day both of them had become believers, Marco had easily maintained his position as head of their family devotions, though he did not do the reading of the Scriptures. Neither illness nor pressing business matters had ever been able to make him relinquish that responsibility even for a day. Now, when the family had gathered very quietly near his bed in the customary manner, he had waved them weakly away. Once he had even complained to Rosa that he could hear them sing. And though Marco's health was definitely on the mend, his attitude had not changed.

One night Rosa suggested that they would come in just to listen to Antonio read the Scriptures together as a family. Marco shook his head and then turned himself toward the wall. Later, when she came to him gently and said, "We can pray together, the two of us," he seemed to evade her eyes.

"You pray," he said, barely above a whisper. And while she prayed, she felt his body jarring the bed spasmodically, as Marco weakly fought against sobs that were racking his emaciated frame.

"What is it, Marco?" Rosa asked, when she had ended her prayer and knelt quietly waiting for him to recover from this storm of emotion so unlike Marco. He considered tears a betrayal of weakness that could be permitted only to children and inadequate women.

"When is Vicente coming?" replied Marco through gasping sobs.

"Sunday. He's coming to take the Sunday service, Marco."

"What day of the week is this?" He had been entirely out of touch with them. He had not listened to the matters that usually had been of supreme importance to him. Marco did not even know the day of the week. He had forgotten Vicente's warm assurance that he would take charge of all the Sunday services here at Santa Inés.

"It's Friday, Marco. And many people are coming to the services. As many as eighty or more. And many are new ones that you've never even met. And they're all praying."

Abruptly Marco turned away from her and soon turned over completely, so that his face was toward the wall. Occasionally a great tearing sob shook his body, but he made no sound. Rosa lay beside him on the bed, praying for whatever it was that had taken Marco's joy and vitality. Marco's asking for Don Vicente confirmed a conviction she already had that his trouble was spiritual rather than solely physical.

Rosa was glad that Don Vicente arrived on a very early truck that Sunday morning. He noted her anxiety as soon as he walked into the patio where she was pouring him a cup of *tinto.*

"Is Marco worse?" he demanded.

"He has been waiting to see you," said Rosa. Then her pent up anxiety broke her own barriers of control, and she whirled from him, brushing the scalding tears from her cheeks. Don Vicente set down his cup at once and put a firm hand on her shoulder.

"Let's go," he said.

Marco lay stiffly straight in bed, his dark eyes deep, burning orbs against the paleness of his face.

"I thought I heard you," he said apathetically, putting out his hand toward his friend.

"You are still in bed?" said Vicente lightly. "I thought we'd be able to count you as part of the Santa Inés congregation today."

Marco shook his head almost imperceptibly, a deep sorrow dulling his eyes, but he did not speak.

"Our Lord understands the pain you are enduring, Marco. He, too, was beaten by officers of the law to provide pleasure for a mocking crowd."

"I may have been beaten like Jesus, but that's where the likeness ends. I'm not even sure if I'm a real *evangélico,* Vicente, even if that's what they beat me for."

"So," said Vicente, his face grave and more intense than ever, "if you had it to do over again, you would recant? Or you are telling me now that you'd be happier in your old ways?"

Tears filled Marco's eyes in spite of his battle to restrain the evidence of his despair. "No," he whispered. "No, that's not the way it is. I never want to go back on any terms, but I may have *slipped* back. I lie here in bed and think what I would have done if I'd had a machete or a gun. I fight off the thought and ask God to forgive them—and me—and the next minute I'm back to the second before they slap those handcuffs on me. Always in my mind, I'm a big hero. I always get the whole bunch of them down in the mud—the crowd jeering at them, not me. I try to forgive them, but it comes back. This is what I'm really like. I'm not like Jesus. I'm not even an *evangélico*."

"What are you, then?" asked Don Vicente gently.

"I just know what I'm *not*," replied Marco. " 'By this shall all men know that ye are my disciples,' " he quoted, " 'if ye have love one to another.' And Jesus said we are to love our enemies."

"You've suffered much for the sake of your faith," said Don Vicente. "Too much to bear, perhaps. Now, I'll have a brief service and then cancel all future meetings here. I'll make it very clear that the witness here is over. And remember, Marco, if you ever want to come into our Ocaña meetings, you're all more than welcome."

"But, Vicente!" Marco was up on his elbow. "That's all right for us. But what about the people who're coming here to hear? You know that many are almost ready to believe. And they have needs as great as my own, even before I knew the Lord." Marco slid his legs to the edge of the bed now. "We have to think of the people!"

"But they may report you again. They are your enemies, in a way, like the police of Ocaña or Totumal."

"I've never heard you talk like this, Vicente!" snapped Marco. "And I'm not going to have you make any such announcement. If you haven't the guts to face the music, then I have!"

Marco caught at the edge of the bed as though he were fighting a wave of dizziness, but he pulled himself upright. "Rosa, where are my pants?"

He glowered at Don Vicente who met his gaze solemnly. "Well, maybe *you* don't care about them—eighty or more, Rosa says, are coming—but God does. They have to hear the *evangelio,* even if I have to get up to preach it."

Rosa became conscious of the subtle glint of triumph in Don Vicente's eyes, though his face was still sternly serious.

"And you not even an *evangélico!*"

"My shoes, Rosa!" growled Marco, weakly struggling into the shirt she had handed him.

"On whose side are you?" continued Don Vicente.

Marco dropped the shoe with a heavy clunk to the floor and looked up at his friend, the thinnest ghost of a smile playing about his pale lips. "Well, if you push me into taking sides, I'll take God's side and the *evangelio.*"

"And it seems Satan, the accuser of the brethren, has taken sides against you. That really leaves you on God's side, doesn't it—when the devil himself is against you?"

Marco did not make any effort to reply.

"How many times have I preached that it is not sin to be tempted or attacked by the devil? It is only sin when we welcome him and entertain him gladly."

"I was entertaining him, all right, but he's miserable company."

"You know what Satan was after, don't you? He'd like to close down the light here in Santa Inés. Marco, when the devil himself recognizes your witness here as important, don't ever forget that, if he can't inspire enough hatred or abuse to get you down, he'll attack you personally. The devil knows that the souls that will hear your witness here in Santa Inés are worth the lifeblood of God's own Son. Santa Inés is important to God, too, remember."

Marco took a few unsteady steps. Vicente led him to a chair. "Now you just wait here while I get Doña Juana's big rocking chair. You're going to sit in our service like a good *evangélico* ought to, but comfortably, like a sick one should."

And when the people had gathered and had sung the lusty praise they felt for restoring their friend and brother in the Lord, Don Vicente preached on the text, "Except a corn of wheat fall into the ground and die, it abideth alone: but if it die, it bringeth forth much fruit. He that loveth his life shall lose it; and he that hateth his life in this world shall keep it unto life eternal."[1]

Later, Marco rested happily in bed with the old fiery look back in his eyes. He took Rosa's hand.

[1]John 12:24-25.

"It's all gone, now—the resentment and wish for vengeance. If they came back right now, I would tell them of the joy of salvation. And if they hit me, I'd know now that Jesus, in me, never stops loving them even if I waver in my remembering it."

15

When You Jar the Jug

FROM THE DAY that Marco won the battle against an enemy more powerful and vicious than the military police, he progressively gained strength. To all appearances, he was his same exuberant, brash self, for he continued his witnessing, undeterred by renewed threats of physical violence to himself, threats against his home and family or threats to stop the Christmas celebration he was advertising at every opportunity.

As Rosa had sensed Marco's depression as spiritual in nature rather than due to his serious injuries, she now became aware of a new undercurrent in his attitude toward his neighbors.

"A cocky rooster"—the police lieutenant's appelative had quite accurately characterized Marco's approach. "Look at me and what I've become. I used to be as evil and as weak as you! And you're bound for hell if you don't change like I did!" Though he had not often used just those words, his implication of moral superiority rather than his evangelical doctrines had often supplied the abrasive that stimulated opposition. Granted, his testimony had rung true, and many men who fought Marco's old problem were drawn to seek the remedy Marco had found effective.

In these past days, Marco had somehow been stripped of that cocksure egoism; and, though he still used the poster of the pilgrim to get his points across, the message that came through portrayed the amazing love of God that reaches through weakness and defeat of an erring mortal to pardon his failures and set him on the road toward eternal fellowship with Himself.

"I don't think God is nearly as concerned about what we've gotten to be on the outside, where people see us," Marco remarked at their own family worship one day, "as what He's been able to do to us on the inside, where nobody can look but He."

Antonio's face lighted with his own interpretation of his father's statement. "Like a jug somebody's carrying around? On the outside it's a jug. It's only when you jar it, and what's inside sloshes out, that you know if it's *tinto* or water from the bottom of the rain barrel."

"With wrigglers in it," chirped Chico.

"Yes," said Marco, chuckling. "The one who filled the jug knows all about it, but it's the jarring that shows up to everybody else what it's got inside."

On the first Sunday of December, Marco was still walking like an old man, doubled over to allay the sharp pains that racked his being from his severe internal injuries. Don Vicente, who had taken the morning service in Ocaña, had come out to hold another service in Santa Inés. Though it meant hours of riding on dark trails, more than eighty people had gathered even for this evening meeting.

"We can expect a hundred or more at the Christmas program," remarked Marco exultantly while he pumped air into the pressure lantern that would be hung from the edge of the veranda roof.

"Wait, Papá," said Antonio, taking over from Marco. "No need for you to pump that up. You're hurting enough."

"I didn't think they'd come to a night meeting like this," Marco continued, "what with getting up so early the next day."

"A night meeting seems to bring more young people," commented Don Vicente.

"Hecklers," retorted Antonio. "They haven't any better way to kill an evening, so they come here to see if they can't make us mad. That's what they're trying to do."

"That's what they come for," replied Don Vicente. "Sometimes they end up kneeling at the edge of the veranda, confessing their sins. We always have to remember that."

An unusually large number of noisy young people shuffled about restlessly at the dark periphery beyond the circle of the lamp's hissing light. During the singing they hooted at each other and made vulgar remarks. After Don Vicente began to preach they mimicked his words or jeered at their context.

Although the rowdies were annoying some members of the audience, Don Vicente was accustomed to their distractions and was hardly aware that the noise toward the front of the house had suddenly grown louder and more argumentative.

"Somebody's trying to get into the store," whispered Rosa. "They're yelling for us to open up the store."

"They know where we are," growled Marco. "And they know we won't open the store on Sunday, anyway."

Even while Marco spoke, a large crowd of men, six of them in police uniform, bounded from the corner of the house, shouting threats and angry imprecations. The congregation, collecting in the patio for the service, scuttled off into the surrounding dark woods where most of their mounts were tethered.

"Who owns this place?"

"You ought to know," snapped Juana Lazzco, who had not moved from her chair on the veranda. "You've been here often enough."

"I've never been here," retorted the commander of the unit. "We've just been stationed here this week. We heard this was a *tienda,* and we want to buy some drinks. Who's the owner?"

"I am," said Marco, "but I don't sell liquor, and I don't open up my store on Sunday."

Obviously the policeman did not believe Marco. He swung around to confer briefly with someone behind him. Then, with a new pretext for entering the store, he announced that they were searching the premises for arms.

"There's no liquor in there," said Germán, reasonably. "Leave us be. We were having a meeting."

"Was this a political rally?" barked the officer.

"No, they're *evangélicos,*" shouted someone from the heckling element.

"Evangélicos?" The officer looked about curiously. "Then this is some of their propaganda? We'll confiscate that, too."

The police, aided by the men who had come with them, had been filling a couple of sacks with what they seemed to consider arms—kitchen knives, personal razors, machetes and hoes for use in farm work. Now they used those machetes and knives to hack at the Bibles, hymnals and other literature they felt was evangelical in nature. Then, with no further pretext of legality, they robbed the Francos of all the money they could find in either the store or the house.

"If you were having a meeting, where's the preacher?"

Having learned from previous experience that his glasses increased his danger of serious injury, Don Vicente had removed them, and so none of the men recognized him.

"Which is the preacher?" barked one of the policemen, grabbing Rosa by the shoulder. Marco, seeing the man's hand on her, spoke up quickly, identifying Don Vicente.

"Well, then, you two will come with us!"

"He's not well," cried Rosa. "Don't take them away!"

"Get a move on," shouted the policeman, grabbing one of the heavy *palos* with which the doors were propped for security.

Rosa was almost beside herself with anxiety. The policemen began to beat Marco and Don Vicente with poles and with the broadsides of Marco's own machetes.

After the other attack here in the patio, they had rejoiced that the rowdies who had attacked Marco and Don Vicente had not been military police, habituated to sadism and who committed murder in the name of the law. The vicious brutality of military police had been demonstrated in Ocaña. That time Marco had escaped death, but by a very narrow margin. These men had come with no other purpose than to make trouble.

Frantic with terror, Rosa found herself on her knees crying to God to find some way of deliverance. Soon, amid her own pleas for help, she became conscious of the children about her, all praying as she was doing, for God to perform a miracle to save Marco's life and the life of their pastor.

By now they were alone on the veranda. The meeting had been broken up, for the people who had been brave enough to remain hidden in the woods would have left during the time the police were searching the house and store. Even Germán and Juana had gone. Rosa could hear shouts of anger or pain as the police drove the men toward the road.

What she was not aware of, until later, was that Juana had followed the military police out onto the trail; and, when she saw Marco staggering under their inhumane bludgeonings, she rushed into the fray, screaming and brandishing an iron kettle in which earlier she had brought a few *bollos* for the Franco family.

"So you'll beat up on a sick man, will you? Well, I'll show you skunks that we're not all full of snake blood!"

So sudden and furious was her attack, flailing blindly at whoever fell within the arc of her wicked weapon, that she scattered the procession. With Juana providing diversion, Vicente found opportunity to draw Marco behind a clump of trees, and from there they slipped back home under the cover of darkness. They could hear Juana following the retreating military detail with her strong-voiced opinions of their characters and lineage until the roar of their truck indicated that they had escaped even from her last bellowed sentiments. She returned a moment later to crow exultantly about her victory over military police.

"They had it coming to them, those filthy bandits," she cried. In her own reaction to the danger, she was chattering excitedly about how they once had robbed and beaten her. She somehow seemed to feel that she had evened an old score, though the military police involved had not been the same ones.

"And somebody who's *not* evangelical had better hang around to see if they're coming back," she averred. "Somebody's got to protect these pacifists who won't fight to save themselves."

As it happened, the police did not return to the house, and the injuries they had inflicted were mostly superficial bruises. When Don Vicente kneeled to praise God for deliverance, Doña Juana—the rough-spoken, strong-armed matron who had cowed a half-dozen police to relinquish their captives—incomprehensibly began to shake with sobs, tears coursing unheeded down her heavy cheeks.

"What is it, Juana?" Rosa knelt beside her, putting her arm around the gross shaking shoulders.

"Who—who's going to fight them off?" the woman wailed. "Who's going to fight them off when I turn into an *evangélica?*"

Don Vicente turned toward her with that familiar glint of amusement beneath his solemn assurance. "Why, then, Juana, we'll have to turn to the Lord."

"Well," she grumped, wiping her tears away with a quick swipe of her sleeve. "Where was He tonight, then? Didn't God know they were taking you in—and Marco still near death from the last time?"

"Maybe He knew He could depend on you to take care of it," returned Don Vicente, chiding her gently.

Marco patted her shoulder reassuringly. "He had to let it happen, Juana, to prove something to me," he said seriously. He looked from Don Vicente to Rosa jubilantly. "And He has! He has!"

Juana must have known that she would soon succumb to this message of love and trust, for at the Christmas program, before a hundred or more of their acquaintances, she and Germán made a public confession of their faith. Others had become believers and made public avowal that their lives were at God's disposition for His sake and the gospel's.

Surprisingly, no untoward antagonism was displayed at this service; but the program in Ocaña, which was held behind barred doors, had turned into a general pandemonium for over half an hour, with men and women under the pews while others dodged bullets fired at point-blank range by a drunken man who had wandered into the service. There, too, God had protected in a miraculous way; not one bullet even so much as grazed anyone in the crowded building.

Shortly, Marco also was preserved from rifle fire. Rosa had

heard the report of the gun during the night. Shooting, especially after a night of drinking and hilarity, was not at all unusual, so Rosa had paid little heed. The whole family had been asleep at that hour.

Next day however, Marco, who was facing the front door during their morning devotions noticed that it was splintered.

"Look, there's a hole right through the door!" he exclaimed. "Rosa, we can't let the children chip at the door like that. That's been done just recently, too."

Don Vicente, who had remained as an overnight guest after a full day of follow-up among the scattered believers, went over to the door to examine the place where a bit of wood appeared to have been gouged out of the door. His expression brought both Rosa and Marco to inspect the hole more carefully.

"Somebody has shot into the house with a rifle."

"Last night!" Rosa cried. "I heard it but paid no attention. I thought someone was just making whoopee."

The men soon found the rifle bullet imbedded in the wall, a few centimeters from where Marco's head would have been, had they not switched around their beds and the children's to make room for Don Vicente in the sala.

"Whoever fired that bullet knew where you sleep," said Don Vicente. "It was no accidental shot."

"Looks like it's keeping God busy just protecting us *evangélicos*," remarked Antonio.

"I'd rather be shot for being about His business," said Marco, "than going through life safely but fearing death every minute!" Then he nodded again, almost happily. "And even if I knew just who did it, I know now that I can forgive him."

"You think they're really after Papá?" said Antonio, with a worried frown. "They've been back again lately, those police. They talked about burning our house down."

"They have to talk big, Toño. It wouldn't be easy to swallow, being chased off by a single woman!"

"We'll be praying for you, Marco," promised Don Vicente.

"A man who would shoot with the intent to kill you could also set your house on fire. We'll ask God to restrain them."

"Who?" wondered Antonio. "Who could it be?"

"Well, we can't go around collecting suspicions," said Marco. "God knows who it is, and He's the one who's protecting us."

A few days later Germán Vanégas came over with a thoughtful scowl. "I'm hearing things again, Marco," he said. "They talk of burning your house down."

Marco tried to make light of the threat, but Germán was insistent that he had heard that a plot was afoot to burn the house.

"You'd better take the family into Ocaña until this blows over," he advised.

When two other people, both with friendly intent, reported that definite plans were afoot, Marco and Rosa decided that the children would be safer sleeping in the woods.

"Of course, they may just want to scare us out, so that they can loot the place again," Marco said. "I'll sleep here to guard the house and store."

For several weeks the children, except for Jonas, the smallest, were packed off to sleep in the wooded areas above and behind the house. They had even made themselves a tent, which they moved from one thicket to another. They seemed to be enjoying it so far, but Rosa knew that the novelty of roughing it would soon wear off.

Santo, the son whose clubfoot had been the means of leading her to faith, came to stand at her shoulder while she peeled plantains for a noon meal. Though Santo was a quiet boy, Rosa felt an extra fondness for this child for whom God had performed the miracle through which her whole life had been given purpose and happiness and peace.

Rosa could not see Santo's face; but, knowing him so well, she could visualize the wistful expression still reminiscent of babyhood, and his hesitation over a request he was afraid she would refuse. What could the boy ask that was so important to him and yet so problematic? A few shrill shrieks in the direction of the highway provided Rosa a clue, and with a sinking heart she realized that perhaps she would have to refuse what Santo wanted.

This Monday, February 25, was the date of the *Carnaval*.[1] The day before, after the service, Don Vicente had cancelled a planned jaunt because it might be dangerous for them on the trails. Rosa had forgotten all about the fiesta, but of course the children hadn't.

If Santo simply wanted a bit of cornstarch to throw into the face of some unwary member of the family, she would not refuse him the innocent diversion. Actually, most of the antics of the young people during the daytime were quite harmless in themselves.

On the other hand, if the children did take part in any fiesta fun, would she be giving them a taste of what the poster in the sala depicted as "of the world"? She wished she had discussed this with Marco before she would be called on to make a decision about it.

Now she felt Santo's hands softly following the contours of her neck and shoulder, and again a great tenderness for the boy welled up in her. His gentle caress, in contrast to Emalina's insistent pokings, made her yearn so much the more to let him have his wish.

Rosa took Santo's hand, as she turned to look into the wistfully importunate face. She pressed her lips to his chubby palm to lessen the hurt of what she might have to say.

"What's on your mind, Santander?" she asked, unconsciously using the form of his name reserved for serious talk.

"It's spooky in the woods, Mamá!" said Santo. "And the boys, they hear the big *tigres*—the ones that eat kids."

Although Rosa was exasperated that the older boys had been teasing Santo and frightening him, she was relieved that he had nothing on his mind that she could not settle for him.

"So," she said indignantly, "they've been trying to scare you, have they? Why don't you go to sleep near Toño?"

"Toño snores so, Mamá. If I'm near him, I won't be able to

[1]Festival of revelry and drinking just before Lent.

listen for when the twigs snap under their paws, or when they cough."

Rosa hugged the sturdy little body to her own. The poor child had been lying there in the woods, awake and straining in terror for sounds of vicious animals. Even the nearness of his older brother and his oblivion to danger added rather than detracted from his fear.

"Would you like to stay in the house and sleep in bed with Papá and me for a few nights?"

The boy nodded silently, but his overwhelming relief was so obvious that Rosa brushed away a tear. How long would they have to send the children out into the woods like this? Was it faith in God's protection if she allowed the neighbors' threats to cause the children such prolonged hardship?

Almost as soon as she had promised Santo the haven of her own bed for the night, Chico appeared to voice his request far more directly.

"If Santo can stay in the house, Mamá, why can't I?"

"It's safer for you in the woods, dear."

"There's *tigres* out there."

"So Carmelo's been scaring you, too?"

"Well, aren't there, Mamá? Aren't there?"

Rosa could not deny the presence of occasional wild cats in the woods. They had robbed her of several pullets.

"Aren't there?" persisted Chico.

"What's he talking about?" demanded Emalina, who had just come into the patio with Carmelo and Santo. "About sleeping in the woods? If Santo can sleep here in the house, why can't we?"

"Because, Emalina, if the people should keep their threat, I could carry Santo and Jonas out of the house. But I couldn't carry you all, and you know it!"

"You don't have to carry me," retorted Emalina firmly. "I can find my own way out of the house in the dark."

"You don't have to carry me," echoed Santo, apparently afraid that he might lose his privilege.

Tive spoke up from the other end of the veranda. "Maybe Chico should stay inside a few nights. Have you noticed his cough? It gets terribly breezy out there towards morning."

"And shivery," added Chico, following his advantage.

Later, when Rosa found Marco alone, she confessed that she had given Santo permission to sleep in the house. She began to relay to him her impression of the children's fears and discomforts, adding that Chico seemed to have a real cold. She was forced to end her account abruptly since the children, sensing her purpose as their advocate, had moved into the room one by one. The eagerly attentive ring closed in on them before she had finished her last hurried remarks.

Marco looked up at the low thatched roof just above their heads, which was dry to the point of explosiveness now during the windy dry season.

"There's not so much dew these days," he argued. "It's been too dry to give anybody a cough. But I'll have to put up a tile roof before the rains. I've got some money saved for it, but it's not near enough yet."

"And in the meantime?"

"Look, Rosa," replied Marco somewhat shortly, "I'm not forcing the children to sleep in the woods for any reason but to protect them. You know it, and so do they. We've had at least half a dozen—more than that—come here and tell us to take care. They won't tell us anything definite. Maybe they can't. So we have to be ready for them all the time."

"If you thought so," said Emalina somewhat peevishly, "you'd dig a hole in the woods and put the money for the tile in there. Money burns up. Why can't we sleep here near the money?"

Marco's eyes twinkled. "Because I'm more careful of you than I am of the money." He scratched reflectively at one of his recent scars still bearing a scab. "Nina is right, though," he said. "If this thatch burns, I can't stop to grab that money from where I've got it hid."

"I can tell you a good place," offered Emalina. "Nobody ever goes there much."

"A good ways off the mule trails?"

"We always sleep away from the trails, Papá," replied Antonio. "Not much point sleeping where everybody can find us."

One of Rosa's smaller kettles, with a tight cover to it, had been commandeered. A touching assortment of strange personal treasures were brought to be included in the buried hoard. Santo brought out a small scripture motto he had won by saying correctly the most Bible verses during the time they had lived in Ocaña. Chico brought a New Testament, also a prize for some sort of achievement. Antonio had some money of his own that he included. Jorge approached with a small rectangular card in his hand that Rosa felt sure was a photograph. He changed his mind, however, before she had been able to see what he held, and shoved it into a pocket.

"But the *niños* stay behind," declared Marco. "No point hiding it, if the little ones know where it is."

"Better put the pot into the wood basket," said Antonio. "And I'll take an axe along and bring back wood."

Emalina lapsed into her childish method of achieving attention. Both her voice and her finger were sharp as she reminded Marco that the idea had been hers in the first place.

"All right," he said, yielding reluctantly. "If you know how to keep a secret. Are you big enough?"

"Sure," retorted Emalina. "I know about Alicia and Manuel—that they're going to get married," she boasted. "I haven't told anybody."

"Oh, no?" snapped Antonio. "Except that you've just told it."

"All of us know. I mean other people."

Afterwards, when they returned with a large load of wood, Emalina walked about stealthily, her eyes wide with the immensity of the secret that had been intrusted to her. Manuel Goméz, who had come for supper, was intrigued with her important airs and began to wheedle for the information with which she was fairly bursting. She however maintained her secret, though the effort was clearly almost more than she could bear.

Marco, watching her with some amusement, tapped Rosa's shoulder. "We'll have to move it when she doesn't know. She'll never keep that secret for a week."

"Manuel's going to sleep here in the granary with me tonight," Antonio announced after some time. "He's staying over, so he can go to Ocaña first thing in the morning. Is that all right?"

No sooner had Antonio mentioned the fact that he would not be going out to the woods than the whole family broke into a clamorous uproar. Every child had a very good reason for sleeping in the house that night, and the older girls were just as emphatic about it as the children. Marco glanced at Rosa helplessly, wanting to acquiesce but knowing that it might not be wise.

Juana and Germán, who had come over with Arturo and Carmen to join the Franco evening devotions, appeared just as the commotion was at its height.

"One thing," said Juana, "there's nobody around tonight. Everybody's in Ocaña at the fiesta."

The chorus of eager pleading recommenced, until Marco relented. "All right. Tonight. But don't tell me I've started something. Tomorrow you go back to the *monte.* You hear?"

The younger ones did a joyous little dance of delight, but the older children were less enthusiastic, since Marco insisted that it was a one-night reprieve. Rosa was happy with their cheerful preparations for their first good night's sleep—as they insisted—for many days. It was good to have them all about her, Rosa thought, just before she slipped off to sleep.

16

But God

ROSA, always a light sleeper, was wide awake the moment she felt Marco jerk to rigid alertness. He raised his head slightly from the pillow, then sat up in bed listening. The dogs were barking in the direction of the road. Some of the celebrants of the *Carnaval* were probably returning from Ocaña, she decided.

Whoever had alighted from the car or truck on the highway was following the trail past their own house into the foothills beyond. In fact, as they lay there in the darkness and listened, it seemed that the passersby were taking far longer than needful.

Why would anyone loiter on the way home at this hour of the night, when everyone had to get up before dawn to work on the farms?

"It sounds as if they might be stealing our chickens, Rosa."

Rosa moaned with frustration. How hard she had worked to raise those pullets. First one of the hens had left the nest, and she had had to walk miles to find another setting hen to take her place. Then, when the chicks had been small, the sky almost always had a circling spiral of hawks ready to pounce on them. It would be very hard to take cheerfully the loss of these precious survivors.

"They were almost big enough to lay eggs," she commented, trying hard to face this trial bravely, if it must occur. And it did seem that Marco was right. By this time the dogs were barking with strange ferocity. Whatever was going on outside was exciting them far more than just a passing group of rowdies on their way home.

"They've got into a fight," muttered Marco, after three shots rang out in quick succession. "Somebody's had too much to drink."

"No, Marco," exclaimed Rosa a moment later. "I think they shot the dogs!"

With a great lunge, Marco left the bed and sprang toward the doors to check the *palos* he had carefully braced against them for security. He stumbled over his sandals as he rushed to the back door and also secured the shutters with a second bolt.

"That I don't like," Rosa heard him muttering apprehensively. "That shooting of our dogs I don't like."

What would those unseen intruders have in mind? Something more serious than stealing chickens, probably. An indistinct hubbub, something like the approach to a busy market or like scores of subdued and excited voices, seemed to come from outside.

"Where are they?" whispered Rosa, getting up and slipping into some clothes. "I can't seem to locate the direction."

"That's what bothers me, Rosa," replied Marco. "They seem to be all around the house."

Rosa recalled the numerous threats to burn their home, but she thought that no one would commit such a crime with witnesses. That was the work of one stealthy wretch who slunk away before he could be recognized. Or was it? It had not been so in Aspasica.

Rosa recalled their new tile roof and walled patio in Aspasica. Even that protection had not kept the mob from breaking in. As she whispered a frightened prayer, she built up a comforting security in reasoning that their home had become important in a recognized evangelical outreach. God was using it as the key to evangelization of the whole area. Would God permit their enemies to thwart His project? Wasn't God personally involved with them? Wasn't their remaining in Santa Inés far more important now than just a place for them to live? She whispered a soundless reminder.

"God, don't let them destroy our home—and Your work!"

Marco's hand was on her shoulder as they both strained tensely to hear what the crowd of people could be doing outside their home. Suddenly Marco's fingers bit into her flesh convulsively.

"They're doing it," he shouted. "They're setting fire to our roof!"

A sudden red glow at one corner of the house was quickly followed by a brisk crackling. Even while Marco shouted for the children to wake up, that the roof was afire, Rosa noticed that flames were licking through the thatch at all four corners of the house, as though the fires had been started on signal. The subdued babble outside now rose to a whoop of triumph.

While she shook Santo awake, Rosa screamed, "Alicia! Tive! The *niños*. Wake the *niños*. The house is on fire!"

"Quick! Quick!" roared Marco. "I'll lead the way out and push them back if I have to." He swung toward Rosa in the dark. "You have Jonas? Give me Santo."

Rosa plunged toward the other room, carrying Jonas. She knew how heavily the children slept, even the girls. No thought could be more horrible than that they had left one behind sleeping. By the time she reached their door, however, the flames overhead shed a billowing light throughout the house. Alicia had Chico in her arms; Tive had Emalina in tow. Both children were bawling with resentment that their sleep had been disturbed. Even as Rosa thrust Carmelo on after the girls, the children's crying changed to a shrill screaming as they wakened to the reality of terror.

She whirled with her own burden, shoving the girls ahead of her toward the door, where Marco had just released the poles supporting the doors.

"Are they all here?" he shouted. "I'll try to hold them back, Rosa. *Niños*—dash for the woods!"

While Marco was shouting directions, he had swept Santo back to his shoulder; and, with Tive's help, he tugged open both the double doors at once.

Rosa caught her breath in horrified amazement at the size

of the mob that seemed to encirle the house completely. As Marco darted forward, the children crowding on his heels, Rosa had a momentary impression of scores of upturned faces, ruddy in the glare from the burning roof, staring in fascination at the blazing thatch. The fire roared and snapped as though the dry thatch had been saturated with gasoline.

A man lunged forward out of the leering, yelling rabble. He appeared doubly evil in the lurid flicker of the flames because he was still wearing his carnival mask. The raging fire overhead probably saved Marco's life, since its light gleamed on the broad machete the murderous brute swung at Marco's head with all his might. Marco dodged just as Rosa screamed, and the children tumbled back into the house, shrieking in fear. A hurried, upward glance showed the thatch a roaring, livid blanket over the heavy beams at which the flames had begun to lick hungrily all across the house.

"Quick, children," cried Rosa. "The other way!"

She dashed to the door that led to the patio. With a practiced flip at the heavy pole, she thrust the door wide open and plunged out, turning to make sure that the children were all close behind.

"Mamá!" shrieked Alicia, at her shoulder. "The gun!"

Whirling about, Rosa felt a gun against her chest before she saw it, but she heard the vicious snarl.

"Another step, Rosa, and you're dead. And so are the rest!"

The assassin knew her by name, she thought vaguely, in the midst of her horror. These masked people around her were people from the foothills around Santa Inés! Marco, close behind, pulled her back into the house.

Stark, overwhelming terror seemed to crush and stun them in a paralyzing embrace as they stumbled back into the buffeting, asphyxiating waves of roaring heat. Rosa felt giddy, as a person drawn under the surface in violent twisting currents of a river in flood—a river of flame. At this moment she did not think of heaven. Only hazily did she wonder at their fate—all of them dying in this fire. Her mind was engulfed, paralyzed in this awful extremity of hopelessness and physical agony.

The children, she saw by the lurid light, were clustered around Marco, who stood with arms aloft in imploring prayer. His habitual resourcefulness had deserted him in this sadistic triumph of his enemies. Rosa choked with a sob of love for him and a wild regret for this ending of Marco's gallant witness, his ministry of love for the very ones who had determined this agonizing death for him—her beloved.

"Oh, God," she wailed. "Can this be true?"

How long would they survive this heat? Would the furnace-like air graciously burn out their lungs and let them suffocate? Or would the flames reach the children before they died? Could she endure to watch them burn to death?

Beside herself with the horror of this thought, Rosa stirred herself from the apathy of partial suffocation. She gasped at Alicia to keep the children together and threw a comforter around them to form a tent against the heat. Shielding her eyes against the blistering heat, Rosa sped to the bedroom and gathered up an armful of pillows with a grim resolve. Suffocation is painless. She could not—she would not allow her babies to roast in the torment of this flame.

Alicia, she saw as she returned, had gathered the younger children under the comforter and was hunched protectively over them. Even so, the children were gasping between short, anguished screams. The whole room seemed to glow with heat. Her tears actually scalded her cheeks.

"God keep me from this sin!" she whimpered. "Find some other way for us, Lord. I don't know if I can do it!"

As if propelled by a mighty arm, Emalina broke away from the others and rushed at the door toward the patio. The door frame under Emalina's fingers was smoldering, and flames flickered out from the wood. Apparently too terrified to notice her burns, the child tugged at the door with all her puny strength. Her thin face flashed back for an instant as she screamed, "Mamá! Mamá! They've gone!"

A moment later they were all huddled together once more, but in the cool, still shadows of the wooded hill a hundred meters from the house.

"Are they coming after us?" whispered Carmelo, his teeth chattering from reaction to his terror and from the sudden change of temperature.

"No," said Tive. "See them, out front?"

Beyond the leaping flames that swept high into the night sky, the mob had huddled together at some distance, staring up in silent fascination. Even now much of the thatch had burned off, exposing the glowing ribs of the blazing roof.

"The heat," Marco ejaculated. "The Lord has driven them back with the heat!" He sank to his knees there under the trees, tears streaming down his face. "God has preserved us alive! God has preserved our family again!"

Even as Marco voiced their gratitude, Rosa saw a sudden bright radiance illumine his face. Startled, she noticed that the sky and woods around them had burst aglow with the same intense light. At that very instant, the air was torn by a thunderous explosion that flung huge blazing rafters high into the now brilliant sky.

"The gasoline!" exclaimed Alicia, muffling her voice with her fingers. "The drum of gasoline you brought for the store, Papá!"

"If we'd stayed in the house just one minute more, Marco," Rosa exclaimed, her voice hushed with awe, "we'd be dead now, every one of us."

"God has preserved us alive," repeated Marco, and murmured, "it's a continuing miracle how He does it!"

"Will they come here?" whimpered Santo. "Will they?"

Evidently the child could not erase the terror of those hideous masks or—perhaps more frightful—faces bared and contorted with fiendish, sadistic passions.

"I don't think anybody saw us come here," comforted Alicia. "They were too busy watching the fire they started."

"Or they'd have hollered," said Emalina. "If they'd have seen us they would have hollered."

"Thank God, thank God, we're all safe," reiterated Marco. "It's hard to believe that all of us are here, alive and unhurt."

With an unusual gesture of sentimentality, Marco stooped to kiss each one of the smaller children and gave the older girls a loving squeeze. As he turned to take Rosa in his arms, he paused.

"Toño! Jorge! Where are the boys? And Manuel?"

Alicia chuckled. "I keep telling you that Toño can sleep through anything. Look at the granary! The door's still closed. They're still asleep in the granary."

Rosa peered back at the still well illuminated yard. The frame of the roof farthest from the explosion remained almost upright, though it sagged inward, drawn down by the weight of the stanchions that had collapsed down into the house. All that remained of the thatch looked like glowing feathers which gusts of wind swirled away in eddies of sparks. The explosion seemingly had torn all combustibles from the front of the house. No part of the roof was visible there, and the flames on that end were flickering up from within the walls. The small granary in which he boys had gone to sleep appeared undisturbed.

"If they didn't sleep through it, they will have slipped out while the mob wasn't looking. Nobody expected them to be in there."

Jonas began to pull at Rosa's skirts, crying softly.

"He stepped on a sticker," said Chico.

"The poor little tyke," murmured Marco. "While I was running, and even until now, I didn't realize it, but not one of us stopped for our shoes." After a moment he added, "Not one of us—except Toño—has any shoes." He chuckled. "I'm glad I got my pants on."

The children had nothing but what they had slept in; and, because they could not be sure when the mob would completely disperse, Marco ordered that they move farther into the woods lest an outcry of the children should invite added violence.

Only as dawn greyed the eastern horizon did they venture out of the sheltering woods. The smaller children had slept a little, though Rosa had had nothing to shield them from the cool night breeze. Morning erased even the peculiar illusion that what had transpired that night at Santa Inés had merely been a horribly vivid nightmare and that daylight would set everything back in focus, and they could go home.

The older girls ran ahead and opened the granary door. Rosa and Marco, each carrying a child, arrived just as Antonio staggered sleepily out into the faint light of morning.

"No!" Rosa heard Antonio's exclamation and saw him swing about toward the house. He uttered a cry of incredulous dismay that brought Manuel and Jorge out as well.

Together they hurried to the still smoldering ruins of what had been their home. The adobe walls, even where they stood erect, had been baked to crumbling cinders. The explosion had caused additional damage.

"You can't build that up again." Manuel spoke into the still-ness of their shock and despair.

Marco and the children waded into the ashes which the night breeze had whirled up into heaps in corners and along the walls.

Charred and shattered utensils and dishes had scattered over the veranda when the cupboard had collapsed in flames. Each in turn poked at some object that protruded from the debris, but not one item was worthy of salvage. Everything they owned had been destroyed beyond any hope of usefulness.

Alicia followed the others to where Rosa stood in what had been their patio. "If it weren't so ghastly," she said, "it would be funny. This is really one time we haven't got a thing to wear!"

Germán wandered over slowly from his own home, his face averted and his eyes to the ground until he came to join their dejected number. He kicked at the charred length of a roof joist before he spoke.

"We didn't wake," he said, with a peculiar catch in his throat, "until just before the whole thing blew up." He glanced momentarily at Marco and cleared his throat. "We thought you all burned in there." He hesitated again. *"They* thought so. We heard them talking. They said they had kept you from coming out."

Marco nodded. He understood his friend's embarrassment. "You couldn't have done anything, Germán, even if you'd wakened sooner. We woke up, but they wouldn't let us through, back or front. But God—" Marco's voice broke.

"Just before the gasoline exploded," said Tive. "God made them go back because of the heat, and Emalina led us out just at the right time."

"If she'd gone out a minute before," added Carmelo, "they were still out there hollering, and they might have killed her. If we'd have stayed a minute longer, we'd not be here to talk about it. That's when the gasoline blew up."

"By the goodness and faithfulness of God, we're alive."

"Well, come over for breakfast," said Germán. "Juana saw you and sent me over to tell you. She's bawling all over the place, and that sort of upsets her. Don't pay any attention if she sounds peevish."

Juana, who had so long worn a gruff mask of harshness, seemed completely unstrung by her own feelings of Christian compassion, still unfamiliar and probably unanalyzed. She banged about the kitchen almost angrily and grumped at everybody, while she made surreptitious swipes at her wet cheeks with a corner of her apron.

While they ate, they discussed possible solutions for their immediate future. When Antonio suggested that he could quickly rig up some sort of temporary shelter, Rosa felt her heart sink. She could not bear to contemplate housekeeping in a one-room shack such as they had had in Tolima. Their small providential cache of money, she knew, would not even buy one outfit of clothing for each of them.

To Rosa's intense relief, Marco shook his head at the proposal, and both Germán and Juana voiced immediate disapproval as well. The mob had not come to Santa Inés to destroy their house, but *them*—the Franco family. To remain on the farm in some sort of temporary shelter seemed a foolhardy invitation to disaster. For a time, at least, they must find refuge elsewhere.

Juana nodded energetically. "You'd be welcome here, even if they burn us down, too," she said, "though I don't know where I'd put you all up."

Marco, still barefoot, caught one of the early trucks bound toward Ocaña, to make some sort of arrangement for them. He returned almost at once to take them all into town. The people of the church meanwhile had assembled enough clothes to cover them for the moment. One of the oil companies of the area heard of their destitution and the violence that had caused it, and sent a contribution toward their immediate needs and to pay rent for the modest house that their evangelical friends had found for them. Marco's brother, Miguel, of Aspasica, sought them out and bought each of them a change of clothing.

Amid those harried, busy days of settling their big family into a new home, Don Vicente came to visit them often to help where he could. Rosa would never forget the first time he came in and wordlessly clasped Marco's hand. Of the two men, thought Rosa as she watched them, Vicente looked as though he had suffered the greatest loss. Marco was exuberantly grateful to God for having preserved them all.

Vicente was grateful for that, too, of course, but Santa Inés had been the focal center for evangelizing an ever increasing area. To contact each home individually—as he would probably need to do, if the people once interested in the gospel would still dare to let him come—and to reach them all would be a physical impossibility. And now he would have to do it all alone. Impoverished by this most recent catastrophe, Marco would not be free to spend any time on evangelistic excursions for months to come. Vicente saw a great work thwarted and cut off in this one brutal gesture of opposition.

Wasn't this what the arch enemy—the spiritual enemy of mankind—had desired? By striking at this family, he was sounding the death knell of a work blossoming into a move-

ment toward spiritual reality over a great and widening territory. For Satan, the mob's action had been a strategic victory.

All this Rosa saw in Vicente's grave face that first day when
he looked at Marco's radiant face.

"Marco," Vicente had said, "God is giving you great grace in
this trial of faith. You don't look like a man who has been impoverished."

"On the contrary," retorted Marco, beaming. "God is showing me that the things that have been happening to me are for
the enriching of my soul. I praise Him, now, for last month's
testing which I couldn't understand then, but which has prepared me to glorify Him in this. He led me to see His love and
His forgiving spirit. This loss? I can't see how He will do it,
Vicente, but I feel it here—" Marco tapped his breast seriously "that this loss is for a greater gain."

Don Vicente looked searchingly into Marco's face. Marco
was so intent on trying to make his pastor see and rejoice with
him in his own spiritual victory, that he was missing Don Vicente's personal battle against discouragement and defeat.

Don Vicente waited three weeks before he took a truck
bound toward Santa Inés to make some house calls in that
neighborhood. Marco knew of his going, and Rosa had seen
the great longing in his eyes to accompany his friend, but he had
had to go to work in the field in which he had hired out as a
daily laborer.

Late that evening Don Vicente knocked at their door. He
had come to their new home directly on his return to Ocaña.
This time Don Vicente's face was radiant with the joy of his own
good news.

"They want to continue the services out there," he cried, almost beside himself with excitement. "They've decided that to
avoid concentrating the enmity of people on one household
they will take the meeting from place to place. Each one knows
what danger he invites by offering his house, but several families are eager for the meetings to be held in their community,
because, they say, they can get many neighbors to come if it

won't be too far to go. The first meeting will be held at Don Cristóbal's house."

"Satan, it looks like, has overplayed his hand this time!"

"Or God has used the enemy's strategy to defeat his own purposes," said Rosa. "Think of how this will spread the *evangelio!*"

It soon became apparent to everyone that the gesture of Satan's emissaries to wipe out the source of evangelical testimony in Santa Inés had resulted, instead, in a dissemination of several widely separated focal points, each as potent as its origin. A service was being held as far to the east as San José, in Don Sixto Machado's home. Antonio was helping the Mateus brothers with a regular service at La Vega del Gusto. People who lived far from these homes were insistent on help in beginning a regular service in their own vicinity.

Before many weeks, Marco was again enthusiastically joining his friend as they tried in vain to follow up all opportunities for evangelistic services. New believers in those Andean foothills had a faith as rugged as the terrain from which they had learned to wrest a living, and they were fearless in proclaiming it.

Often someone converted at the first meetings of a new area service had come from an amazing distance. Immediately he began such a strenuous witness in his own neighborhood that the newly born congregation became mother to another congregation immediately. Marco had provided a living demonstration of a man totally committed to the cause of Christ and the dissemination of His gospel; and, because they had seen no example of a more dilute *evangelio,* such commitment came to be the expected norm of each new evangelical. Reality of faith and the resulting reality of the power of Christ transformed other lives and drew ever-increasing numbers to share that same quality of belief.

So rapidly was the evangelical faith received, and over so large an area, that soon only for very special conferences did leaders from the far edges of the mushrooming movement try to meet with other leaders in the widespread region. Out of apparent disaster, God had multiplied the effectiveness of Marco Franco's witness in Santa Inés beyond estimation.

Stormy days lay ahead for each of those burgeoning congregations, and the archenemy was soon to bare his teeth again. But these churches thrived on opposition.

At the dedication service of a chapel for one of those magnificent congregations, Don Vicente invited Marco to speak.

"I haven't much to say to you," Marco said, "except what the Sacred Scriptures say better than I could." Then from the treasury of carefully stored counsel, he quoted from one of Paul's letters to a growing church in Corinth: " 'My beloved brethren, be ye steadfast, unmovable, always abounding in the work of the Lord, forasmuch as ye know that your labor is not in vain in the Lord.' "

"And then," added Don Vicente, "you will begin to bear the likeness of your heavenly Father. In Him is 'no variableness, neither shadow of turning.' "[1]

---

[1]James 1:17.